A-LEVEL AND AS-LEVEL   MATHE

A-LEVEL
AND AS-LEVEL

LONGMAN
REFERENCE
GUIDES

MATHEMATICS

John Reynolds

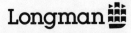

LONGMAN A AND AS-LEVEL REFERENCE GUIDES

Series editors: Geoff Black and Stuart Wall

TITLES AVAILABLE
Biology
Chemistry
English
Geography
Mathematics
Physics

Longman Group UK Limited,
Longman House, Burnt Mill, Harlow,
Essex CM20 2JE, England
and Associated Companies throughout the world.

© Longman Group UK Limited 1991

First published 1991
Fourth Impression 1993

British Library Cataloguing in Publication Data

Reynolds, John
　Mathematics.
　1. Great Britain. Secondary schools. Curriculum
　subjects: Mathematics. Examinations
　I. Title
　510.76

　ISBN 0–582–06398–1

Set in 10/12pt Century Old Style.

Printed in Singapore

ACKNOWLEDGEMENTS

Thanks are extended to Stuart Wall and Geoff Black for their editing and most useful suggestions at each stage of production.

HOW TO USE THIS BOOK

Throughout yourA-level and AS-level course you will be coming across terms, ideas and definitions that are unfamiliar to you. The Longman Reference Guides provide a quick, easy-to-use source of information, fact and opinion. Each main term is listed alphabetically and, where appropriate, cross-referenced to related terms.

- Where a term or phrase appears in **different type** you can look up a separate entry under that heading elsewhere in the book.
- Where a term or phrase appears in **different type** and is set between two arrowhead symbols ◄ ►, it is particularly recommended that you turn to the entry for that heading.

ACCELERATION

This is the rate of change of **speed** or **velocity** with respect to time. The standard unit is metres per second per second (m/s^2). The *gradient* on a velocity/time graph will represent the acceleration.

◀ Kinematics, Polar components ▶

ALTERNATIVE HYPOTHESIS

◀ Hypothesis ▶

ANGLE

 ANGLE MEASURES

Angles are measured in either degrees or **radians**.

Degrees

- One complete revolution $= 360°$
- One-quarter of a complete revolution $= 90° = 1$ right-angle
- $1° = 60$ minutes $(60')$; 1 minute $= 60$ seconds $(60'')$

Radians

- One complete revolution $= 2\pi$ radians $= 2\pi^c$
- One radian is the angle subtended at the centre of a circle by an arc of the circle equal in length to the radius of the circle.

Degrees	0°	30°	45°	60°	90°	180°	360°
Radians	0	$\dfrac{\pi^c}{6}$	$\dfrac{\pi^c}{4}$	$\dfrac{\pi^c}{3}$	$\dfrac{\pi^c}{2}$	π^c	$2\pi^c$

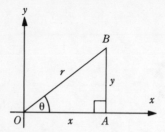

Fig. A.1

CIRCULAR FUNCTIONS

For any acute angle $\theta = AOB$, say, of a right-angled triangle OAB (Fig. A.1)

$$\sin \theta = \frac{\text{Opposite}}{\text{Hypotenuse}} = \frac{AB}{OB} = \frac{y}{r}$$

$$\cos \theta = \frac{\text{Adjacent}}{\text{Hypotenuse}} = \frac{OA}{OB} = \frac{x}{r}$$

$$\tan \theta = \frac{\text{Opposite}}{\text{Adjacent}} = \frac{AB}{OA} = \frac{y}{x}$$

Further, $\operatorname{cosec} \theta = \dfrac{1}{\sin \theta}$, $\sec \theta = \dfrac{1}{\cos \theta}$, $\cot \theta = \dfrac{1}{\tan \theta}$

TRIGONOMETRIC RATIOS FOR A GENERAL ANGLE

Angles measured in an anticlockwise sense from the positive x-axis are positive. Angles measured in a clockwise sense from the positive x-axis are negative – see Fig. A.2.

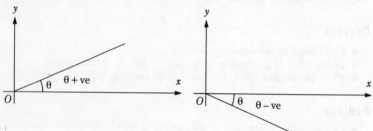

Fig. A.2

Worked example

Show, in relation to a cartesian diagram, angles of

a) 125°, b) −60°, c) $\dfrac{5\pi^c}{4}$ d) −210°

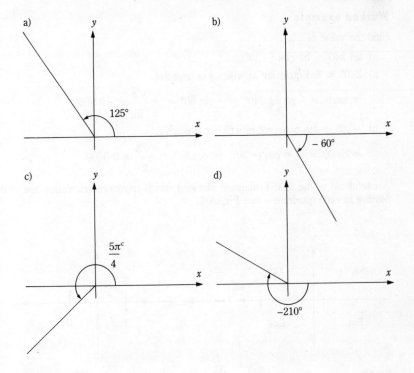

Fig. A.3

Fig. A.3 shows the angles a) to d).

▶ QUADRANTS

The cartesian axes divide a plane into four quadrants.
$0° \rightarrow 90°$ 1st quadrant, $90° \rightarrow 180°$ 2nd quadrant,
$180° \rightarrow 270°$ 3rd quadrant, $270° \rightarrow 360°$ 4th quadrant.

2nd quadrant ↑ 1st quadrant	
3rd quadrant | 4th quadrant	

| x negative ↑ x positive |
y positive | y positive
x negative | x positive
y negative | y negative

The trigonometric ratio of any angle is then obtained by determining the quadrant connected with the angle, the sign of x or y within that quadrant and the associated acute angle made with the positive (or negative) x-axis. Irrespective of the quadrant in which the angle lies, r is always taken as positive.

Worked example

Find the value of

  a) sin 240°, b) cos (−30°)

  a) 240° ⇒ 3rd quadrant in which y is negative

$$\Rightarrow \sin\theta = \frac{y}{r} \Rightarrow \sin 240° = -\sin 60° = -\frac{\sqrt{3}}{2} \text{ or } -0.8660$$

  b) −30° ⇒ 4th quadrant in which x is positive

$$\Rightarrow \cos\theta = \frac{x}{r} \Rightarrow \cos(-30°) = \cos 30° = \frac{\sqrt{3}}{2} \text{ or } 0.8660$$

A useful aid is the CAST diagram showing which trigonometric ratios are *positive* in each quadrant – see Fig. A.4.

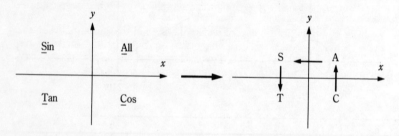

Fig. A.4

  Thus

  a) sin 240° ⇒ third quadrant ⇒ tangent only positive
     ⇒ sin 240° = − sin 60° = −0·8660
  b) cos (−30°) ⇒ fourth quadrant ⇒ cosine only positive
     ⇒ cos (−30°) = cos 30° = 0·8660

Worked example

Find a) tan 740°, b) sin 320°, c) sec 600°

  a) 740° = 360° + 360° + 20° ⇒ 1st quadrant ⇒ *all* positive
     ⇒ tan 740° = tan 20° = 0·3640
  b) 320° ⇒ 4th quadrant ⇒ cosine only positive
     ⇒ sin 320° = − sin 40° = −0·6428
  c) 600° = 360° + 240° ⇒ 240° in 3rd quadrant ⇒ tan only positive

$$\Rightarrow \sec 600° = \frac{1}{\cos 600°} = -\frac{1}{\cos 60°} = -2$$

◀ Trigonometric equation, Trigonometric function, Trigonometric identity ▶

ANGLE OF FRICTION

◀ Friction ▶

APPROXIMATE INTEGRATION

It is not always possible to find an **integral** of a given function of x, for example

$$\int e^{x^2} dx,$$ since there is no a **function**, say $f(x)$, whose **derivative** with respect to x is e^{x^2}. However, an *approximate* value of a definite integral such as

$$\int_0^1 e^{x^2} dx$$ can be found by equating the integrand e^{x^2} to y and regarding the problem of **integration** as that of finding the area of the region between the curve $y = e^{x^2}$, the x-axis and the ordinates given by the limits of the integral, i.e. $x = 0$ and $x = 1$. Two such methods are of importance at A-level and its equivalent: the Trapezium rule and Simpson's rule.

◀ Simpson's rule, Trapezium rule ▶

ARC LENGTH

Given the graph of the function $y = f(x)$, the arc length L between the points (x_1, y_1) and (x_2, y_2) is given by

$$L = \int_{x_1}^{x_2} \left\{ \sqrt{1 + \left(\frac{dy}{dx}\right)^2} \right\} dx$$

In cases where the curve is defined parametrically in terms of θ, the arc length between the points with parametric values θ_1, θ_2 is given by

$$L = \int_{\theta_1}^{\theta_2} \left\{ \sqrt{\left(\frac{dx}{d\theta}\right)^2 + \left(\frac{dy}{d\theta}\right)^2} \right\} d\theta$$

We illustrate with two examples.

Worked example A

Calculate the arc length of the curve $y = x^{\frac{3}{2}}$ between the points $(0,0)$ and $(1,1)$.

Here

$$\frac{dy}{dx} = \frac{3}{2} x^{\frac{1}{2}}$$

and

$$1 + \left(\frac{dy}{dx}\right)^2 = 1 + \frac{9x}{4}$$

Thus

$$\text{arc length} = \int_0^1 \left(1 + \frac{9x}{4}\right)^{\frac{1}{2}} dx$$

$$= \left[\frac{\left(1 + \dfrac{9x}{4}\right)^{\frac{3}{2}}}{\dfrac{3}{2} \cdot \dfrac{9}{4}}\right]_0^1$$

$$= \frac{8}{27}\left\{\left(\frac{13}{4}\right)^{\frac{3}{2}} - 1\right\}$$

$$= 1 \cdot 44$$

Worked example B

Find the arc length of the **parabola** defined parametrically by $x = at^2$, $y = 2at$ between the points $(a, 2a)$ (for which $t = 1$) and $(4a, 4a)$ (for which $t = 2$)

Here

$$\frac{dx}{dt} = 2at \text{ and } \frac{dy}{dt} = 2a$$

Thus

$$\text{arc length} = \int_1^2 \{\sqrt{(2at)^2 + (2a)^2}\} dt = 2a\int_1^2 \sqrt{1 + t^2}\, dt$$

To evaluate this integral, put
$$t = \sinh u$$
so that $dt = \cosh u\, du$
When $t = 1$, $u = \sinh^{-1}1$ $(= \alpha$, say), and
When $t = 2$, $u = \sinh^{-1}2$ $(= \beta$, say)

Thus

$$\text{arc length} = 2a\int_\alpha^\beta \sqrt{1 + \sinh^2 u} \cdot \cosh u\, du$$

$$= 2a\int_\alpha^\beta \cosh^2 u\, du$$

$$= a\int_\alpha^\beta (1 + \cosh 2u)\, du$$

$$= a\left[u + \frac{1}{2}\sinh 2u\right]_{\alpha}^{\beta}$$

$$= a\left[u + \sinh u \cosh u\right]_{\alpha}^{\beta}$$

$$= a[\sinh^{-1}2 + 2\sqrt{1 + 2^2} - \sinh^{-1}1 - 1\sqrt{1 + 1^2}]$$

$$= a(2\sqrt{5} - \sqrt{2} + \sinh^{-1}2 - \sinh^{-1}1)$$

$$= 3 \cdot 62a$$

AREA

Area is the amount of space inside a flat two-dimensional (2D) shape, and is measured in squares, square centimetres or square metres, for example.

▶ COMMON AREAS

- Area of **rectangle** = length × breadth
- Area of **triangle** = ½base length × height
- Area of **parallelogram** = base length × height
- Area of **trapezium** = average length of parallel sides × perpendicular distance between them
- Area of **circle** = πr^2, where r is the radius
- Area of **sector** = $\dfrac{x \pi r^2}{360}$ where $x°$ is the angle of the sector.

▶ AREA UNDER A CURVE

For questions involving the area of the region between a curve, the x- or y-axis and the appropriate ordinates or abscissae, it is necessary to commit to memory the appropriate **integrals**. They can, however, be quite easily built up by considering the area of an appropriate elementary strip, regarding the integral sign as standing for the summation of the areas as designated by the limits of the integral (see Fig. A.5). The area of the region between two curves can be dealt with in similar manner.

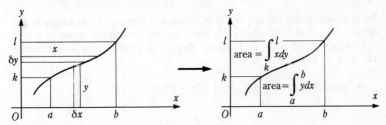

Fig. A.5

AREA

In calculating such areas it is advisable to sketch the curves, so that mistakes are not made should part of the area be below the x-axis and therefore counted as negative, and so a difference of two areas is obtained rather than their sum. Take a curve with equation $y = f(x)$ which crosses the x-axis between $x = a$ and $x = c$, at $x = b$, say, as shown in Fig. A.6. Then the area of the region bounded by the curve $y = f(x)$, the x-axis and the ordinates at $x = a$, $x = c$ is given by:

$$\int_a^b y\,dx - \int_b^c y\,dx = \int_a^b f(x)\,dx + \left| \int_b^c f(x)\,dx \right|$$

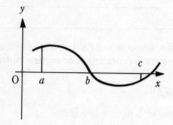

Fig. A.6

Worked example A

Sketch the arc of the curve with equation $y = 2x - x^2$ for which y is positive. Find the area of the finite region which lies between this arc and the x-axis (Fig. A.7). You should be able to recognise the equation as that of a **parabola**.

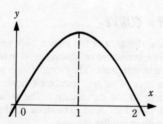

Fig. A.7

By completing the square of the x terms and writing the equation in the form $y = 1 - (x-1)^2$ it can be seen that the maximum value of y is 1 and occurs when $x = 1$. Further, the curve crosses the x-axis where $x(2 - x) = 0 \Rightarrow x = 0$ or 2

$$\Rightarrow \text{Required area} \Rightarrow \int_0^2 y\,dx = \int_0^2 (2x - x^2)\,dx = \left[x^2 - \frac{x^3}{3} \right]_0^2$$

$$= 4 - \frac{8}{3} = \frac{4}{3}$$

Worked example B

Find the area of the finite region bounded by the curves with equation $y = x^2$, $y^2 = x$.

For such a question it is absolutely essential to sketch the curves, as in Fig. A.8.

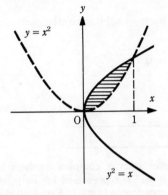

Clearly, the curves meet at the point $(1, 1)$. Thus:

$$\text{Required area} = \int_0^1 x^{\frac{1}{2}}dx - \int_0^1 x^2 dx$$

$$= \frac{2}{3}\left[x^{\frac{3}{2}}\right]_0^1 - \frac{1}{3}\left[x^3\right]_0^1$$

$$= \frac{2}{3} - \frac{1}{3} = \frac{1}{3}$$

Fig. A.8

Worked example C

Show that the area enclosed by the **ellipse** with equation $\dfrac{x^2}{a^2} + \dfrac{y^2}{b^2} = 1$ is πab (see Fig. A.9).

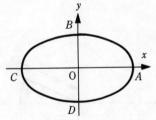

Fig. A.9

The **parametric equations** of this ellipse are $x = a\cos\theta$, $y = b\sin\theta$

At A, $\theta = 0$. At B, $\theta = \dfrac{\pi}{2}$ and for points on the ellipse between A

and B, $0 \le \theta \le \dfrac{\pi}{2}$

Area enclosed by the ellipse $= 4 \times$ Area OAB

$$= 4\int_0^a y dx = 4\int_{\frac{\pi}{2}}^0 b\sin\theta . (-a\sin\theta\, d\theta) \text{ since}$$

$y = b\sin\theta$ and $dx \equiv -a\sin\theta\, d\theta$

$$\Rightarrow \text{Area} = -4ab \int_{\frac{\pi}{2}}^{0} \sin^2\theta \, d\theta = -2ab \int_{\frac{\pi}{2}}^{0} (1 - \cos 2\theta) \, d\theta$$

$$= -2ab \left[\theta - \sin 2\theta \right]_{\frac{\pi}{2}}^{0} = -2ab \left[0 - 0 - \frac{\pi}{2} + \frac{1}{2} \sin \pi \right] = \pi ab$$

Note: the limits to the integral in terms of θ are $\dfrac{\pi}{2}$ and 0 since when

$x = 0$, $\theta = \dfrac{\pi}{2}$ and when $x = a$, $\theta = 0$.

◀ Integration ▶

ARGAND DIAGRAM

An Argand diagram is a graphical representation of **complex numbers** in which the complex number $z = x + iy = re^{i\theta}$ is represented by the point with cartesian coordinates (x, y) or polar coordinates (r, θ). In Fig. A.10 the ordinary two-dimensional diagram is used to represent a complex number, the real part x being measured along the x-axis or real axis, and the imaginary part y being measured along the y-axis or imaginary axis.

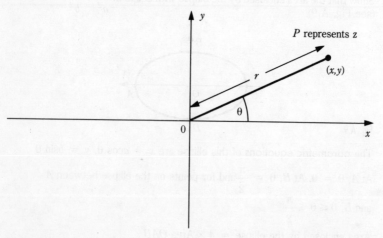

Fig. A.10

The complex number $z_1 = 4 + 2i$ is therefore represented by the point A in Fig. A11. B represents $-2 - 3i$, C represents $-4 + 3i$, D represents $2 + i0$ and E represents i (see Fig. A.11).

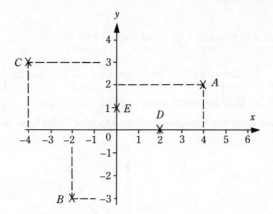

Fig. A.11

ARGUMENT

If P represents the **complex number** $z = x + iy$ then the length of OP, usually denoted by r, $|z|$ or $|x + iy|$, is called the **modulus** of z. The angle $\theta = P\hat{O}x$ is called the argument of z and is written as $\arg z = \arg (x + iy) = \theta = \arctan \left(\dfrac{y}{x}\right)$. The examining boards have agreed to use the convention that $-\pi < \arg z \leqslant \pi$ (Fig. A.12).

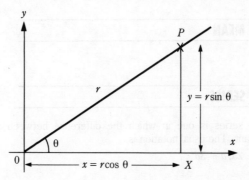

Fig. A.12

In finding θ, you must plot the complex number on an Argand diagram (Fig. A.13), since there is an infinite number of angles whose tangent is $\left(\dfrac{y}{x}\right)$; two of these lie in $(-\pi, \pi)$, but only one of these corresponds to the unique position of P. The value of θ in $(-\pi, \pi)$ is known as the *principal value* of the argument.

Thus

$$z_1 = 2 + 3i \Rightarrow \arg(2 + 3i) = \arctan\left(\frac{3}{2}\right) = \theta_1, \text{ say,}$$

$$z_2 = -2 - 3i \Rightarrow \arg(-2 - 3i) = \arctan\left(\frac{-3}{-2}\right) = \arctan\left(\frac{3}{2}\right) = \theta_2,$$

say, $\theta_1 = 56.3°$ or 0.983^c, $\theta_2 = -123.7° = -2.16^c$

◀ Argand diagram, Complex number, Modulus, Polar form ▶

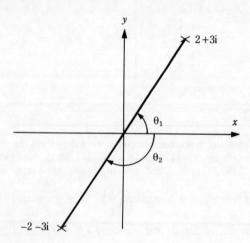

Fig. A.13

ARITHMETIC MEAN

◀ Mean ▶

ARITHMETIC SERIES

An arithmetic series is one in which the difference between successive terms is constant. The usual notation is

$$a, a + d, a + 2d, a + 3d \ldots$$

where

a = first term

and d = common difference

If l denotes the nth term, then

$$l = a + (n - 1)d$$

If S_n denotes the sum of the first n terms, then

$$S_n = \frac{n}{2}(a + l) = \frac{n}{2}[2a + (n - 1)d]$$

The formula for S_n is easily proved, as is now shown –

$S_n = a + (a + d) + (a + 2d) + (a + 3d) + \ldots + [a + (n - 1)d]$

Reversing the order of the terms on the R.H.S.

$S_n = [a + (n - 1)d] + [a + (n - 2)d] + [a + (n - 3)d] + \ldots a$

Adding the two equations

$2S_n = [2a + (n - 1)d] + [2a + (n - 1)d] + \ldots n$ times

$2S_n = n[2a + (n - 1)d] \Rightarrow S_n = \dfrac{n}{2}[2a + (n - 1)d]$

or $S_n = \dfrac{n}{2}[a + a + (n - 1)d] = \dfrac{n}{2}[a + l]$

Worked example

The 9th term of an arithmetic series is -1 and the sum of the first 9 terms is 45. Find   i) the common difference,   ii) the sum of the first 15 terms.

First write down, in algebraic form, the information given

$n = 9, l = -1, S_9 = 45$

Then look at the formulae and choose the one containing only one unknown.

$S_n = \dfrac{n}{2}(a + l) \Rightarrow 45 = \dfrac{9}{2}[a + (-1)] \Longleftrightarrow a = 11$

$l = a + (n - 1)d \Rightarrow -1 = 11 + 8d \Longleftrightarrow d = -\dfrac{3}{2}$

$S_n = \dfrac{n}{2}[2a + (n - 1)d] \Rightarrow S_{15} = \dfrac{15}{2}\left[22 + 14\left(-\dfrac{3}{2}\right)\right] = \dfrac{15}{2}$

AVERAGE

There are three different types of average: **mode, median** and **mean**.
◀ Mean, Median, Mode ▶

B

BAYES' THEOREM

◀ Probability ▶

BIASED ESTIMATOR

◀ Estimator ▶

BINOMIAL

An algebraic expression consisting of two terms.

$$2x - y, \; x^3 + y^3, \; \frac{x}{y} - \frac{y}{x^2}$$

◀ Binomial distribution, Binomial expansion ▶

BINOMIAL DISTRIBUTION

Let n independent trials be carried out, each having two outcomes which we can call 'success' and 'failure'. Further, let the probability of success in each trial be p. Let X be the total number of successes obtained in the n trials.

Then X is said to have a binomial distribution with parameters (n, p), abbreviated to $B(n, p)$.

The probability function of the binomial distribution is

$$p_x = P(X = x) = {}^nC_x p^x q^{n-x} \text{ (where } q = 1 - p) \text{ for } x = 0, 1, \dots n$$

This follows by considering a sequence of successes and failures containing x successes, for example:

$$\underbrace{SS \dots S}_{x} \quad \underbrace{FF \dots F}_{n-x}$$

This has probability $p^x q^{n-x}$. There are ${}^nC_x$ such sequences, leading to the above result.

It can be shown by division that

$$\frac{p_{x+1}}{p_x} = \frac{(n-x)p}{(x+1)q}$$

or $\quad p_{x+1} = \dfrac{(n-x)p}{(x+1)q} p_x$

This result can be used for the calculation of successive binomial probabilities.

Many statistical tables include a table of binomial probabilities. The quantity usually tabulated is

$$F(x; n, p). = \sum_{y=0}^{x} {}^nC_y \, p^y \, q^{n-y} = P(X \leqslant x \,|\, X \text{ is } B(n, p))$$

Single probabilities can be found using the result

$$P(X = x \,|\, X \text{ is } B(n, p)) = F(x; n, p) - F(x-1; n, p)$$

▶ MEAN AND VARIANCE OF BINOMIAL DISTRIBUTION

The standard results here are

$$E(X) = np \text{ and } \text{Var}(X) = npq$$

The simplest proof is to let

$$X_i = 1 \text{ if the } i\text{th trial is a success}$$
$$= 0 \text{ if the } i\text{th trial is a failure}$$

Then

$$E(X_i) = p \times 1 + q \times 0 = p$$

and $\quad \text{Var}(X_i) = E(X_i^2) - [E(X_i)]^2$
$$= p \times 1 + q \times 0 - p^2$$
$$= p(1-p) = pq$$

Then,

$$X = \sum_{i=1}^{n} X_i$$

so that

$$E(X) = E\left(\sum_{i=1}^{n} X_i\right)$$
$$= \sum_{i=1}^{n} E(X_i)$$
$$= \sum_{i=1}^{n} p$$
$$= np$$

and

$$\text{Var}(X) = \text{Var}\left(\sum_{i=1}^{n} X_i\right)$$
$$= \sum_{i=1}^{n} \text{Var}(X_i)$$
$$= \sum_{i=1}^{n} pq$$
$$= npq$$

▶ ASYMPTOTIC APPROXIMATIONS

Poisson approximation

Let X be $B(n, p)$ so that

$$p_x = {}^nC_x p^x (1-p)^{n-x}$$

$$= \frac{n(n-1)(n-2)\dots(n-x+1)}{x!} \left(\frac{\mu}{n}\right)^x \left(1 - \frac{\mu}{n}\right)^{n-x}$$

where $\mu = E(X) = np$.

We now consider the limiting form of p_x as $n \to \infty$, keeping μ constant. This implies that $p \to 0$. Now,

$$p_x = \frac{\mu^x}{x!} \frac{n(n-1)\dots(n-x+1)}{n.n\dots n} \left(1 - \frac{\mu}{n}\right)^n \left(1 - \frac{\mu}{n}\right)$$

$$= \frac{\mu^x}{x!} \left(1 - \frac{1}{n}\right)\left(1 - \frac{2}{n}\right)\dots\left(1 - \left(\frac{x-1}{n}\right)\right)\left(1 - \frac{\mu}{n}\right)^n\left(1 - \frac{\mu}{x}\right)$$

It follows that

$$\lim_{n\to\infty} p_x = \frac{\mu^x}{x!} e^{-\mu}$$

since $\lim_{n\to\infty} \left(1 - \frac{\mu}{n}\right)^n = e^{-\mu}$

and $\lim_{n\to\infty} \left(1 - \frac{\mu}{n}\right)^{-x} = 1$

This result is used in practice for large n and small p, in which case, if X is $B(n, p)$,

$$P(X = x) = {}^nC_x p^x q^{n-x} \approx \frac{\mu^x e^{-\mu}}{x!}$$

where $\mu = np$.

It is not possible to give a definitive rule on when the Poisson approximation can be used, since this depends on what degree of accuracy is acceptable. Rules are, however, given in many texts – for instance, $n \geq 50$ and $p \leq 0.1$. We can test this rule by calculating probabilities and their Poisson approximations for the $B(50, 0.1)$ distribution; these are shown in the table. The errors in the central part of the distribution (i.e. around the mean $np = 5$) are approximately 5 per cent, which may or may not be acceptable.

x	0	1	2	3	4	5	6	7
Exact $P(X = x)$	0·0052	0·0286	0·0779	0·1386	0·1809	0·1849	0·1541	0·1076
Poisson approx.	0·0067	0·0337	0·0842	0·1404	0·1755	0·1755	0·1462	0·1044

Normal approximation

Let X be $B(n, p)$ with n large, but p not close to 0 or 1. Then, X has the approximate distribution $N(np, npq)$. Again, it is not possible to give a definitive rule on when the normal approximation can be used. Rules are, however, given in many texts – for instance $n \geqslant 50$ and $0 \cdot 2 \leqslant p \leqslant 0 \cdot 8$. A continuity correction should be used with this approximation, so that if X is $B(n, p)$ and the above conditions are satisfied,

$$P(a \leqslant X \leqslant b) = \sum_{x=a}^{b} {}^nC_x p^x q^{n-x} \approx \Phi\left(\frac{b + \frac{1}{2} - np}{\sqrt{npq}}\right) - \Phi\left(\frac{a - \frac{1}{2} - np}{\sqrt{npq}}\right)$$

where Φ denotes the distribution function of the standardised normal distribution $N(0, 1)$, and a, b are integers.

Worked example

A fair coin is tossed 100 times. Calculate the probability that the number of 'heads' obtained lies between 48 and 55 (inclusive).

Here X is $B(100, \frac{1}{2})$, so that

$$P(48 \leqslant X \leqslant 55) \approx \Phi\left(\frac{55 + \frac{1}{2} - 50}{\sqrt{25}}\right) - \Phi\left(\frac{48 - \frac{1}{2} - 50}{\sqrt{25}}\right)$$

$$= \Phi(1 \cdot 1) - \Phi(-0 \cdot 5)$$
$$= \Phi(1 \cdot 1) - [1 - \Phi(0 \cdot 5)]$$
$$= 0 \cdot 5558$$

The exact value is found, using binomial tables, to be
$$F(55; 100; 0 \cdot 5) - F(47; 100, 0 \cdot 5) = 0 \cdot 86437 - 0 \cdot 30865$$
$$= 0 \cdot 5557$$

indicating the accuracy of this approximation.
◀ Normal distribution, Poisson distribution ▶

BINOMIAL EXPANSION

The basic result here is that, for n a positive integer,

$$(a + b)^n = a^n + na^{n-1}b + \frac{n(n-1)}{2!} a^{n-2}b^2 + \frac{n(n-1)(n-2)}{3!} a^{n-3}b^3$$
$$+ \ldots + nab^{n-1} + b^n$$

$$= \sum_{r=0}^{n} {}^nC_r a^r b^{n-r} = \sum_{r=0}^{n} {}^nC_r a^{n-r}b^r$$

where

$${}^nC_r = \frac{n!}{r!\,(n-r)!}$$

and $n!$ (n factorial) is defined by
$$n! = n(n-1)\ldots 2.1$$

(NB. 0! is taken to be 1.) Putting $n = 4$, for example, we find that
$$(a + b)^4 = a^4 + 4a^3b + 6a^2b^2 + 4ab^3 + b^4$$
A special case is obtained by putting $a = 1$, $b = x$ so that

$$(1 + x)^n = 1 + nx + \frac{n(n - 1)x^2}{2!} + \frac{n(n - 1)(n - 2)x^3}{3!} + \ldots \qquad \text{(i)}$$

If n is a positive integer, the expansion terminates with the term x^n. For example, with $n = 4$,
$$(1 + x)^4 = 1 + 4x + 6x^2 + 4x^3 + x^4$$
If, however, n is not a positive integer, expression (i) gives an infinite series, i.e. it never terminates. This series is convergent for $|x| < 1$.

In this case,

$$(1 + x)^n = \sum_{r=0}^{\infty} \frac{n(n - 1)(n - 2) \ldots (n - r + 1)x^r}{r!}$$

(NB. We interpret the first term $(r = 0)$ to be 1.) For example, putting $n = \frac{1}{2}$,

$$(1 + x)^{\frac{1}{2}} = 1 + \frac{x}{2} - \frac{x^2}{8} + \frac{x^3}{16} + \ldots$$

This result can be used to derive rational approximations to square roots of integers. For example, putting $x = \frac{1}{3}$,

$$\left(\frac{4}{3}\right)^{\frac{1}{2}} \approx 1 + \frac{1}{6} - \frac{1}{72} + \frac{1}{432} = \frac{499}{432}$$

or $\quad \dfrac{2}{\sqrt{3}} \approx \dfrac{499}{432}$

i.e. $\quad \sqrt{3} \approx \dfrac{864}{499}$

BOW'S NOTATION

Bow's notation is used for labelling the spaces in a space diagram with capital letters. When this notation is followed by the respective small letters for vertices in the force diagram (polygon), it provides an easy check on the directions of the forces, and it also ensures that the forces are taken in order.

◀ Triangle (polygon) of forces ▶

BRACKET

Algebraic operations often involve the use of brackets, and it is absolutely essential for students to become familiar with the use of and the removal of brackets. Remember when removing brackets that if the sign before the bracket is positive, the + and − signs inside the bracket are unaltered. If the sign before the bracket is −, the + and − signs inside the brackets change to − and + respectively. Remember also that inner brackets should always be removed first.

Three worked examples

Simplify $3(2xy + z) - 4(xy - 2z) + 2(z - xy)$
$$\Rightarrow 6xy + 3z - 4xy + 8z + 2z - 2xy = 13z$$

Simplify $3 - x - 2[1 - 3(x - y)]$
$$\Rightarrow 3 - x - 2[1 - 3x + 3y] = 3 - x - 2 + 6x - 6y = 1 + 5x - 6y$$

Solve the equation $(x - 2)(x + 3) = x(x - 1)$
$$\Rightarrow x(x + 3) - 2(x + 3) = x(x - 1)$$
$$\Rightarrow x^2 + 3x - 2x - 6 = x^2 - x \Rightarrow x^2 + 3x - 2x - 6 - x^2 + x = 0$$
$$\Rightarrow 2x - 6 = 0 \Rightarrow 2x = 6 \Rightarrow x = 3$$

CARTESIAN COORDINATES

◀ Coordinates ▶

CARTESIAN EQUATIONS

◀ Curve sketching ▶

CARTESIAN FORM

◀ Vector, Vector geometry ▶

CAST DIAGRAM

◀ Angle, Trigonometric function ▶

CENTRAL LIMIT THEOREM

Let X_1, X_2, ... X_n be a random sample of size n from a distribution, not necessarily normal, with finite mean μ and finite variance σ^2.

The central limit theorem states that, for large n,

$$\sum_{i=1}^{n} X_i \quad \text{is approximately N}(n\mu, n\sigma^2)$$

Variations of the theorem are that

$$\bar{X} = \frac{\sum_{i=1}^{n} X_i}{n} \quad \text{is approximately N}\left(\mu, \frac{\sigma^2}{n}\right)$$

and $\dfrac{\bar{X} - \mu}{\sigma/\sqrt{n}}$ is approximately N$(0, 1)$

It is impossible to state how large n must be in order to use this theorem, although some textbooks do this. This depends on how near to normality the sampled distribution is.

- If the distribution is normal, then $n = 1$ gives an exact result.
- If the distribution is uniform, then $n \geq 12$ gives an acceptable approximation.
- If the distribution is exponential, which is markedly non-normal, then even $n = 100$ does not give a very good approximation.

Worked example A

The sugar content per litre bottle of a soft drink is known to be distributed with mean 5·8 and standard deviation 1·2. A sample of 900 bottles is taken at random and the sugar content of each bottle is measured. Estimate to three decimal places the probability that the mean sugar content of the 900 bottles will be less than 5·85.

Since X is distributed with $\mu = 5 \cdot 8$, $\sigma^2 = (1 \cdot 2)^2$ and $n = 900$

$\Rightarrow \bar{X}$ is approximately normally distributed $N\left(5 \cdot 8, \dfrac{(1 \cdot 2)^2}{900}\right)$

Hence $P(\bar{X} < 5 \cdot 85) = \Phi \dfrac{5 \cdot 85 - 5 \cdot 8}{\dfrac{1 \cdot 2}{\sqrt{900}}} = \Phi(1 \cdot 25) = 0 \cdot 8944$

$= 0 \cdot 894$ (to 3 decimal places)

Worked example B

A firm produces alternators for cars. The alternators are known to have a mean lifetime of 8 years with standard deviation 6 months. Forty samples of 144 alternators produced by the firm are tested. Estimate the number of samples which would be expected to have a mean lifetime of more than 8 years and 1 month

Let X months be the lifetime of an alternator. Then X is distributed with mean 96 months and standard deviation 6 months. The sample size, n, is 144 which is large, hence $\bar{X}$ the mean sample life is approximately distributed

$$N\left(96, \frac{6^2}{144}\right)$$

That is

$$SE_{\bar{X}} = \frac{6}{\sqrt{144}} = \frac{1}{2}$$

Hence $P(\bar{X} < 97) = \Phi\left(\dfrac{1}{\frac{1}{2}}\right) = \Phi(2) = 0 \cdot 97725$

$\Rightarrow$ Of 40 samples, $40 \times 0 \cdot 97725 = 39 \cdot 09$ would be expected to have a mean lifetime of less than 8 years and 1 month. So only approximately 1 sample would be expected to have a mean lifetime of more than 8 years and 1 month.

◀ Normal distribution ▶

CENTRAL LOCATION/TENDENCY (MEASUREMENT)

◀ Mean, Median, Mode ▶

CENTRE OF MASS

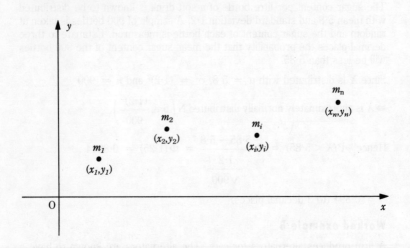

Fig. C.1

Consider first the situation of a number of discrete masses located at various points, as shown, for instance, in Fig. C.1. Let a mass m_i be located at the point $(x_i, y_i)(i = 1, 2, \ldots n)$. Then,

$$\text{Total moment about } y\text{-axis} = \sum_{i=1}^{n} m_i x_i$$

and

$$\text{Total moment about } x\text{-axis} = \sum_{i=1}^{n} m_i y_i$$

The coordinates of the centre of mass $(\bar{x}, \bar{y})$ are therefore given by

$$\bar{x} = \frac{\sum_{i=1}^{n} m_i x_i}{\sum_{i=1}^{n} m_i}$$

and

$$\bar{y} = \frac{\sum_{i=1}^{n} m_i y_i}{\sum_{i=1}^{n} m_i}$$

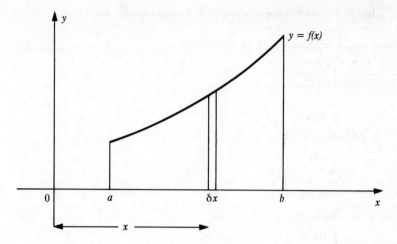

Fig. C.2

Consider now a uniform lamina bounded by the curve $y = f(x)$, the ordinates $x = a$ and $x = b$ and the x-axis as shown in Fig. C.2. Let the density of the lamina be ρ/unit area. Consider a thin strip as shown. Then,

x-Moment of strip $= x \cdot \rho y \delta x$

so that

$$\text{Total } x\text{-Moment of lamina} = \int_a^b \rho xy \, dx$$

Furthermore,

y-Moment of strip $= \dfrac{1}{2} y \cdot \rho y \delta x$

so that

$$\text{Total } y\text{-Moment of lamina} = \int_a^b \frac{1}{2} \rho y^2 \, dx$$

Now

Mass of strip $= \rho y \delta x$

so that

$$\text{Total mass of lamina} = \int_a^b \rho y \, dx$$

CENTRE OF MASS

Thus, if $(\bar{x}, \bar{y})$ denote the coordinates of the centre of the mass,

$$\bar{x} = \frac{\displaystyle\int_a^b \rho xy\,dx}{\displaystyle\int_a^b \rho y\,dx}$$

$$= \frac{\displaystyle\int_a^b xy\,dx}{\displaystyle\int_a^b y\,dx}$$

$$= \frac{\displaystyle\int_a^b xf(x)\,dx}{\displaystyle\int_a^b f(x)\,dx}$$

$$\bar{y} = \frac{\displaystyle\int_a^b \frac{1}{2}\rho y^2\,dx}{\displaystyle\int_a^b \rho y\,dx}$$

$$= \frac{\displaystyle\frac{1}{2}\int_a^b y^2\,dx}{\displaystyle\int_a^b y\,dx}$$

$$= \frac{\displaystyle\frac{1}{2}\int_a^b \left\{f(x)\right\}^2\,dx}{\displaystyle\int_a^b f(x)\,dx}$$

Worked example

Find the centroid of the uniform lamina bounded by the line $y = x$, the ordinate $x = a$ and the x-axis – see Fig. C.3.

Here $$\bar{x} = \frac{\displaystyle\int_0^a xy\,dx}{\displaystyle\int_0^a y\,dx}$$

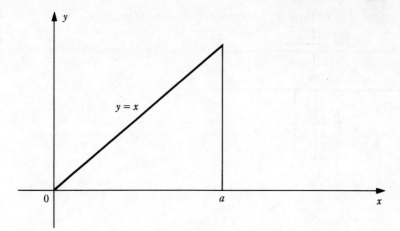

Fig. C.3

$$= \frac{\displaystyle\int_0^a x^2 \, dx}{\displaystyle\int_0^a x \, dx}$$

$$= \frac{\dfrac{1}{3}\Big[x^3\Big]_0^a}{\dfrac{1}{2}\Big[x^2\Big]_0^a}$$

$$= \frac{\dfrac{1}{3}a^3}{\dfrac{1}{2}a^2}$$

$$= \frac{2}{3}a$$

Also, $\quad \bar{y} = \dfrac{\dfrac{1}{2}\displaystyle\int_0^a y^2 \, dx}{\displaystyle\int_0^a y \, dx}$

$$= \frac{\dfrac{1}{2}\displaystyle\int_0^a x^2 \, \mathrm{d}x}{\displaystyle\int_0^a x \, \mathrm{d}x}$$

$$= \frac{\dfrac{1}{6}\left[x^3\right]_0^a}{\dfrac{1}{2}\left[x^2\right]_0^a}$$

$$= \frac{\dfrac{1}{6}a^3}{\dfrac{1}{2}a^2}$$

$$= \frac{1}{3}a$$

▶ CENTRE OF MASS AND FORCES

This is an important concept required in the study of **forces** acting on a rigid body.

Body (uniform)	Centre of mass location
Circular arc, angle 2θ, radius r	$\dfrac{r\sin\theta}{\theta}$ from centre
Circular sector, angle 2θ, radius r	$\dfrac{2r\sin\theta}{3\theta}$ from centre
Triangular lamina ABC mid-point of BC is D	at G, intersection of medians, e.g. $\overrightarrow{AG} = \dfrac{2}{3}\overrightarrow{AD}$
Solid right circular cone, height h	$\dfrac{3}{4}h$ from vertex
Solid hemisphere, radius r	$\dfrac{3}{8}r$ from centre
Hemispherical shell, radius r	$\dfrac{1}{2}r$ from centre

The weight of the particles which make up a rigid body form a set of forces all directed towards the earth's centre and we assume that these forces are parallel. The resultant of the weights is equal in magnitude to the sum of the weights of the particles. This sum is called the *weight of the body* and it acts through a definite point called the *centre of mass of the body*. For uniform, symmetrical bodies, the position of the centre of mass coincides with the centre of symmetry; for instances, the centre of mass of a uniform straight rod is at the midpoint of the rod; the centre of mass of a thin, uniform square plate is at the centre of the square. Often, the position of the centre of mass of a body is determined by **integration** using the result that the sum of the moments of the weights of all the particles making up the body about any point is equal to the moment of the weight of the whole body about the same point.

Some standard results for uniform bodies are often given in the formula booklets issued by the examination boards, and the above table gives some of these. Check carefully with your own booklet, but remember that you may be asked to prove any result by integration at the start of a question.

◀ Forces, Integration, Moments, Rigid body ▶

CENTRIPETAL ACCELERATION

◀ Circular motion, Kinematics ▶

CENTROIDS

◀ Centre of mass ▶

CHAIN RULE

The chain rule is a rule for finding the **derivative** of a function of a function. The rule states that if u is a function of v where v is a function of x, then

$$\frac{du}{dx} = \frac{du}{dv} \cdot \frac{dv}{dx}$$

The result can be generalised:

$$\frac{du}{dx} = \frac{du}{dv} \cdot \frac{dv}{dw} \cdot \frac{dw}{dx}$$

The result in function notation is that

$$\frac{d}{dx}[f \circ g(x)] = [f' \circ g(x)] \times g'(x)$$

where ′ denotes differentiation with respect to x.

Worked example

Find the derivative of $(1 + \sin x)^2$.

Using the first notation above, we let
$$u = v^2$$
where $v = 1 + \sin x$

Now, $\dfrac{du}{dx} = \dfrac{du}{dv} \cdot \dfrac{dv}{dx}$

$\qquad = 2v \cdot \cos x$

$\qquad = 2(1 + \sin x) \cos x$

Using the second notation, with

$f(x) = x^2$ and $g(x) = 1 + \sin x$

$\dfrac{d}{dx}[f \circ g(x)] = [f' \circ g(x)] \times g'(x)$

$\qquad = 2(1 + \sin x) \cos x$

CHI-SQUARED (χ^2) TEST (GOODNESS OF FIT)

Let an experiment have n outcomes. Suppose we wish to test the null hypothesis

H_0: the ith outcome has probability π_i $\qquad (\sum\limits_{i=1}^{n} \pi_i = 1)$

against all alternatives.

To test H_0, suppose that the experiment is repeated N times and the ith outcome occurs O_i times.

Under H_0, let E_i denote the expected number of times the ith outcome occurs so that $E_i = N\pi_i$. Then, the statistic used to measure the discrepancy between the observations and those predicted by H_0 is

$$X^2 = \sum_{x=1}^{n} \frac{(O_x - E_x)^2}{E_x}$$

It can be shown that for large N, X^2 has approximately the χ^2-distribution with $(n-1)$ degrees of freedom. In practice, the common 'rule of thumb' is that all the E_x's should be at least 5. If any values are less than this, then some outcomes will have to be combined.

A special case of the situation being considered is the fitting of a distribution to experimental data, as in these examples.

Worked example A

The data in the table refer to the number of errors made by a typist on pages of a book. Test the hypothesis H_0 that the Poisson distribution with mean $1 \cdot 5$ is an acceptable fit to these data.

Number of errors (x)	0	1	2	3	4	5	6	7 or more
Number of pages (O_x)	14	25	32	19	5	3	2	0

Here, the probabilities associated with each value of x under H_0 are

$$p_x = \frac{1 \cdot 5^x e^{-1 \cdot 5}}{x!}$$

The values of E_x are therefore

$$E_x = 100 \times \frac{1 \cdot 5^x e^{-1 \cdot 5}}{x!}$$

since there are 100 pages in the book. The values of E_x are given by the figures shown in the second table. (NB. The last probability is 1 minus the sum of all the others.) Since the expected frequencies in the last four categories are less than 5, we combine them to give a category of 4 errors or more, which gives the information shown in the third table.

Number of errors (x)	0	1	2	3	4	5	6	7 or more
Expected number of pages E_x	22·313	33·470	25·102	12·551	4·707	1·412	0·353	0·092

Number of errors (x)	0	1	2	3	4 or more
O_x	14	25	32	19	10
E_x	22·313	33·470	25·102	12·551	6·564

It follows that

$$X^2 = \frac{(14 - 22 \cdot 313)^2}{22 \cdot 313} + \frac{(25 - 33 \cdot 470)^2}{33 \cdot 470} + \ldots + \frac{(10 - 6 \cdot 564)^2}{6 \cdot 564}$$

$$= 12 \cdot 248$$

At a significance level of 5 per cent, the appropriate critical value is $\chi^2_{\cdot 95}(4) = 9 \cdot 488$. The computed value is greater than this, so that the Poisson distribution with mean 1·5 is not an acceptable fit to the data.

It is possible to generalise the null hypothesis in this problem to

H_0: The number of errors made per page is Poisson distributed.

The difference here is that although the distribution is specified, the mean is not.

We can, however, use the data to estimate the mean to allow the expected frequencies to be calculated. The only modification we need make to the test procedure is to subtract one degree of freedom. More generally, one degree of freedom is subtracted for each parameter estimated.

Worked example B

The data shown in the table refer to the number of errors made by a typist on pages of a book. Test the hypothesis H_0 that the Poisson distribution is an acceptable fit to these data.

Number of errors (x)	0	1	2	3	4	5	6	7 or more
Number of pages (O_x)	14	25	32	19	5	3	2	0

Since the mean is not specified, we estimate by the mean of the data.

$$\text{Mean} = \frac{(1 \times 25) + (2 \times 32) + (3 \times 19) + (4 \times 5) + (5 \times 3) + (6 \times 2)}{100}$$

$$= 1 \cdot 93$$

We therefore take

$$p_x = \frac{1 \cdot 93^x e^{-1 \cdot 93}}{x!}$$

and

$$E_x = 100 \times \frac{1 \cdot 93^x e^{-1 \cdot 93}}{x!}$$

The values of E_x are given by the second table. Again, we have to combine the last four categories. Even though E_4 exceeds 5, the remaining E_x's sum to less than 5 so that they have to be combined with E_4. This gives the information shown in the third table.

Number of errors (x)	0	1	2	3	4	5	6	7 or more
E_x	14·515	28·014	27·033	17·391	8·391	3·239	1·042	0·375

Number of errors (x)	0	1	2	3	4 or more
O_x	14	25	32	19	10
E_x	14·515	28·014	27·033	17·391	13·047

Thus,

$$X^2 = \frac{(14 - 14 \cdot 515)^2}{14 \cdot 515} + \frac{(25 - 28 \cdot 014)^2}{28 \cdot 014} + \ldots + \frac{(10 - 13 \cdot 047)^2}{13 \cdot 047}$$

$$= 2 \cdot 116$$

There are now 3 degrees of freedom, and at significance level 5 per cent, the appropriate critical value is $\chi^2_{.95}(3) = 7 \cdot 815$. The computed value is less than this, so that the Poisson distribution is an acceptable fit to the data.

CHORD

◀ Circle ▶

CIRCLE

A circle is the locus of a point which moves in such a way that its distance from a fixed point, called the centre, is equal to a constant, called the radius.

▶ EQUATION OF A CIRCLE

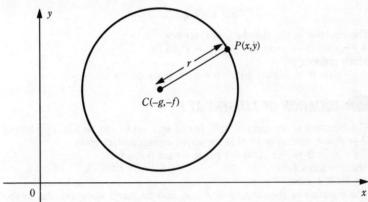

Fig. C.4

Let $P(x, y)$ be a general point on the circle in Fig. C.4. Then, if $C(-g, -f)$ denotes the centre and r the radius,

$$CP = \sqrt{(x + g)^2 + (y + f)^2} = r$$

whence

$$(x + g)^2 + (y + f)^2 = r^2$$

or, expanding

$$x^2 + y^2 + 2gx + 2fy + g^2 + f^2 - r^2 = 0$$

i.e. $x^2 + y^2 + 2gx + 2fy + c = 0$

where $c = g^2 + f^2 - r^2$

Conversely, the circle having equation

$$x^2 + y^2 + 2gx + 2fy + c = 0$$

has centre $(-g, -f)$ and radius $\sqrt{g^2 + f^2 - c}$.

▶ PARAMETRIC COORDINATES

In the special case $f = g = 0$, in which the centre is at the origin, the equation of the circle is

$$x^2 + y^2 = r^2$$

The point $P(r \cos \theta,\ r \sin \theta)$ lies on this circle for all θ since
$$(r \cos \theta)^2 + (r \sin \theta)^2 = r^2(\cos^2 \theta + \sin^2 \theta)$$
$$= r^2$$

▶ EQUATION OF CHORD

Let $P(r \cos \theta,\ r \sin \theta)$, $Q(r \cos \phi,\ r \sin \phi)$ be two points on the circle. Then

$$
\begin{aligned}
\text{Gradient of chord } PQ &= \frac{r \sin \theta - r \sin \phi}{r \cos \theta - r \cos \phi} \\[2mm]
&= \frac{2 \cos \tfrac{1}{2}(\theta + \phi) \sin \tfrac{1}{2}(\theta - \phi)}{-2 \sin \tfrac{1}{2}(\theta + \phi) \sin \tfrac{1}{2}(\theta - \phi)} \\[2mm]
&= -\cot \tfrac{1}{2}(\theta + \phi)
\end{aligned}
$$

The equation of the chord PQ is therefore
$$y - r \sin \theta = -\cot \tfrac{1}{2}(\theta + \phi)\ (x - r \cos \theta)$$
which reduces to
$$y - r \sin \theta = -x \cot \tfrac{1}{2}(\theta + \phi) + r \cot \tfrac{1}{2}(\theta + \phi) \cos \theta$$

▶ EQUATION OF TANGENT AT P

The equation of the tangent at P $(r \cos \theta,\ r \sin \theta)$ can be found by letting $Q \to P$, i.e. putting $\phi = \theta$ in the above equation. This gives
$$y - r \sin \theta = -x \cot \theta + r \cot \theta + r \cot \theta \cos \theta$$
which reduces to
$$y \sin \theta + x \cos \theta = r$$
The equation of the tangent at P can also be found using calculus in the following way.
$$x = r \cos \theta : y = r \sin \theta$$
$$\frac{dx}{d\theta} = -r \sin \theta : \frac{dy}{d\theta} = r \cos \theta$$
Thus, the gradient of the tangent at P is given by
$$\frac{dy}{dx} = \frac{dy}{d\theta} \Big/ \frac{dx}{d\theta}$$
$$= -\frac{r \cos \theta}{r \sin \theta} = -\cot \theta$$
The equation of the tangent at P is therefore
$$y - r \sin \theta = -\cot \theta\ (x - r \cos \theta)$$
or
$$y \sin \theta + x \cos \theta = r$$

CIRCULAR FUNCTION

◀ Angle ▶

CIRCULAR MOTION

A particle moving in a circle of constant radius r with angular velocity $\dot\theta$ has tangential velocity component $r\dot\theta$. The acceleration components $r\ddot\theta$ tangentially and $r\dot\theta^2$ towards the centre. This acceleration component towards the centre is called the *centripetal acceleration*, and an alternative expression for it is v^2/r, where $v = r\dot\theta$ denotes the speed.

Circular motion can only be maintained if there is a force providing the necessary centripetal acceleration.

The following example shows how energy principles can be combined with circular motion.

Worked example

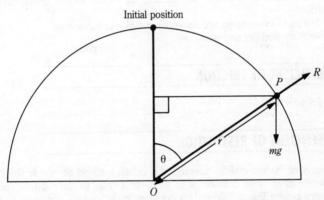

Fig. C.5

Fig. C.5 shows the circular cross-section of a smooth log. A particle of mass m is placed at the highest point and slightly displaced so that it slides down the log. Find the reaction R when OP makes an angle θ with the vertical.

Let v denote the speed of the particle in the position shown. Then, taking the reference level for potential energy as the initial position of the particle,

Initial energy = Initial kinetic energy + Initial potential energy
$$= 0 + 0$$
$$= 0$$

Energy in position shown = Kinetic energy + potential energy
$$= \tfrac{1}{2}mv^2 - mgr(1 - \cos\theta)$$

Using **Conservation of Energy**,
$$\tfrac{1}{2}mv^2 - mgr(1 - \cos\theta) = 0$$
so that
$$v^2 = 2gr(1 - \cos\theta)$$

Centripetal acceleration $= \dfrac{v^2}{r}$
$$= 2g(1 - \cos\theta)$$

Resolving towards the centre,

$$mg \cos \theta - R = \frac{mv^2}{r}$$

so that

$$R = mg \cos \theta - 2mg(1 - \cos \theta)$$
$$= mg(3 \cos \theta - 2)$$

We observe that R changes from positive to negative when

$$3 \cos \theta - 2 = 0$$

$$\cos \theta = \frac{2}{3}$$

or

$$\theta = \cos^{-1}\left(\frac{2}{3}\right) \approx 48°$$

Since R cannot be negative, the particle leaves the surface of the log in this position.

◀ Force, Non-uniform circular motion, Polar components (of velocity and acceleration) ▶

COEFFICIENT OF FRICTION

◀ Friction ▶

COEFFICIENT OF RESTITUTION

When two bodies collide directly, the relative speed at which the bodies separate after their collision is in a constant ratio to the relative speed of closure before the collision. This constant ratio for two particular bodies is called their coefficient of restitution and is usually denoted by e, where $0 \leq e \leq 1$.

Suppose we have two particles A and B moving in the same straight line with constant speeds u_A and u_B, and that they collide. After the collision A and B move in the same line, as shown in Fig. C.6, with speeds v_A and v_B.

By the law stated above

$$\text{Coefficient of restitution} = e = \frac{v_B - v_A}{u_A - u_B}$$

Fig. C.6   *before collision*   *after collision*

If we also know the masses of A and B (suppose they are m_A and m_B), then by the **conservation of momentum** principle, we have

$$m_A u_A + m_B u_B = m_A v_A + m_B v_B$$

In questions it is usual to have m_A, m_B, u_A, u_B and e given, and by using both **Newton's experimental law** and the conservation of momentum principle, v_A and v_B can be found.

When solving problems, draw a clear diagram for each stage; that is, one for before the collision and another for after the collision. Write down clear equations and state the principle being applied. Marks are awarded for these vital stages. Then, make sure each step in your solution is clear. Often you will be asked to find the loss in kinetic energy due to the collision. In the case just presented this loss is:

$$\frac{1}{2}m_A u_A^2 + \frac{1}{2}m_B u_B^2 - \frac{1}{2}m_A v_A^2 - \frac{1}{2}m_B v_B^2$$

and you would be expected to substitute in the values of v_A and v_B found earlier before giving the final answer.

Also, you may be asked to find the magnitude of the impulse exerted by A on B in the collision; this is *the change in the momentum of B alone*.

Impulse exerted by A on B $= m_B(v_B - u_B)$

NB. The *loss in kinetic energy* is found from the *whole system* under consideration but the *impulse* is found by consideration of the change in momentum of *one member of the pair*.

◀ Impulse, Momentum ▶

COFACTOR

The cofactor of an element of a determinant (or square matrix) is the determinant obtained by removing the row and column containing the element and applying the appropriate sign.

◀ Matrix/Matrices ▶

COLLISION

◀ Coefficient of restitution, Impact (direct) ▶

COMBINATION

A combination of r objects from n is a selection of r of the objects in which the order of selection is ignored. The number of combinations of r objects from n is denoted by ^nC_r or $\binom{n}{r}$ and

$$^nC_r = \frac{n(n-1)\dots(n-r+1)}{r!}$$
$$= \frac{n!}{r!\,(n-r)!}$$

where $n!$ (n factorial) is defined by
$$n! = n(n-1)\ldots 2.1$$
For example, the number of combinations of 3 letters from the 5 letters A, B, C, D, E is given by

$$^5C_3 = \frac{5 \times 4 \times 3}{1 \times 2 \times 3} = 10$$

The ten combinations are: ABC, ABD, ABE, ACD, ACE, ADE, BCD, BCE, BDE, CDE.

The following worked examples illustrate the methods used.

Worked example A

Find the number of ways of selecting five children from a group of twelve children.

If the group contains an equal number of boys and girls, find the number of different selections which contain   i) 2 girls and 3 boys;   ii) at least 3 boys.

The number of ways of selecting five children from 12 children is

$$\binom{12}{5} = \frac{12!}{5!\,7!} = \frac{12.11.10.9.8}{1.2.3.4.5} = 792$$

i) If the selection contains 2 girls and 3 boys, it is necessary to select 2 girls from 6 girls and 3 boys from 6 boys.
   The number of ways of selecting the 2 girls is
$$\binom{6}{2} = \frac{6.5}{1.2} = 15$$

   The number of ways of selecting the 3 boys is
$$\binom{6}{3} = \frac{6.5.4}{1.2.3} = 20$$

Any of the selections of girls can be taken with any of the selections of boys ⇒ total number of selections containing 2 girls and 3 boys is
$$\binom{6}{2} \cdot \binom{6}{5} = 15 \times 20 = 300$$

ii) If the selection contains at least 3 boys it could contain:
   a) 3 boys and 2 girls,   b) 4 boys and 1 girl or   c) 5 boys.
   Number of selections containing 3 boys and 2 girls is
$$\binom{6}{3} \cdot \binom{6}{2} = 300$$

Number of selections containing 4 boys and 1 girl is
$$\binom{6}{4} \cdot \binom{6}{1} = \frac{6.5}{1.2} \cdot \frac{6}{1} = 90$$

Number of selections containing 5 boys is
$$\binom{6}{5} = \frac{6}{1} = 6$$

Total number of selections containing at least 3 boys is $300 + 90 + 6 = 396$

Worked example B

In how many ways can 8 different books be divided into i) two groups of 5 books and 3 books; ii) two groups of 4 books and 4 books?

Two groups of 5 and 3 $\Rightarrow \begin{pmatrix} 8 \\ 5 \end{pmatrix} = \begin{pmatrix} 8 \\ 3 \end{pmatrix} = \dfrac{8.7.6}{1.2.3} = 56$ ways

Two groups of 4 and 4 $\Rightarrow \dfrac{1}{2} \begin{pmatrix} 8 \\ 4 \end{pmatrix} = \dfrac{1}{2} \cdot \dfrac{8.7.6.5}{1.2.3.4} = 35$ ways

◄ Permutation ►

COMBINATION OF EVENTS

◄ Probability ►

COMPLEX NUMBER

If we apply the quadratic equation formula to the equation
$$x^2 - 4x + 13 = 0$$
we obtain

$$x = \frac{4 \pm \sqrt{4^2 - 4 \times 13}}{2}$$

$$= \frac{4 \pm \sqrt{-36}}{2}$$

$$= \frac{4 \pm \sqrt{36 \times (-1)}}{2}$$

$$= \frac{4 \pm 6\sqrt{-1}}{2}$$

$$= 2 \pm 3i \text{ where } i = \sqrt{-1}$$

Although $\sqrt{-1}$ does not exist in the real world, this analysis leads us to define a complex number in the following way
Let $z = x + iy$
where x, y are real numbers and $i^2 = -1$. Then, z is called a complex number.
x is called the real part of z, written $\text{Re}(z)$.
y is called the imaginary part of z, written $\text{Im}(z)$.

Complex numbers can be represented graphically on an **Argand diagram**, in which the complex number $x + iy$ is represented by the point (x, y) – see Fig. C.7. The horizontal axis (x-axis) is called the *real axis* and the vertical axis (y-axis) the *imaginary axis*.

The **modulus** of z, written $|z|$, is defined as $\sqrt{x^2 + y^2}$; this equals OP on Fig. C.7.

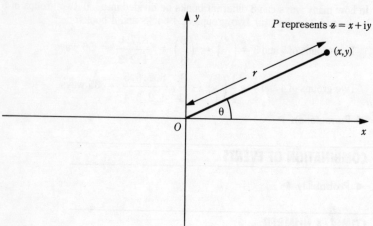

Fig. C.7

The **argument** of z, written $\arg(z)$, is defined as the angle θ satisfying

$$\theta = \tan^{-1}\left(\frac{y}{x}\right)$$

where the quadrant of θ depends in the usual way on the signs of x, y. Fig. C.7. shows the geometrical interpretation of θ. It is customary to take $-\pi < \theta \leq \pi$ (or $180° < \theta \leq 180°$)
The complex conjugate of $x + iy$ is defined as $x - iy$.

▶ *ALGEBRAIC OPERATIONS ON COMPLEX NUMBERS*

Addition and subtraction

$$(x_1 + iy_1) \pm (x_2 + iy_2) = (x_1 \pm x_2) + i(y_1 \pm y_2)$$

Multiplication

$$\begin{aligned}(x_1 + iy_1)(x_2 + iy_2) &= x_1x_2 + ix_1y_2 + ix_2y_1 + i^2y_1y_2 \\ &= (x_1x_2 - y_1y_2) + i(x_1y_2 + x_2y_1)\end{aligned}$$

Division

$$\frac{(x_1 + iy_1)}{(x_2 + iy_2)} = \frac{(x_1 + iy_1)(x_2 - iy_2)}{(x_2 + iy_2)(x_2 - iy_2)}$$

$$= \frac{x_1x_2 - ix_1y_2 + ix_2y_1 - i^2y_1y_2}{x_2^2 + ix_2y_2 - ix_2y_2 - i^2y_2^2}$$

$$= \frac{x_1x_2 + y_1y_2 + i(x_2y_1 - x_1y_2)}{x_2^2 + y_2^2}$$

$$= \frac{x_1x_2 + y_1y_2}{x_2^2 + y_2^2} + \frac{i(x_2y_1 - x_1y_2)}{x_2^2 + y_2^2}$$

▶ POLAR FORM

Since $x = r \cos \theta$ and $y = r \sin \theta$, it follows that
$$x + iy = r \cos \theta + ir \sin \theta$$
$$= r(\cos \theta + i \sin \theta)$$
We now consider this right-hand side. Put
$$u = \cos \theta + i \sin \theta$$
Then, differentiating,

$$\frac{du}{d\theta} = -\sin \theta + i \cos \theta$$

$$= i^2\sin \theta + i \cos \theta$$

$$= i(\cos \theta + i \sin \theta)$$

$$= iu$$

Integrating,

$$\int \frac{du}{u} = i \int d\theta$$

$$\log_e u = i\theta + \text{Constant}$$

When $\theta = 0$, $u = 1$ so that
$$0 = 0 + \text{Constant}$$

or Constant $= 0$
and $\log_e u = i\theta$
or $u = \cos \theta + i \sin \theta = e^{i\theta}$

Thus
$$x + iy = re^{i\theta}$$

The fact that the polar form involves powers means that multiplication, division and calculation of powers is easier using this polar form.

An alternative notation for $x + iy$ in **polar form** is $r \angle \theta$.

Multiplication

$$r_1e^{i\theta_1} \times r_2e^{i\theta_2} = r_1r_2e^{i(\theta_1+\theta_2)}$$

Division

$$\frac{r_1 e^{i\theta_1}}{r_2 e^{i\theta_2}} = \frac{r_1}{r_2} e^{i(\theta_1 - \theta_2)}$$

Powers

$$(re^{i\theta})^n = r^n e^{in\theta}$$

Note that this last result is true for all n, including fractional values. This enables nth roots to be calculated, as is illustrated in the following example.

Worked example

Find the three cube roots of unity.
Now
$$1 = e^{i0} = e^{i,2\pi} = e^{i,4\pi}$$
So that
$$1^{\frac{1}{3}} = e^{i0} \text{ or } e^{i,2\pi/3} \text{ or } e^{i,4\pi/3}$$
In cartesian form, the roots are
$$e^0 = 1$$
or
$$e^{i,2\pi/3} = \cos\frac{2\pi}{3} + i\sin\frac{2\pi}{3} = -\frac{1}{2} + \frac{\sqrt{3}}{2}i$$
or
$$e^{i,4\pi/3} = \cos\frac{4\pi}{3} + i\sin\frac{4\pi}{3} = -\frac{1}{2} - \frac{\sqrt{3}}{2}i$$

COMPOSITE FUNCTION

Two functions f and g can be combined to give a composite function. Unfortunately, the GCE A-level boards do not accept a uniform notation for a composite function, and you must therefore be familiar with that used by your board. The alternative notations are fg = f.g = f∘g ≡ f[g(x)], the f composite of g. For this function to exist the **domain** of f must contain the **range** of g.

You must note that the order of the composition is important, for in general $f[g(x)] \neq g[f(x)]$. The composite function fg is determined by
i) finding $g(x)$, and then   ii) finding $f[g(x)]$.

Worked example A

$f(x) = 3x + 1, \ x\epsilon\mathbb{R}$
$g(x) = 2x - 4, \ x\epsilon\mathbb{R}$
Find i) fg, ii) gf
$fg(x) = f(2x - 4) = 3(2x - 4) + 1 = 6x - 11, \Rightarrow fg : x \mapsto 6x - 11$
$gf(x) = g(3x + 1) = 2(3x + 1) - 4 = 6x - 2 \Rightarrow gf : x \mapsto 6x - 2$

Worked example B

Given that f and g are functions defined by

$$f(x) = x + \frac{\pi}{2}, \quad g(x) = \sin\left(\frac{1}{2}x - \frac{\pi}{4}\right), \quad x \in \mathbb{R}$$

show that, when $x = \dfrac{5\pi}{4}$, $f[g(x)] - g[f(x)] = \dfrac{\pi}{2}$

$$f[g(x)] = \sin\left(\frac{1}{2}x - \frac{\pi}{4}\right) + \frac{\pi}{2} \Rightarrow f\left[g\left(\frac{5\pi}{4}\right)\right] = \sin\left(\frac{3\pi}{8}\right) + \frac{\pi}{2}$$

$$g[f(x)] = \sin\left[\frac{1}{2}\left(x + \frac{\pi}{2}\right) - \frac{\pi}{4}\right] = \sin\frac{1}{2}x \Rightarrow g\left[f\left(\frac{5\pi}{4}\right)\right]$$

$$= \sin\left(\frac{5\pi}{8}\right) = \sin\left(\frac{3\pi}{8}\right)$$

Hence $f\left[g\left(\dfrac{5\pi}{4}\right)\right] - g\left[f\left(\dfrac{5\pi}{4}\right)\right] = \dfrac{\pi}{2}$

Worked example C

Given that $f(x) = x^3$ and $g(x) = 2^x$, $x \in \mathbb{R}$, state the range of
a) f,   b) g,   c) fg
Show that $(fg)^{-1} = g^{-1}f^{-1}$
  $f(x) = x^3$, $x \in \mathbb{R} \Rightarrow$ range of f is $\mathbb{R}$
  $g(x) = 2^x$, $x \in \mathbb{R} \Rightarrow$ range of g is $\mathbb{R}^+$
  $fg(x) = f(2^x) = (2^x)^3 = 2^{3x} \Rightarrow$ range of fg is $\mathbb{R}^+$

$$y = 2^{3x} \Rightarrow \text{for the inverse } (fg)^{-1}, \; x = 2^{3y} \text{ or } y = \frac{1}{3}\log_2 x$$

i.e. $(fg)^{-1}(x) = \dfrac{1}{3}\log_2 x$

$f(x) = x^3 \Rightarrow y = x^3 \Rightarrow$ for the inverse f^{-1}, $x = y^3$ or $y = x^{\frac{1}{3}}$
$g(x) = 2^x \Rightarrow y = 2^x \Rightarrow$ for the inverse g^{-1}, $x = 2^y$ or $y = \log_2 x$

$$\Rightarrow g^{-1}f^{-1}(x) = g^{-1}\left(x^{\frac{1}{3}}\right) = \log_2 x^{\frac{1}{3}} = \frac{1}{3}\log_2 x = (fg)^{-1}(x)$$

$$\Rightarrow (fg)^{-1} = g^{-1}f^{-1}$$

Worked example D

Composite functions can be extended to include, for instance, f(gh) or (fg)h for any f, g, h for which the composites are defined.
Given $f: x \mapsto (2 + x)^3$, $x \in \mathbb{R}$
       $g: x \mapsto \sin x$, $x \in \mathbb{R}$
       $h: x \mapsto \sqrt{x}$, $x \in \mathbb{R}^+$

Find   a) f(gh)(x),   b) (fg)h(x)

$$gh(x) = g(\sqrt{x}) = \sin \sqrt{x}$$
$$\Rightarrow fgh(x) = f(\sin \sqrt{x}) = (2 + \sin \sqrt{x})^3$$
$$h(x) = \sqrt{x}, \ fg(x) = (2 + \sin x)^3$$
$$\Rightarrow (fg)h(x) = (fg)(\sqrt{x}) = (2 + \sin \sqrt{x})^3$$

NB. In this case (fg)h(x) $\equiv$ f(gh)(x)

This result is not only true for the above functions, but is true for any f, g, h for which the composites are defined.

◀ Function, Domain, Mapping ▶

COMPRESSION

A pressing or squeezing force.

CONE

◀ Solid shape ▶

CONFIDENCE INTERVAL

Let $X_1, X_2, \ldots X_n$ be a **random sample** from a distribution whose **probability density function** (or *probability function* in the case of a discrete distribution) contains an unknown parameter θ. Let $L(X_1, X_2, \ldots X_n)$, $U(X_1, X_2, \ldots X_n)$ denote statistics, i.e. functions of the random sample, such that

$$P(L \leqslant \theta \leqslant U) = 1 - \alpha \qquad \text{(typically, } \alpha = 0 \cdot 05)$$

In other words, $[L, U]$ is a random interval which contains θ with probability $1 - \alpha$.

Let $l(x_1, x_2, \ldots x_n)$, $u(x_1, x_2, \ldots x_n)$ denote the numerical values of L, U when the **random variables** $X_1, X_2, \ldots X_n$ are replaced by their numerical values $x_1, x_2, \ldots x_n$. Then

$$[l, u]$$

is called a $100(1 - \alpha)$ per cent confidence interval for θ; l, u are called the (lower and upper) confidence limits.

The following standard $100(1 - \alpha)$ per cent **confidence limits** are included in one or more A-level syllabuses.

In Cases 1 to 3 following,

$$\bar{x} = \frac{\sum_{i=1}^{n} x_i}{n} \text{ and } \hat{\sigma}^2 = \frac{\sum_{i=1}^{n} (x_i - \bar{x})^2}{n - 1}$$

where $x_1, x_2, \ldots x_n$ denotes a random sample from the normal distribution $N(\mu, \sigma^2)$.

Case 1: Estimation of μ (σ^2 known)

$$\bar{x} \pm \Phi^{-1}\left(1 - \frac{1}{2}\alpha\right) \cdot \frac{\sigma}{\sqrt{n}}$$

where $\Phi^{-1}(p)$ denotes the 100 pth percentile of the $N(0, 1)$ distribution. For the special case $\alpha = 0.05$, the 95 per cent confidence limits are

$$\bar{x} \pm 1.96 \frac{\sigma}{\sqrt{n}}$$

Case 2: Estimation of μ (σ^2 unknown)

$$\bar{x} \pm t_{1-\frac{1}{2}\alpha}(n - 1) \cdot \frac{\hat{\sigma}}{\sqrt{n}}$$

where $t_p(n - 1)$ denotes the 100 pth percentile of the **Student's t-distribution** with $(n - 1)$ degrees of freedom.

Case 3: Estimation of σ^2

$$\left[\frac{(n - 1)\,\hat{\sigma}^2}{\varkappa^2_{1-\frac{1}{2}\alpha}(n - 1)}, \frac{(n - 1)\,\hat{\sigma}^2}{\varkappa^2_{\frac{1}{2}\alpha}(n - 1)} \right]$$

where $\varkappa^2_p\,(n - 1)$ denotes the 100 pth percentile of the Student's $t-$ distribution with $(n - 1)$ degrees of freedom.

In cases $4 \simeq 5$

$$\bar{x} = \frac{\sum\limits_{i=1}^{m} x_i}{m} \text{ and } \bar{y} = \frac{\sum\limits_{i=1}^{n} y_i}{n}$$

where $x_1, x_2, \ldots x_m$ and $y_1, y_2 \ldots y_n$ denote random samples from normal distributions $N(\mu_x, \sigma_x{}^2)$, $N(\mu_y, \sigma_y{}^2)$.

Case 4: Estimation of $\mu_x - \mu_y$ ($\sigma_x{}^2$ and $\sigma_y{}^2$ known)

$$\bar{x} - \bar{y} \pm \Phi^{-1}\left(1 - \frac{1}{2}\alpha\right) \sqrt{\frac{\sigma_x{}^2}{m} + \frac{\sigma_y{}^2}{n}}$$

where $\Phi^{-1}(p)$ denotes the 100 pth percentile of the $N(0, 1)$ distribution.

Case 5: Estimation of $\mu_x - \mu_y$ ($\sigma_x{}^2$ and $\sigma_y{}^2$ unknown but assumed equal)

$$\bar{x} - \bar{y} \pm t_{1-\frac{1}{2}\alpha}(m + n - 2) \sqrt{\frac{(m - 1)\sigma_{\hat{x}}{}^2 + (n - 1)\sigma_{\hat{y}}{}^2}{m + n - 2}} \sqrt{\frac{1}{m} + \frac{1}{n}}$$

where $\hat{\sigma}_x{}^2 = \dfrac{\sum\limits_{i=1}^{m}(x_i - \bar{x})^2}{m - 1}$ and $\hat{\sigma}_y{}^2 = \dfrac{\sum\limits_{i=1}^{n}(y_i - \bar{y})^2}{n - 1}$

Case 6: Estimation of binomial *p*

If x successes are obtained in n independent trials, each having probability p, then an approximate $100(1 - \alpha)$ per cent confidence limits for p for large n are

$$\hat{p} \pm \Phi^{-1}\left(1 - \frac{1}{2}\alpha\right)\sqrt{\frac{\hat{p}(1 - \hat{p})}{n}}$$

where $\hat{p} = x/n$

◀ Random variable ▶

CONFIDENCE LIMIT

◀ Confidence interval ▶

CONNECTED PARTICLES

The motions of particles connected by inelastic strings can be determined using the simple laws of motion. This can be illustrated with an example.

Worked example

Particles of mass m_1, m_2 are connected to the two ends of a light inelastic string which passes over a fixed pulley. The system is released from rest.

Find   i) the acceleration of the particles;   ii) the tension in the string. (See Fig. C.8.)

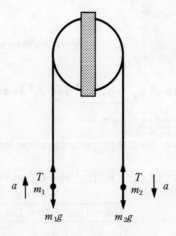

Fig. C.8

Let T denote the tension in the string – this remains constant throughout the string.

We assume (for convenience) that $m_2 > m_1$. Let m_2 descend with acceleration a so that m_1 ascends with acceleration a. The equations of motion of the two particles are

$$m_2 g - T = m_2 a \qquad \text{(i)}$$
$$T - m_1 g = m_1 a \qquad \text{(ii)}$$

Adding these equations,

$$(m_2 - m_1)g = (m_1 + m_2)a$$

so that

$$a = \frac{(m_2 - m_1)g}{(m_1 + m_2)}$$

Substituting back,

$$T = m_2 g - \frac{m_2(m_2 - m_1)g}{(m_1 + m_2)}$$
$$= \frac{2m_1 m_2 g}{(m_1 + m_2)}$$

CONSERVATION OF ENERGY/MOMENTUM

◀ Circular motion, Energy, Mechanical energy, Momentum, Work ▶

CONSERVATIVE SYSTEM OF FORCES

◀ Mechanical energy ▶

CONSISTENT EQUATIONS

A set of equations is consistent if it has a solution, not necessarily unique.

CONSTANT OF INTEGRATION

◀ Integration ▶

COORDINATE GEOMETRY

For all GCE A-level and equivalent syllabuses you are expected to be familiar with the various forms for the equation of a straight line, a circle, and the simple forms for the parabola, ellipse and hyperbola. You must be able to find the equations of tangents and normals to curves and to deal with simple loci problems. The formulae you should understand and be able to use are given here.

▶ STRAIGHT LINE

$ax + by + c = 0$	general equation of straight line
$y = mx + c$	straight line, gradient m, intercept on y-axis $(0, c)$
$\dfrac{x}{a} + \dfrac{y}{b} = 1$	straight line, intercept on x-axis $(a, 0)$, y-axis $(0, b)$
$y - y_1 = m(x - x_1)$	straight line, gradient m, passes through point (x_1, y_1)
$\dfrac{y - y_1}{y_2 - y_1} = \dfrac{x - x_1}{x_2 - x_1}$	straight line, passes through the points (x_1, y_1), (x_2, y_2)

Two lines are parallel if their gradients m_1 and m_2 are equal $\Rightarrow m_1 = m_2$
Two lines are perpendicular if their gradients m_1 and m_2 are such that $m_1 m_2 = -1$.
The perpendicular distance of the point (x_1, y_1) from the straight line

$$ax + by + c = 0 \text{ is } \frac{|ax_1 + by_1 + c|}{\sqrt{(a^2 + b^2)}}$$

▶ CIRCLE

The general equation of the circle is $x^2 + y^2 + 2gx + 2fy + c = 0$, a second-degree equation in which there is no term in xy and coefficient of x^2 equal to the coefficient of y^2

$x^2 + y^2 = r^2$, circle, centre origin, radius r.
$(x - a)^2 + (y - b)^2 = r^2$, circle, centre (a, b), radius r.
$x^2 + y^2 + 2gx + 2fy + c = 0 \Rightarrow (x + g)^2 + (y + f)^2 = g^2 + f^2 - c$
i.e. circle centre $(-g, -f)$, radius $\sqrt{(g^2 + f^2 - c)}$.
$(x - x_1)(x - x_2) + (y - y_1)(y - y_2) = 0$, circle having (x_1, y_1) and (x_2, y_2) as coordinates of the extremities of a diameter.

▶ PARABOLA

$y^2 = 4ax$, parametric equations, $x = at^2$, $y = 2at$

▶ ELLIPSE

$\dfrac{x^2}{a^2} + \dfrac{y^2}{b^2} = 1$, parametric equations, $x = a\cos\theta$, $y = b\sin\theta$

▶ HYPERBOLA

$\dfrac{x^2}{a^2} - \dfrac{y^2}{b^2} = 1$, parametric equations, $x = a\sec\theta$, $y = b\tan\theta$

or $x = a\cosh\theta$, $y = b\sinh\theta$

RECTANGULAR HYPERBOLA

$xy = c^2$, parametric equations, $x = ct, y = \dfrac{c}{t}$

◀ Circle, Ellipse, Hyperbola, Linear, Parabola ▶

COORDINATES

Coordinates are used to fix the position of a point. We consider the two-dimensional and three-dimensional cases separately.

TWO-DIMENSIONAL CASE

Cartesian coordinates

To fix the position of a point, we take two perpendicular axes (as shown in Fig. C.9) – called the x-axis and y-axis – which intersect at the origin O. The coordinates of the general point P are defined as the perpendicular distance of P from the y-axis (called the x coordinate or *abscissa*) and the perpendicular distance of P from the x-axis (called the y coordinate or *ordinate*).

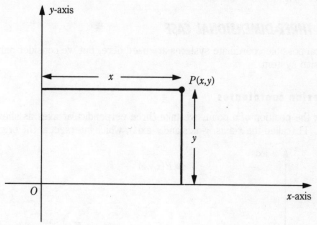

Fig. C.9

Polar coordinates

To fix the position of a point, we define an initial line and an origin (Fig. C.10). The coordinates of the general point P are defined as the distance of P from the origin O (the r coordinate) and the angle between the initial line and OP (the θ coordinate measured in an anticlockwise direction). It is customary to take $-\pi < \theta \leq \pi$ (or $180° < \theta \leq 180°$ in degrees).

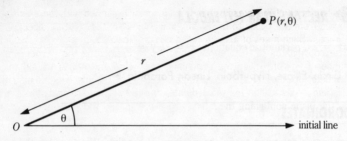

Fig. C.10

Relationship between cartesian and polar coordinates

If we take the initial line as the x-axis, and the y-axis as perpendicular to this, then the relationships between (x, y) and (r, θ) are

$$x = r \cos \theta; \qquad y = r \sin \theta$$

and $\quad r = \sqrt{x^2 + y^2}; \quad \theta = \tan^{-1}\left(\dfrac{y}{x}\right)$

In calculating the value of θ, the angle is taken in that quadrant giving the correct sign for $\sin \theta$ and $\cos \theta$.

▶ THREE-DIMENSIONAL CASE

Several possible coordinate systems are used here, but we consider only the cartesian system.

Cartesian coordinates

To fix the position of a point, we take three perpendicular axes as shown in Fig. C.11 (called the x-axis, y-axis and z-axis), which intersect at the origin O.

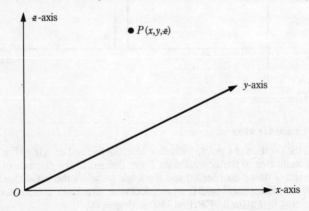

Fig. C.11

The orientation of the axes is such that if a screw is aligned with the z-axis and screwed from the x-axis to the y-axis, it will move in the positive direction of the z-axis. Such a set of axes is called a *right-handed set*.

The coordinates of the general point P are defined as the perpendicular distance of P from the plane containing the y-axis and z-axis (called the x coordinate), the perpendicular distance of P from the plane containing the z-axis and x-axis (called the y coordinate) and the perpendicular distance of P from the plane containing the x-axis and y-axis (called the z-coordinate).

CORRELATION COEFFICIENT (KENDALL'S τ)

Given n pairs of observations (x_1, y_1), (x_2, y_2), ... (x_n, y_n), let u_i, v_i denote respectively the rank of x_i when the x values are ranked and the rank of y_i when the y values are ranked. (NB. The ranking can be in either ascending or descending order, but must be the same for both.)

Consider the two pairs of observations (x_i, y_i), (x_j, y_j) with ranks (u_i, v_i), (u_j, v_j). These two pairs are called *concordant* if $x_i - x_j$ (or $u_i - u_j$) and $y_i - y_j$ (or $v_i - v_j$) have the same signs; the pairs are *discordant* if $x_i - x_j$ (or $u_i - u_j$) and $y_i - y_j$ (or $v_i - v_j$) have different signs.

Let D denote the number of discordant pairs out of the ${}^nC_2 = n(n-1)/2$ possible pairs. Then the Kendall's τ is defined as

$$\tau = 1 - \frac{4D}{n(n-1)}$$

Note that i) if $D = 0$, then $\tau = 1$; and ii) if $D = n(n-1)/2$ (its maximum value), then $\tau = -1$. We illustrate the calculation of τ by means of an example.

Worked example

Two judges are asked to rank 6 wines in order of preference. The results are as follows (1 = best, 6 = worst):

Wine	A	B	C	D	E	F
Judge 1	5	1	3	2	6	4
Judge 2	6	4	1	2	5	3

Calculate Kendall's τ.

Note here that, as often happens in practice, the data are presented in the form of ranks, so that no preliminary ranking operation is required. There are ${}^6C_2 = 15$ pairings and these are shown below, together with an indication of whether they are concordant (Con) or discordant (Dis).

AB (Con)	AC (Con)	AD (Con)	AE (Dis)	AF (Con)
BC (Dis)	BD (Dis)	BE (Con)	BF (Dis)	CD (Dis)
CE (Con)	CF (Con)	DE (Con)	DF (Con)	EF (Con)

Thus, $D = 5$

and $\tau = 1 - \dfrac{4 \times 5}{6 \times 5} = \dfrac{1}{3}$

The calculation can be done diagrammatically as shown.

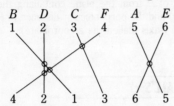

Here, the rankings are rearranged so that the Judge 1 rankings are in order. Equal ranks are then joined by straight lines and the number of discordant pairs (D) is given by the number of intersections (here 5, as was found earlier).

In the case of ties, each equal value is given a ranking equal to the mean of the ranks which would have been given if the values had been slightly different. Suppose that the two pairs of observations (x_i, y_i), (x_j, y_j) have ranks (u_i, v_i), (u_j, v_j). Then, in the case of ties, either $u_i = u_j$ (corresponding to $x_i = x_j$) or $v_i = v_j$ (corresponding to $y_i = y_j$); it is, of course, possible to have a double tie in which $u_i = u_j$ and $v_i = v_j$. We consider all these case to be half-concordant, and half-discordant, contributing $\frac{1}{2}$ to the total number (D) of discordant pairs.

In broad terms, a value of τ around 0 indicates no association between the two quantities being measured, here the judges' order of preference. A positive value of τ indicates a *positive association*, which means a tendency for high values (or ranks) of the one variable to be associated with high values (or ranks) of the other variable and low values (or ranks) of the one variable to be associated with low values (or ranks) of the other variable.

▶ HYPOTHESIS TESTING

Because of the sampling variability of τ, the interpretation of τ should be made within the framework of hypothesis testing.

An appropriate null hypothesis is

H_0: No association between the variables

Tables of critical values of τ for the possible alternative hypothesis are included in many sets of statistical tables. The possible alternatives are

  H_1: Association between the variables (2-tailed alternative)
or H_1: Positive association between the variables (1-tailed alternative)
or H_1: Negative association between the variables (1-tailed alternative)

We illustrate by means of an example.

Worked example

The value of the Kendall's τ between 6 pairs of ranks is $\frac{1}{3}$. Test, at the 5 per cent significance level, the hypothesis that the rankings are positively associated.

Here we use a 1-tailed test, and we find from tables that the appropriate critical value is 0·6. Since the computed value is less than this, we reject the alternative hypothesis that the rankings are positively associated.

In other words, there is insufficient evidence here that the judges are in agreement.

◄ Correlation coefficient (Spearman rank), Correlation coefficient (product moment) ►

CORRELATION COEFFICIENT (PRODUCT MOMENT)

The (product moment) correlation coefficient ρ of the random variables X and Y is defined by

$$\rho = \frac{\text{Cov}(X, Y)}{\sqrt{\text{Var}(X)\,\text{Var}(Y)}}$$

where $\text{Var}(X)$, $\text{Var}(Y)$ denote the variances of X, Y respectively and $\text{Cov}(X, Y)$ (the covariance of X, Y) is given by

$$\text{Cov}(X, Y) = \text{E}(XY) - \text{E}(X)\text{E}(Y)$$

It can be shown that $-1 \leq \rho \leq 1$.

If X, Y are independent, then $\rho = 0$.

If X, Y are linearly related, then $\rho = +1$ or -1 according as to whether Y increases or decreases with X.

If $\rho = 0$, it does not follow that X, Y are independent. However, if X, Y have a bivariate normal distribution, then $\rho = 0$ *does* imply independence and in this case ρ can be used as a measure of association between X, Y. Given n pairs of observations (x_1, y_1), (x_2, y_2), ... (x_n, y_n), ρ can be estimated by the sample (product moment) correlation coefficient

$$r = \frac{\dfrac{1}{n} \sum_{i=1}^{n} x_i y_i - \bar{x}\bar{y}}{\sqrt{\left(\dfrac{1}{n} \sum_{i=1}^{n} x_i^2 - \bar{x}^2\right)\left(\dfrac{1}{n} \sum_{i=1}^{n} y_i^2 - \bar{y}^2\right)}}$$

where $\bar{x} = \sum_{i=1}^{n} x_i/n$ and $\bar{y} = \sum_{i=1}^{n} y_i/n$

Alternatively

$$r = \frac{S_{xy}}{\sqrt{S_{xx}S_{yy}}}$$

where

$$S_{xx} = \sum_{i=1}^{n} x_i^2 - n\bar{x}^2$$

$$S_{yy} = \sum_{i=1}^{n} y_i^2 - n\bar{y}^2$$

and

$$S_{xy} = \sum_{i=1}^{n} x_i y_i - n\bar{x}\bar{y}$$

It can be shown that $-1 \leqslant r \leqslant 1$.

The following example illustrates the calculation of r.

Worked example

The marks obtained by a class in examinations in Pure Mathematics and Statistics are given below. Calculate the sample correlation coefficient.

Student	A	B	C	D	E	F	G	H
Pure Maths (x)	62	50	83	71	69	42	71	33
Statistics (y)	70	53	79	53	71	53	69	35

We find, using a calculator, that
$\Sigma x = 481 : \Sigma y = 483 : \Sigma xy = 30489$
$\Sigma x^2 = 30929 : \Sigma y^2 = 30595$
Since $n = 8$,

$$S_{xx} = 30929 - 8 \times \left(\frac{481}{8}\right)^2 = 2008 \cdot 875$$

$$S_{yy} = 30595 - 8 \times \left(\frac{483}{8}\right)^2 = 1433 \cdot 875$$

$$S_{xy} = 30489 - 8 \times \left(\frac{481}{8}\right) \times \left(\frac{483}{8}\right) = 1448 \cdot 625$$

Thus

$$r = \frac{S_{xy}}{\sqrt{S_{xx}S_{yy}}}$$

$$= \frac{1448 \cdot 625}{\sqrt{2008 \cdot 875 \times 1433 \cdot 875}}$$

$$\approx 0 \cdot 854$$

In broad terms, a value of r around 0 indicates independence of X, Y. A positive value of r indicates *positive association*, which means a tendency for high values of X to be associated with high values of Y and low values of X to be associated with low values of Y. The greater the value of r, the greater this association. In this case, for example, the calculated value of r indicates that students who are good (or bad) at Pure Mathematics are also good (or bad) at

Statistics. A negative value of r indicates *negative association*, which means a tendency for high values of X to be associated with low values of Y and low values of X to be associated with high values of Y.

▶ HYPOTHESIS TESTING

Since r is only an estimate of ρ, the interpretation of r should really be done within the framework of hypothesis testing.

We now consider some tests of hypothesis on ρ assuming X, Y have a bivariate normal distribution.

Testing the hypothesis $H_0: \rho = 0$

The null hypothesis $H_0: \rho = 0$ corresponds to X, Y being independent. It can be shown that, under H_0,

$$T = R \sqrt{\frac{n-2}{1-R^2}}$$

has the **student's t-distribution** with $(n-2)$ degrees of freedom. This result can be used to obtain the critical region dependent upon the alternative hypothesis H_1. These are, taking a significance level of 5 per cent,

$H_1: \rho \neq 0$ Critical region $|T| > t_{.975}(n-2)$ (2-tailed test)
$H_1: \rho > 0$ Critical region $T > t_{.95}(n-2)$ (1-tailed test)
$H_1: \rho < 0$ Critical region $T < -t_{.95}(n-2)$ (1-tailed test)

where $t_p(n)$ denotes the 100pth percentile of the Student's t distribution with n degrees of freedom. Similar results can be given for other significance levels. Alternatively, some sets of statistical tables give critical values for the computed sample correlation coefficient itself. These should be used if available. This can be illustrated with an example.

Worked example

The sample correlation coefficient of 10 pairs of observations on a pair of variables X, Y was 0.423. Test, at the 5 per cent significance level, the hypothesis that X, Y are independent.

Here, we take $H_0: \rho = 0$ and $H_1: \rho \neq 0$, since the wording (or rather the lack of it) suggests that a 2-sided alternative is appropriate here. Transforming,

$$t = r \sqrt{\frac{n-2}{1-r^2}}$$
$$\approx 1.320$$

Since $t_{.975}(8) = 2.306$, the critical region is
$|t| > 2.306$

The computed value does not lie in the critical region so that we cannot reject the null hypothesis of independence.

Alternatively, we find from a table of critical values of r that the appropriate critical region here is

$$|r| > 0.6319$$

Again, the computed value of 0.423 does not lie in the critical region, which leads us to the same conclusion as before.

Testing the hypothesis $H_0 : \rho = \rho_0 (\neq 0)$

The relevant result here is that, under H_0, for large n

$$Z \text{ is approximately } N\left(S, \frac{1}{n-3}\right)$$

where

$$Z = \frac{1}{2}\log_e\left(\frac{1+R}{1-R}\right)\left(= \tanh^{-1}R\right)$$

and

$$S = \frac{1}{2}\log_e\left(\frac{1+\rho}{1-\rho}\right)\left(= \tanh^{-1}\rho\right)$$

Z is called the Fisher Z-transform, and values of this transform and its inverse are given in statistical tables.

It follows by standardising that
$(Z - S)\sqrt{n-3}$ is approximately $N(0, 1)$

This result can be used to obtain the critical region dependent upon the alternative hypothesis H_1. These are, taking a significance level of 5 per cent,

$H_1 : \rho \neq \rho_0$ Critical region $|Z - S_0|\sqrt{n-3} > 1.96$
$H_1 : \rho > \rho_0$ Critical region $(Z - S_0)\sqrt{n-3} > 1.645$
$H_1 : \rho < \rho_0$ Critical region $(Z - S_0)\sqrt{n-3} < -1.645$

Worked example

The sample correlation coefficient of 25 pairs of observations on a pair of variables X, Y was 0.532. Test, at the 5 per cent significance level, the hypothesis that $\rho = 0.2$ against the alternative that $\rho > 0.2$.

We find, using Fisher Z-transform tables, that
$$Z = 0.5929$$
and $S_0 = 0.2027$
Since $n = 25$,
$$(Z - S_0)\sqrt{n-3} = (0.5929 - 0.2027)\sqrt{25-3}$$
$$\approx 1.83$$

Since this value exceeds 1.645, we accept the alternative hypothesis, namely $\rho > 0.2$.

▶ CONFIDENCE INTERVAL CALCULATION

The Fisher Z-transform can also be used to construct a confidence interval for ρ. The basic result here is that, for large n, $\tanh^{-1} R$ is approximately

$$N\left(\tanh^{-1} \rho, \frac{1}{n-3}\right)$$

It follows from this that a 95 per cent confidence interval for ρ is

$$\left[\tanh\left(\tanh^{-1}r - \frac{1\cdot96}{\sqrt{n-3}}\right), \tanh\left(\tanh^{-1}r + \frac{1\cdot96}{\sqrt{n-3}}\right)\right]$$

We can illustrate this result by means of an example.

Worked example

The sample correlation coefficient of 25 samples of observations on a pair of variables X, Y was $0\cdot532$. Calculate a 95 per cent confidence interval for ρ.

We find, using Fisher $\mathcal{Z}$-transform tables, that
$$\mathcal{Z} = \tan h^{-1} 0\cdot532 = 0\cdot5929$$

The 95 per cent confidence interval for ρ is therefore

$$\left[\tanh\left(0\cdot5929 - \frac{1\cdot96}{\sqrt{22}}\right), \tanh\left(0\cdot5929 + \frac{1\cdot96}{\sqrt{22}}\right)\right]$$

which is $[0\cdot1733, 0\cdot7661]$
◀ Correlation coefficient (Kendall's τ), Correlation coefficient (Spearman rank) ▶

CORRELATION COEFFICIENT (SPEARMAN RANK)

Given n pairs of observations (x_1, y_1), (x_2, y_2), ... (x_n, y_n), let u_i, v_i denote respectively the rank of x_i when the x values are ranked and the rank of y_i when the y values are ranked. (NB. The ranking can be either in ascending order or descending order, but must be the same for both.)

Consider the pairs of ranks (u_1, v_1), (u_2, v_2), ... (u_n, v_n). Then the Spearman rank correlation coefficient of the original (x, y) sample is defined as the product moment correlation coefficient of the ranking (u, v), that is

$$r_s = \frac{\frac{1}{n}\sum_{i=1}^{n}u_i v_i - \bar{u}\bar{v}}{\sqrt{\left(\frac{1}{n}\sum_{i=1}^{n}u_i^2 - \bar{u}^2\right)\left(\frac{1}{n}\sum_{i=1}^{n}v_i^2 - \bar{v}^2\right)}} \tag{1}$$

where $\bar{u} = \dfrac{\sum_{i=1}^{n}u_i}{n}$ and $\bar{v} = \dfrac{\sum_{i=1}^{n}v_i}{n}$

Since both sets of ranks $u_1, u_2 \ldots u_n$ and $v_1, v_2 \ldots v_n$ are permutations of the first n integers $1, 2 \ldots n$, this expression can be simplified to

$$r_s = 1 - \frac{6 \sum_{i=1}^{n} d_i^2}{n(n^2 - 1)} \qquad (2)$$

where $d_i = u_i - v_i$

In the case of ties, each equal value is given a ranking equal to the mean of the ranks which would have been given if the values had been slightly different. In this case, formulae 1) and 2) give slightly different answers, and 2) is used.

We can illustrate the calculation of r_s by means of an example.

Worked example

The marks obtained by a class in examinations in Pure Mathematics and Statistics are given below. Calculate the Spearman rank correlation coefficient.

Student	A	B	C	D	E	F	G	H
Pure Maths (x)	62	50	83	71	69	42	71	33
Statistics (y)	70	53	79	53	71	53	69	35

The rankings are given below.

Student	A	B	C	D	E	F	G	H
Pure Maths	5	6	1	2·5	4	7	2·5	8
Statistics	3	6	1	6	2	6	4	8
|Rank difference|	2	0	0	3·5	2	1	1·5	0
(Rank difference)^2	4	0	0	12·25	4	1	2·25	0

We see that $\Sigma d^2 = 23 \cdot 25$. Since $n = 8$,

$$r_s = 1 - \frac{6 \times 23 \cdot 25}{8(8^2 - 1)}$$

$$\approx 0 \cdot 723$$

In broad terms, a value for r_s around 0 indicates no association between the two quantities being measured, here the marks in Pure Mathematics and Statistics. A positive value of r_s indicates a *positive association*, which means a tendency for high values of the one variable to be associated with high values of the other variable and low values of the one variable to be associated with low values of the other variable. In this case, for example, the calculated value of r_s indicates that students who are good (or bad) at Pure Mathematics are also good (or bad) at Statistics. A negative value of r_s indicates a *negative association*, which means a tendency for high values of the one variable to be associated with low values of the other variable and vice versa.

▶ HYPOTHESIS TESTING

Because of the sampling variability of r_s, the interpretation of r_s should really

be done within the framework of hypothesis testing. An appropriate null hypothesis is H_0: No association between the variables.
Tables of critical values of r_s for the various possible alternative hypotheses are included in many sets of statistical tables.
The possible alternatives are

H_1: Association between the variables (2-tailed alternative)

or H_1: Positive association between the variables (1-tailed alternative)

or H_1: Negative association between the variables (1-tailed alternative)

Worked example

The value of the Spearman rank correlation coefficient between 8 pairs of observations is $0 \cdot 723$. Test, at the 5 per cent significance level, the hypothesis that the variables are positively associated.

Here we use a 1-tailed test and we find from tables that the appropriate critical value is $0 \cdot 6429$. Since the computed value exceeds this, we accept the alternative hypothesis that the variables are positively associated.

◄ Correlation coefficient (Kendall's τ), Correlation coefficient (product moment) ►

COSINE RULE

The cosine rule for a triangle (Fig. C.12) states that
$$a^2 = b^2 + c^2 - 2bc \cos A.$$
Two other versions of the rule can be derived by cyclic rotation
$$a \rightarrow b \rightarrow c \rightarrow a.$$
To prove this result, drop a perpendicular from C to AB. Referring to the diagram (Fig. C.12),
$$CF = b \sin A; \ AF = b \cos A$$
so that $\ BF = AB - AF = c - b \cos A$
Using Pythagoras' theorem in the triangle BFC,
$$BC^2 = BF^2 + CF^2$$
or $\ a^2 = (c - b \cos A)^2 + b^2 \sin^2 A$
$$= c^2 - 2bc \cos A + b^2(\cos^2 A + \sin^2 A)$$
$$= b^2 + c^2 - 2bc \cos A$$

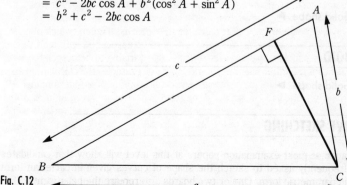

Fig. C.12

CROSS PRODUCT

◄ Vector product ►

COUPLE

A couple consists of two parallel **forces** equal in magnitude but opposite in sign. The **moment** of a couple is the product of the magnitude of the force times the perpendicular distance between them.

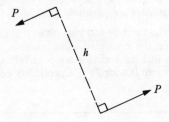

Fig. C.13

The couple shown in Fig. C.13 has moment Ph and the sign of the moment is taken as positive because the turning effect of the couple is in an anticlockwise sense. Further, a couple has the same moment about any point in its plane of action and may be replaced by any pair of equal and opposite parallel forces acting in opposite directions, provided that their moment has the same magnitude and sense as the couple.

◄ Moment of a force ►

CUBE

◄ Solid shape ►

CUBOID

◄ Solid shape ►

CURVE SKETCHING

A glance at most examination papers at this level will show that candidates are frequently asked to sketch the shape of curves given in cartesian form and in parametric form. One or two boards also require the polar form.

CARTESIAN EQUATIONS

The questions to ask yourself are as follows.

  i) Is the curve symmetrical about the x-axis? (That is, does the equation contain even powers of y only?)
 ii) Is the curve symmetrical about the y-axis? (That is, does the equation contain even powers of x only?)
iii) Is the curve symmetrical about the origin? (That is, does the equation stay the same when x is replaced by $(-x)$ and y is replaced by $(-y)$?)
 iv) What happens to y if x is made large? What happens to x if y is made large?
  v) Are there any values of x which make y infinite? Are there any values of y which make x infinite?
 vi) Where does the curve cross the axes?

Finally, if the answers to the questions are not sufficient to sketch the curve, determine the maximum and minimum values of y. Use of the sign of $f'(x)$ also helps to sketch the curve $y = f(x)$

Worked example A

Sketch the curve $y^2 = 4(x - 1)$

  i) the curve contains even powers of y only $\Rightarrow$ symmetrical about the x-axis
 ii) not symmetrical about y-axis
iii) if $x < 1$, then $4(x - 1) < 0 \Rightarrow y^2 < 0$ which is impossible. Hence curve only exists for $x \geqslant 1$
 iv) when $x = 1$, $y = 0 \Rightarrow$ crosses x-axis at $(1, 0)$
  v) when x is large, y also is large
 vi) $y^2 = 4(x - 1) \Rightarrow 2y\dfrac{\mathrm{d}y}{\mathrm{d}x} = 4 \Rightarrow \dfrac{\mathrm{d}y}{\mathrm{d}x} = \dfrac{2}{y} \to \infty$ as $y \to 0$

$\Rightarrow$ curve is as shown in Fig. C.14.

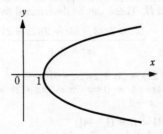

Fig. C.14

Worked example B

Sketch the curve $y = \dfrac{3x + 2}{x(x - 2)}$

   i) curve is not symmetrical about either axis
  ii) if x is large and positive, y is very small and positive
      if x is large and negative, y is very small and negative
 iii) the values $x = 0$ and $x = 2$ make y infinite. If $x = 0 +$, i.e. x is
      positive and just greater than 0, then y is negative and very large
      i.e. $x \to 0 +,\ y \to -\infty$
      If $x \to 0-,\ y \to +\infty$
      If $x \to 2-,\ y \to -\infty$ and if $x \to 2+,\ y \to +\infty$
  iv) curve crosses the x-axis when $x = -\frac{2}{3}$
      $\Rightarrow$ curve is therefore as shown in Fig. C.15.

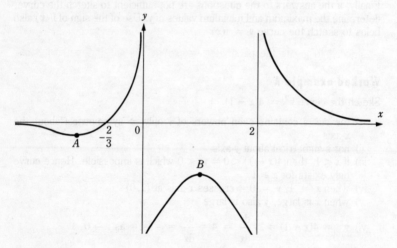

Fig. C.15

The only question left unresolved by the previous working is the position of
the turning points A and B. These can be determined by **differentiation**

$$y = \frac{3x + 2}{x^2 - 2x} \Rightarrow \frac{dy}{dx} = \frac{(x^2 - 2x)3 - (3x + 2)(2x - 2)}{(x^2 - 2x)}$$

$$\Rightarrow \frac{dy}{dx} = 0 \Rightarrow 3(x^2 - 2x) - (3x + 2)(2x - 2) = 0$$
$$\Rightarrow 3x^2 + 4x - 4 = 0 \Leftrightarrow (3x - 2)(x + 2) = 0$$
$$\Rightarrow x = \tfrac{2}{3} \text{ or } -2$$

When $x = \frac{2}{3}$, $y = -4\frac{1}{2} \Rightarrow B \equiv (\frac{2}{3}, -4\frac{1}{2})$
When $x = -2$, $y = -\frac{1}{2} \Rightarrow A \equiv (-2, -\frac{1}{2})$
You should note that no part of the curve exists for $-4\frac{1}{2} < y < -\frac{1}{2}$

This can also be shown as follows

$$y = \frac{3x + 2}{x(x - 2)} \Rightarrow x^2y - x(2y + 3) - 2 = 0$$

$$x\in\mathbb{R} \Rightarrow B^2 - 4AC \geqslant 0 \Rightarrow (2y + 3)^2 + 8y \geqslant 0$$
$$\Rightarrow 4y^2 + 20y + 9 \geqslant 0$$
$$\Rightarrow (2y + 9)(2y + 1) \geqslant 0$$
$$\Rightarrow y \leqslant -4\tfrac{1}{2} \cup y \geqslant -\tfrac{1}{2}$$

▶ PARAMETRIC EQUATIONS

There are no general rules for sketching curves whose equations are given in parametric form. It is sometimes easy to eliminate the variable parameter and obtain a cartesian equation from which the curve can be sketched. You can look for symmetry and find $\dfrac{dy}{dx}$ as an aid to sketching the curve, but you may be reduced to giving the parameter various values and plotting individual points.

Worked example

Sketch the curve whose parametric equations are $x = t^2 + 1$, $y = 2t$

$$y = 2t \Rightarrow t = \frac{y}{2} \Rightarrow x = \left(\frac{y}{2}\right)^2 + 1 \Rightarrow y^2 = 4(x - 1)$$

$\Rightarrow$ the curve is the same as that shown in Fig. C.14 for the earlier example.

▶ POLAR EQUATIONS

(You should omit this section if polar coordinates are not contained within your syllabus.)

A point may be identified in a plane by reference to a fixed line (called the initial line) and a fixed point (called the pole) on the line. Conventionally we take the fixed line as the positive x-axis and the origin O as the pole.

A point P is then identified by the polar coordinates (r, θ), where θ is the angle through which a straight line, coincident with the initial line, must be rotated in an anticlockwise direction in order to pass through P, and r is the distance of P from O. (See Fig. C.16.)

It is normal practice to define $r > 0$ and θ in $-\pi < \theta \leqslant \pi$. Under these conditions the cartesian coordinates (x, y) and corresponding polar coordinates (r, θ) for a point P are related by $(x, y) \equiv (r\cos \theta, r\sin \theta)$.

When sketching a curve whose equation is given in polar form you should ask the following questions:

  i) Is the curve symmetrical about the initial line? (That is, does the equation remain the same if θ is replaced by $-\theta$?)
  ii) Is the curve symmetrical about a line through the pole and perpendicular

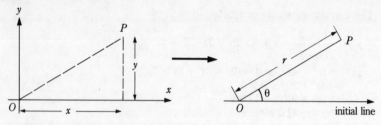

Fig. C.16

to the initial line? (That is, does the equation remain the same if θ is replaced by (π − θ?)

iii) Is the curve symmetrical about the origin? (That is, does the equation remain the same if θ is replaced by (π + θ?)

Finally, note the values of θ for which r has special values, i.e. for which $r = 0$, $r =$ maximum value. If the curve $r = f(θ)$ passes through the pole, it behaves like $f(θ) = 0$ there. The solution of this equation gives the half-lines which are tangents to the curve at the pole.

Worked example

Sketch the curve $r = 3 + 2\cos θ$

$f(θ) = 3 + 2\cos θ \Rightarrow f(-θ) = 3 + 2\cos (-θ) = 3 + 2\cos θ = f(θ)$
⇒ curve is symmetrical about the initial line
$f(π − θ) = 3 + 2\cos (π − θ) = 3 − 2\cos θ \neq f(θ)$

⇒ curve is not symmetrical about the line $θ = \dfrac{π}{2}$

It is therefore necessary to determine r as θ increases from 0 to π

$$θ = 0 \Rightarrow r = 5, \qquad θ = \frac{π}{2} \Rightarrow r = 3, \qquad θ = π \Rightarrow r = 1$$

As θ increases from 0 to π, r steadily decreases from 5 to 1
⇒ curve $r = 3 + 2\cos θ$ is as shown in Fig. C.17.

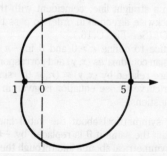

Fig. C.17

▶ *TRANSFORMATIONS AND CURVES*

As well as being able to sketch curves, it is necessary to be able to interpret the effect of certain simple transformations, namely for $y = f(x)$ state the significance of:

i) $y = af(x)$, ii) $y = f(x) + a$, iii) $y = f(x - a)$, iv) $y = f(ax)$

where a is a known constant. We shall consider a to be a positive constant.

i) $y = af(x)$. Multiplication by a positive constant $a, a > 1$, simply increases the y value to a times the original value. The effect then is to stretch the curve out in the direction of the y-axis to give a curve of the form shown in Fig. C.18.

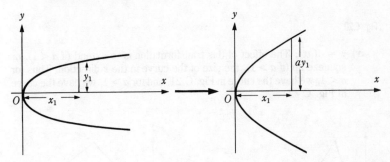

Fig. C.18

ii) $y = f(x) + a$. This transformation does not affect the shape of the curve. It simply moves it through a distance a in the positive direction of the y-axis to give a curve of the form shown in Fig. C.19.

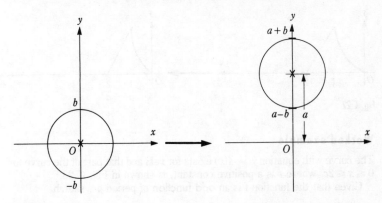

Fig. C.19

iii) $y = f(x - a)$. This transformation again does not affect the shape of the curve. It simply moves the curve through a distance a in the positive direction of the x-axis to give a curve of the form shown in Fig. C.20.

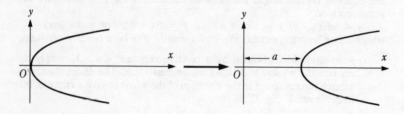

Fig. C.20

iv) $y = f(ax)$. The effect of this transformation is to extend (if $a < 1$), or squeeze up (if $a > 1$), the size of the curve in the x-direction. Thus for $a < 1$, we have the curve in Fig. C.21, and for $a > 1$, we have the curve in Fig. C.22.

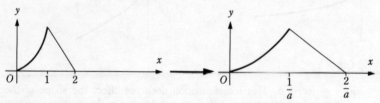

Fig. C.21

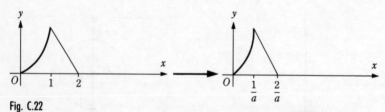

Fig. C.22

Worked example

The curve with equation $y = f(x)$ exists for $x \in \mathbb{R}$ and that part of the curve for $0 \leqslant x \leqslant 2c$, where c is a positive constant, is shown in Fig. C.23.

Given that the function f is an **odd function** of period $4c$, sketch

i) the curve $y = f(x)$ for $-2c \leqslant x \leqslant 2c$
ii) the curve $y = f(2c)$ for $-2c \leqslant x \leqslant 2c$
iii) the curve $y = f(x - c)$ for $0 \leqslant x \leqslant 2c$
iv) the curve $y = 2f(x)$ for $0 \leqslant x \leqslant 2c$

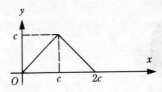

Fig. C.23

The curves are shown in Figs. C.24–C.27.

i) $y = f(x) \Rightarrow$ (Fig. C.24)

ii) $y = f(2c) \Rightarrow$ (Fig. C.25)

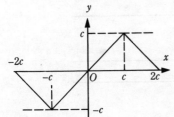

Fig. C.24

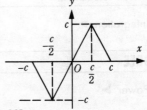

Fig. C.25

iii) $y = f(x - c) \Rightarrow$ (Fig. C.26)

iv) $y = 2f(x) \Rightarrow$ (Fig. C.27)

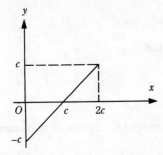

Fig. C.26

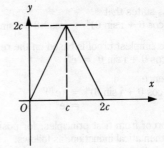

Fig. C.27

◀ Coordinates, Curve sketching, Parametric equations ▶

CYLINDER

◀ Solid shape ▶

DEFINITE INTEGRAL

◀ Integration ▶

DEGREE

◀ Power ▶

DE MOIVRE'S THEOREM

This states that
$$(\cos \theta + i \sin \theta)^n = \cos n\theta + i \sin n\theta$$

The simplest proof is based on the result that
$$\cos \theta + i \sin \theta = e^{i\theta}$$

whence
$$(\cos \theta + i \sin \theta)^n = (e^{i\theta})^n$$
$$= e^{in\theta}$$

A proof from first principles, for positive integral n, can also be given using mathematical induction, as follows.

Let the result be true for $n = k$, that is
$$(\cos \theta + i \sin \theta)^k = \cos k\theta + i \sin k\theta$$

Consider
$$(\cos \theta + i \sin \theta)^{k+1} = (\cos \theta + i \sin \theta)^k(\cos \theta + i \sin \theta)$$
$$= (\cos k\theta + i \sin k\theta)(\cos \theta + i \sin \theta)$$
$$= \cos k\theta \cos \theta - \sin k\theta \sin \theta +$$
$$i (\sin k\theta \cos \theta + \cos k\theta \sin \theta)$$
$$= \cos (k + 1)\theta + i \sin (k + 1)\theta$$

This is the assumed result with $k + 1$ replacing k. Thus if the result is true for $n = k$, then it is true for $n = k + 1$. The result is clearly true for $n = 1$ since both sides reduce to $\cos \theta + i \sin \theta$. This completes the proof by induction. The result is also true when n is not a positive integer.
◀ Complex number ▶

DERIVATIVE (OR DIFFERENTIAL COEFFICIENT)

The derivative $f'(x)$ of $f(x)$ is defined by

$$f'(x) = \lim_{h \to 0} \frac{f(x + h) - f(x)}{h}$$

Diagramatically, this appears as shown in Fig. D.1. Since
$$PA = RB = f(x)$$
$$\text{and} \quad QB = f(x + h)$$
it follows that
$$QR = QB - RB$$
$$= f(x + h) - f(x)$$
Since also
$$PR = h,$$

$$f'(x) = \lim_{h \to 0} \frac{QR}{PR}$$
$$= \lim_{h \to 0} \tan Q\hat{P}R$$

Thus, $f'(x)$ is the limiting value of the gradient of the chord PQ as Q approaches P, which means that it gives the gradient of the tangent at P. Another commonly used notation is
$$PR = \delta x; \quad QR = \delta y$$
Thus δx, δy represent the increases, or increments, in x, y respectively moving from P to Q. The notation for the derivative is then

$$\frac{dy}{dx} = \lim_{\delta x \to 0} \frac{\delta y}{\delta x}$$

The process of finding a derivative is called *differentiation*.

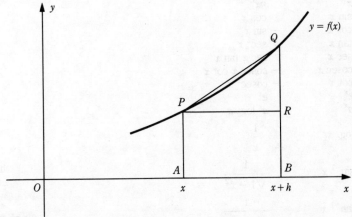

Fig. D.1

Worked example

Find the derivative of $f(x) = \dfrac{1}{x}$

Here,

$$\frac{f(x+h) - f(x)}{h} = \frac{\dfrac{1}{(x+h)} - \dfrac{1}{x}}{h}$$

$$= \frac{x - (x+h)}{hx(x+h)}$$

$$= \frac{-1}{x(x+h)}$$

Thus,

$$f'(x) = \lim_{h \to 0} \frac{-1}{x(x+h)}$$

$$= -\frac{1}{x^2}$$

▶ LIST OF STANDARD DERIVATIVES

Function	Derivative
$f(x)$	$f'(x)$
x^n	nx^{n-1}
$\sin x$	$\cos x$
$\cos x$	$-\sin x$
$\tan x$	$\sec^2 x$
$\sec x$	$\sec x \tan x$
$\operatorname{cosec} x$	$-\operatorname{cosec} x \cot x$
$\cot x$	$-\operatorname{cosec}^2 x$
e^x	e^x
a^x	$a^x \log_e a$
$\log_e x$	$\dfrac{1}{x}$
$\sin^{-1} x$	$\dfrac{1}{\sqrt{1 - x^2}}$
$\tan^{-1} x$	$\dfrac{1}{1 + x^2}$

▶ BASIC RULES OF DIFFERENTIATION

The basic rules of differentiation include the five listed below.

1 $y = cf(x)$, c a constant, $\Rightarrow \dfrac{dy}{dx} = cf'(x)$;

for example $y = 7x^3 \Rightarrow \dfrac{dy}{dx} = 21x^2$

2 $y = u \pm v$, u and v functions of x, $\Rightarrow \dfrac{dy}{dx} = \dfrac{du}{dx} \pm \dfrac{dv}{dx}$

for example, $y = 3\sin x + 2x^5 \Rightarrow \dfrac{dy}{dx} = 3\cos x + 10x^4$

3 $y = uv \Rightarrow \dfrac{dy}{dx} = u\dfrac{dv}{dx} + v\dfrac{du}{dx}$

for example $y = x^2 \tan x \Rightarrow \dfrac{dy}{dx} = x^2(\sec^2 x) + 2x\tan x$

4 $y = \dfrac{u}{v} \Rightarrow \dfrac{dy}{dx} = \dfrac{v\dfrac{du}{dx} - u\dfrac{dv}{dx}}{v^2}$

5 $y = f(u)$ where $u = g(x)$, i.e. a function of a function of x

$\Rightarrow \dfrac{dy}{dx} = \dfrac{dy}{du} \cdot \dfrac{du}{dx}$ often referred to as the *chain rule*.

for example $y = \sin 3x$, i.e. $y = \sin u$ where $u = 3x$

$\Rightarrow \dfrac{dy}{dx} = \cos u . 3 = 3\cos 3x$

NB. a) a special case of this rule is $\dfrac{dy}{dx} = \left(\dfrac{1}{\dfrac{dx}{dy}} \right)$

For example, $x = \sin 3y \Rightarrow \dfrac{dx}{dy} = 3\cos 3y \Rightarrow \dfrac{dy}{dx} = \left(\dfrac{1}{\dfrac{dx}{dy}} \right) = \dfrac{1}{3\cos 3y}$

b) the rule can be extended $\Rightarrow \dfrac{dy}{dx} = \dfrac{dy}{du} \cdot \dfrac{du}{dv} \cdot \dfrac{dv}{dx}$

For example, $y = \cos^2(3x)$ i.e. $y = u^2$ where $u = \cos v$ and $v = 3x$

DERIVATIVE

$$\Rightarrow \frac{dy}{du} = 2u = 2\cos v = 2\cos 3x, \quad \frac{du}{dv} = -\sin v = -\sin 3x, \quad \frac{dv}{dx} = 3$$

$$\Rightarrow \frac{dy}{dx} = \frac{dy}{du} \cdot \frac{du}{dv} \cdot \frac{dv}{dx} = 2\cos 3x \, (-\sin 3x) \cdot 3 = -6\cos 3x \sin 3x$$

This rule enables the table of derivatives to be generalised.

▶ GENERALISED DERIVATIVES

y	$\dfrac{dy}{dx}$
$u^n = [f(x)]^n$	$n[f(x)]^{n-1} f'(x)$
$\sin f(x)$	$f'(x) \cos f(x)$
$\cos f(x)$	$-f'(x) \sin f(x)$
$\tan f(x)$	$f'(x) \sec^2 f(x)$
$\ln f(x)$	$\dfrac{f'(x)}{f(x)}$
$e^{f(x)}$	$f'(x) e^{f(x)}$
$\arcsin f(x)$	$\dfrac{f'(x)}{\sqrt{[1 - (f(x))^2]}}$
$\arccos f(x)$	$\dfrac{-f'(x)}{\sqrt{[1 - (f(x))^2]}}$
$\arctan f(x)$	$\dfrac{f'(x)}{1 + (f(x))^2}$

Eight examples

1 $y = 7(x+2)^4 \Rightarrow \dfrac{dy}{dx} = 7 \cdot 4 \cdot (x+2)^3 \cdot 1 = 28(x+2)^3$

2 $y = \sqrt{(2+x^3)} = (2+x^3)^{\frac{1}{2}} \Rightarrow \dfrac{dy}{dx} = \frac{1}{2}(2+x^3)^{-\frac{1}{2}} \cdot 3x^2 = \dfrac{3x^2}{2\sqrt{(2+x^3)}}$

3 $y = e^{4x} - e^{-3x} \Rightarrow \dfrac{dy}{dx} = 4e^{4x} - (-3)e^{-3x} = 4e^{4x} + 3e^{-3x}$

4 $y = \tan 2x \Rightarrow \dfrac{dy}{dx} = (\sec^2 2x) \cdot 2 = 2\sec^2 2x$

5 $y = \sin 3x \cos 2x \Rightarrow \dfrac{dy}{dx} = 3\cos 3x \cos 2x + \sin 3x \, (-2\sin 2x)$

$$= 3\cos 3x \cos 2x - 2\sin 3x \sin 2x$$

6 $y = 2\sin^3 (4x) \Rightarrow \dfrac{dy}{dx} = 2.3\sin^2 (4x) \cdot (\cos 4x)(4) = 24\sin^2 4x \cos 4x$

7 $y = \text{arc sin } (3x) \Rightarrow \dfrac{dy}{dx} = \dfrac{3}{\sqrt{(1 - (3x)^2)}} = \dfrac{3}{\sqrt{(1 - 9x^2)}}$

8 $y = \dfrac{e^{2x}}{\sin 3x} \Rightarrow \dfrac{dy}{dx} = \dfrac{\sin 3x \cdot 2e^{2x} - e^{2x} \cdot 3 \cos 3x}{\sin^2 3x}$

▶ MASTERING DIFFERENTIATION

With practice students usually become efficient at differentiation. Usually marks are lost either because the standard results have not been learnt properly, or because sufficient care has not been taken in 'talking oneself' through the necessary operations. First you should recognise the form of the function, then you should 'talk yourself' through the basic rules to be used.

In example 2, $y = \sqrt{(2 + x^3)}$, you should first recognise y as a function of x raised to the power of $\dfrac{1}{2}$. Differentiation therefore involves multiplying by the power $\left(\dfrac{1}{2}\right)$, reducing the power by 1, $(2 + x^3)^{-\frac{1}{2}}$, and finally multiplying by the derivative of the expression inside the bracket, $(3x^2)$.

Thus $\dfrac{dy}{dx} = \dfrac{1}{2} \cdot (2 + x^3)^{-\frac{1}{2}} \cdot (3x^2) = \dfrac{3x^2}{2\sqrt{(2 + x^3)}}$

Derivatives involving products or quotients simply add extra lines to the working. In example 8, $y = \dfrac{e^{2x}}{\sin 3x}$, you should recognise that the quotient rule is required.

$$= \dfrac{\begin{array}{c}(\text{denominator})(\text{derivative of numerator}) \\ - (\text{numerator})(\text{derivative of denominator})\end{array}}{(\text{denominator})^2}$$

For $\dfrac{d}{dx}(e^{2x})$, the derivative of an exponential, we have the exponential, (e^{2x}), multiplied by the derivative of the index, (2).

$$\Rightarrow \dfrac{d}{dx}(e^{2x}) = 2e^{2x}$$

For $\dfrac{d}{dx}(\sin 3x)$, the derivative of a sine, we have a cosine, $(\cos 3x)$, multiplied by the derivative of $3x$, (3)

$$\Rightarrow \dfrac{d}{dx}\sin 3x = 3 \cos 3x$$

$$\Rightarrow \dfrac{dy}{dx} = \dfrac{\sin 3x \cdot 2e^{2x} - e^{2x} \cdot 3 \cos 3x}{\sin^2 3x}$$

DETERMINANT

◀ Matrix/matrices ▶

DIFFERENTIAL COEFFICIENT

◀ Derivative ▶

DIFFERENTIAL EQUATION

A differential equation is an equation which contains at least one differential coefficient. The *order* of a differential equation is the order of the highest differential coefficient present. The *solution* of a differential equation is an equation relating the variables, but containing no differential coefficients. The *general solution* is a solution containing arbitrary constants. A *particular solution* is a solution obtained from the general solution by using boundary conditions; it contains no arbitrary constants.

Here we can consider three types of differential equation included in the A-level curriculum.

▶ TYPE 1 VARIABLES SEPARABLE

Consider the equation

$$\frac{dy}{dx} = f(x)g(y)$$

The x and y terms can be separated to give

$$\int \frac{dy}{g(y)} = \int f(x)dx$$

These two integrals can be evaluated separately.

Worked example

Solve the differential equation

$$\frac{dy}{dx} = 2xe^y$$

given that $y = 0$ when $x = 1$.

We separate the variables to give

$$\int e^{-y}dy = \int 2xdx$$

Integrating

$$-e^{-y} = x^2 + A$$

where A is an arbitrary constant.

Since $y = 0$ when $x = 1$,

$$-1 = 1 + A$$

whence $A = -2$

Thus,

$$-e^{-y} = x^2 - 2$$
$$\text{or} \quad e^{-y} = 2 - x^2$$

giving

$$-y = \log_e(2 - x^2)$$
$$\text{or} \quad y = -\log_e(2 - x^2)$$

▶ TYPE 2 EQUATIONS SOLVABLE USING INTEGRATION FACTOR

Consider the equation

$$\frac{dy}{dx} + Py = Q$$

where P, Q are functions of x.

The method of solution is to multiply the left-hand side by a factor I (a function of x) chosen to make the left-hand side the derivative of a product. Multiplying by I,

$$I\frac{dy}{dx} + IPy = IQ$$

If the left-hand side is the derivative of a product, it must by Iy. Now

$$\frac{d}{dx}(Iy) = I\frac{dy}{dx} + y\frac{dI}{dx}$$

This will give the left-hand side if

$$y\frac{dI}{dx} = IPy$$

or, separating the variables,

$$\int \frac{dI}{I} = \int P dx$$

whence $\log_e I = \int P dx$

or $\qquad I = e^{\int P dx}$

(NB. We have not inserted an arbitrary constant since we are looking for any I which will give us the derivative of a product.)

Thus the differential equation can be written

$$\frac{d}{dx}(ye^{\int Pdx}) = Qe^{\int Pdx}$$

whence integrating,

$$ye^{\int Pdx} = \int Qe^{\int Pdx}dx$$

Worked example

Find the general solution of the differential equation

$$\frac{dy}{dx} + \frac{3y}{x} = x^2$$

Here

$$P = \frac{3}{x}$$

so that

$$\int Pdx = 3\int \frac{dx}{x}$$

$$= 3\log_e x$$
$$= \log_e x^3$$

The integrating factor is

$$I = e^{\int Pdx}$$
$$= e^{\log_e x^3}$$
$$= x^3$$

Multiplying through by I.

$$x^3\frac{dy}{dx} + 3x^2y = x^5$$

or

$$\frac{d}{dx}(yx^3) = x^5$$

Integrating

$$yx^3 = \frac{x^6}{6} + B$$

(B an arbitrary constant) or

$$y = \frac{x^3}{6} + \frac{B}{x^3}$$

This is the general solution.

▶ TYPE 3   SECOND-ORDER EQUATIONS WITH CONSTANT COEFFICIENTS

Consider the equation

$$a\frac{d^2y}{dx^2} + b\frac{dy}{dx} + cy = 0$$

We try the solution

$$y = e^{mx}$$

for which

$$\frac{dy}{dx} = me^{mx}$$

and

$$\frac{d^2y}{dx^2} = m^2e^{mx}$$

This satisfies the differential equation if

$$am^2 e^{mx} + bme^{mx} + ce^{mx} = 0$$

or

$$am^2 + bm + c = 0$$

This is called the auxiliary equation, and it has two roots α, β. Then

$$y = e^{\alpha x} \text{ and } y = e^{\beta x}$$

are both solutions to the differential equation.

The general solution is given by

$$y = Ae^{\alpha x} + Be^{\beta x}$$

If α, β are real, the solution is normally given in this form. If however, α, β are complex, then this can be transformed to a more useful form.

Let

$$\alpha = \lambda + i\mu$$
$$\beta = \lambda - i\mu$$

Then,

$$\begin{aligned} y &= Ae^{(\lambda+i\mu)x} + Be^{(\lambda-i\mu)x} \\ &= e^{\lambda x}(Ae^{i\mu x} + Be^{-i\mu x}) \\ &= e^{\lambda x}[A(\cos \mu x + i \sin \mu x) + B(\cos \mu x - i \sin \mu x)] \\ &= e^{\lambda x}(C \cos \mu x + D \sin \mu x) \end{aligned}$$

where $C = A + B$ and $D = i(A - B)$ are arbitrary constants. This can be illustrated with an example.

Worked example

Find the general solution to the differential equation

$$\frac{d^2y}{dx^2} - 4\frac{dy}{dx} + 13y = 0$$

The auxiliary equation is

$$m^2 - 4m + 13 = 0$$

Thus,

$$\alpha, \beta = \frac{4 \pm \sqrt{16 - 52}}{2} = 2 \pm 3i$$

The general solution is therefore
$$y = e^{2x}(A \cos 3x + B \sin 3x)$$
A special case arises when $\alpha = \beta$. In this case, the general solution is
$$y = (A + Bx)e^{\alpha x}$$
A more general differential equation is

$$a\frac{d^2y}{dx^2} + b\frac{dy}{dx} + cy = f(x)$$

The general solution is made up of two components:

i) The *complementary function* which is the general solution to the differential equation obtained by replacing $f(x)$ by zero.

ii) A *particular integral* depending upon $f(x)$. This can be found by trial and error, as follows
$$f(x) = e^{\gamma x}; \text{ try } y = ke^{\gamma x}$$
$$f(x) = a_n x^n + a_{n-1}x^{n-1} + \ldots a_0; \text{ try } y = b_n x^n + b_{n-1}x^{n-1} + \ldots + b_0$$

The method involves substituting the trial solution into the differential equation. The example which follows provides an illustration of this point.

Worked example

Find the general solution to the differential equation

$$\frac{d^2y}{dx^2} - 4\frac{dy}{dx} + 3y = x^2 + 1$$

The auxiliary equation is
$$m^2 - 4m + 3 = 0$$
$$(m - 1)(m - 3) = 0$$
i.e. $\alpha = 1, \beta = 3$.

The complementary function is
$$y = Ae^x + Be^{3x}$$
As a particular integral, try
$$y = b_2 x^2 + b_1 x + b_0$$
Here

$$\frac{dy}{dx} = 2b_2 x + b_1$$

and

$$\frac{d^2y}{dx^2} = 2b_2$$

Substituting into the differential equation,
$$2b_2 - 4(2b_2 x + b_1) + 3(b_2 x^2 + b_1 x + b_0) = x^2 + 1$$
or $\quad 3b_2 x^2 + (3b_1 - 8b_2)x + 3b_0 - 4b_1 + 2b_2 = x^2 + 1$
Equating coefficients of like terms
$$3b_2 = 1$$
$$3b_1 - 8b_2 = 0$$
$$3b_0 - 4b_1 + 2b_2 = 1$$

Solving,

$$b_2 = \frac{1}{3}$$

$$b_1 = \frac{8}{3} \cdot \frac{1}{3} = \frac{8}{9}$$

$$b_0 = \frac{1 + \left(4 \times \frac{8}{9}\right) - \left(2 \times \frac{1}{3}\right)}{3} = \frac{35}{27}$$

The general solution is therefore

$$y = Ae^x + Be^{3x} + \frac{1}{3}x^2 + \frac{8}{9}x + \frac{35}{27}$$

DIFFERENTIATION

Differentiation is the process of finding a **derivative**.
◄ Derivative ►

DISCRIMINANT

◄ Quadratic equation ►

DISPLACEMENT

This is the distance moved in a particular direction.

Note that this is a **vector** quantity, and the direction should be either very obvious (movement along a straight track, for example) or clearly stated, so that the displacement is not mixed up with a simple distance, which is a **scalar**.
◄ Scalar, Vector, Velocity ►

DISTRIBUTION FUNCTION (CUMULATIVE)

The distribution function $F(x)$ of the random variable X is defined by

$$F(x) = P(X \leq x) \quad \text{for all } x$$

If X is discrete with **probability** function p_x, then

$$F(x) = \sum_{y \leq x} p_y$$

If X is continuous with **probability density function** $f(x)$, then

$$F(x) = \int_{-\infty}^{x} f(y)dy$$

Reversing this result,
$$f(x) = F'(x)$$

All distribution functions $F(x)$ have the following properties:

   i) $F(x)$ is a non-decreasing function for all x.
   ii) $\lim_{x \to \infty} F(x) = 1$
   iii) $\lim_{x \to \infty} F'(x) = 0$

DOMAIN

In mathematics we constantly attempt to explain physical happenings by relating a physical quantity x, say, to another physical quantity y. We usually produce sets of ordered pairs of the quantities (x_1, y_1), (x_2, y_2), (x_3, y_3) ... (x_n, y_n) to form a relation.

There are various notations for expressing a relation other than listing the set of ordered pairs. If, for instance, it is known that each y is the square of the corresponding x value then the relation can be expressed as
$$y = x^2$$
The set of the first elements $\{x_1, x_2, x_3 \ldots x_n\}$ of the pairs of the relation is called the domain of the relation. The set of the second elements $\{y_1, y_2, y_3, \ldots y_n\}$ of the pairs of the relation is called the *range* of the relation.

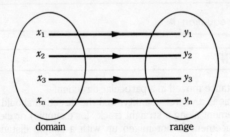

or

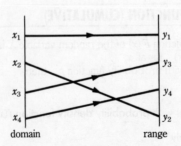

Fig. D.2

A relation can be represented diagramatically as shown in Fig. D.2. A relation in which each element of the domain is associated with one and only one element of the range is called a **function**.

◀ Function, Mapping ▶

DOT PRODUCT

◀ Scalar product ▶

---

e

---

e is the base of natural logarithms, and has the approximate value 2·718. There are two simple definitions of e, as shown below.

▶ DEFINITION 1

$$e = 1 + 1 + \frac{1}{2!} + \frac{1}{3!} + \frac{1}{4!} + \ldots$$

$$= \sum_{r=0}^{\infty} \frac{1}{r!} \text{ (taking } 0! = 1)$$

▶ DEFINITION 2

$$e = \lim_{n \to \infty} \left(1 + \frac{1}{n}\right)^n$$

Many students find it difficult to believe that the limit on the right-hand side has any value other than 1. Detailed examination of this limit is beyond the A-level syllabus, but students can convince themselves of the validity of Definition 2 by evaluating $\left(1 + \dfrac{1}{n}\right)^n$ for large n using a calculator, for example (to three decimal places),

$$\left(1 + \frac{1}{100}\right)^{100} = 2·705$$

$$\left(1 + \frac{1}{1000}\right)^{1000} = 2·717$$

and so on. (NB. Rounding errors will defeat any attempt to make n too large.)
◀ Logarithm ▶

EFFICIENCY

◀ Power ▶

ELASTIC ENERGY

◀ Energy ▶

ELLIPSE

An ellipse is the locus of a point which moves in such a way that the ratio of its distance from a fixed point (the focus) to its distance from a fixed line (the directrix) is equal to a constant less than 1. This constant is called the *eccentricity*, *e*. The standard equation of the ellipse can be derived by taking the coordinates of the focus as (*ae*, 0) and the equation of the directrix as $x = a/e$ (see Fig. E.1).

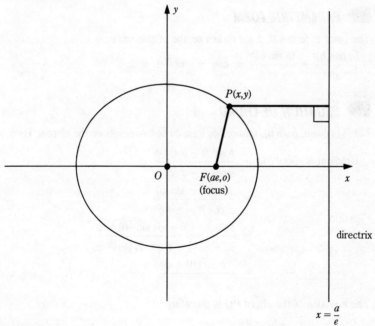

Fig. E.1

If $P(x, y)$ is any point on the ellipse, then
$$PF = \sqrt{(x - ae)^2 + y^2}$$

If D denotes the foot of the perpendicular from P to the directrix, then

$$PD = \frac{a}{e} - x$$

Since $PF = ePD$, it follows that

$$\sqrt{(x - ae)^2 + y^2} = e\left(\frac{a}{e} - x\right) = a - ex$$

or, squaring,

$$(x - ae)^2 + y^2 = (a - ex)^2$$

i.e. $\quad x^2 - 2xae + a^2e^2 + y^2 = a^2 - 2aex + e^2x^2$

which reduces to

$$\frac{x^2}{a^2} + \frac{y^2}{a^2(1 - e^2)} = 1$$

or $\quad \dfrac{x^2}{a^2} + \dfrac{y^2}{b^2} = 1$

where $b^2 = a^2(1 - e^2)$

▶ PARAMETRIC FORM

The point P ($a \cos \theta$, $b \sin \theta$) lies on the ellipse since

$$\frac{(a \cos \theta)^2}{a^2} + \frac{(b \sin \theta)^2}{b^2} = \cos^2 \theta + \sin^2 \theta = 1$$

▶ EQUATION OF CHORD

Let P ($a \cos \theta$, $b \sin \theta$), Q($a \cos \phi$, $b \sin \phi$) be two points on the ellipse. Then,

$$\begin{aligned}
\text{Gradient of chord } PQ &= \frac{b \sin \theta - b \sin \phi}{a \cos \theta - a \cos \phi} \\
&= \frac{b(\sin \theta - \sin \phi)}{a(\cos \theta - \cos \phi)} \\
&= \frac{b . 2 \cos \frac{1}{2}(\theta + \phi) \sin \frac{1}{2}(\theta - \phi)}{a . -2\sin \frac{1}{2}(\theta + \phi) \sin \frac{1}{2}(\theta - \phi)} \\
&= \frac{-b \cot \frac{1}{2}(\theta + \phi)}{a}
\end{aligned}$$

The equation of the chord PQ is therefore

$$y - b \sin \theta = \frac{-b \cot \frac{1}{2}(\theta + \phi)}{a}(x - a \cos \theta)$$

which reduces to

$$ay - ab \sin \theta = -bx \cot \tfrac{1}{2}(\theta + \phi) + ab \cot \tfrac{1}{2}(\theta + \phi) \cos \theta$$

▶ EQUATION OF TANGENT

The equation of the tangent at $P(a \cos \theta, b \sin \theta)$ can be found by letting $Q \to P$, that is, putting $\phi = \theta$ in the above equation. This gives

$$ay - ab \sin \theta = -bx \cot \theta + ab \cot \theta \cos \theta$$

which reduces to

$$ay \sin \theta + bx \cos \theta = ab$$

The equation of the tangent at P can be found using calculus in the following way.

$$x = a \cos \theta; \quad y = b \sin \theta$$

$$\frac{dx}{d\theta} = -a \sin \theta; \quad \frac{dy}{d\theta} = b \cos \theta$$

Thus the gradient of the tangent at P is given by

$$\frac{dy}{dx} = \frac{dy}{d\theta} \Big/ \frac{dx}{d\theta}$$

$$= \frac{-b \cot \theta}{a}$$

The equation of the tangent at P is therefore

$$y - b \sin \theta = \frac{-b \cot \theta}{a} (x - a \cos \theta)$$

which reduces to

$$ay \sin \theta + bx \cos \theta = ab$$

▶ EQUATION OF NORMAL

The gradient of the normal at $P(a \cos \theta, b \sin \theta)$ is given by

$$-1 \Big/ \frac{dy}{dx} = \frac{a \tan \theta}{b}$$

The equation of the normal at P is therefore

$$y - b \sin \theta = \frac{a \tan \theta}{b} (x - a \cos \theta)$$

or $\quad by \cos \theta - ax \sin \theta = -(a^2 - b^2) \sin \theta \cos \theta$

ENERGY

Energy is the capacity to do work. It is a **scalar**, measured in joules. Three of the many forms in which energy exists are described here.

ENERGY (CONSERVATION OF)

 *KINETIC ENERGY*

The kinetic energy of a particle of mass m moving with speed v is equal to $\frac{1}{2}mv^2$.

 *POTENTIAL ENERGY*

The potential energy of a particle of mass m height h above the reference level is equal to mgh.

 *ELASTIC ENERGY*

The elastic energy of a string of natural length l and modulus of elasticity λ when extended an amount x is equal to $\lambda x^2/2l$.
◀ Force, Power, Work ▶

ENERGY (CONSERVATION OF)

The principle of conservation of **energy** states that the total energy of a system is conserved. In practice, however, some energy is always lost in the form of heat and so forth.
◀ Energy, Mechanical Energy (conservation of), Work ▶

EQUATIONS AND IDENTITIES

An equality such as $6(x - 2) = 24$, which is true only when $x = 6$, is called an equation. An equality such as $x^2 - 4 = (x - 2)(x + 2)$, which is true for *all* real values of x, is called an identity and as such is written

$$x^2 - 4 \equiv (x - 2)(x + 2)$$

The following identities frequently occur in mathematics and you should become familiar with them. They can all be proved by multiplying out the brackets.

$$(x + y)^2 \equiv x^2 + 2xy + y^2$$
$$(x - y)^2 \equiv x^2 - 2xy + y^2$$
$$(x + y)^3 \equiv x^3 + 3x^2y + 3xy^2 + y^3$$
$$(x - y)^3 \equiv x^3 - 3x^2y + 3xy^2 - y^3$$
$$(x + y)(x - y) \equiv x^2 - y^2$$
$$(x + y)(y + z)(z + x) \equiv x^2(y + z) + y^2(z + x) + z^2(x + y) + 2xyz$$

Worked examples

1 Find the product $(x + y + 2)(x + y - 2)$

$$(x + y + 2)(x + y - 2) \equiv [(x + y) + 2][(x + y) - 2] \equiv (x + y)^2 - 2^2$$
$$\equiv x^2 + 2xy + y^2 - 4$$

2   Find the product $(x - 3y + 2z)^2$

$(x - 3y + 2z)^2 \equiv [(x - 3y) + 2z]^2 \equiv (x - 3y)^2 + 2(x - 3y).2z + (2z)^2$
$\equiv x^2 - 6xy + 9y^2 + 4xz - 12yz + 4z^2$

3   Find the product $(a - 2)^3(a + 2)^3$

$(a - 2)^3(a + 2)^3 \equiv [(a - 2)(a + 2)]^3 = (a^2 - 4)^3$
$\equiv (a^2)^3 - 3(a^2)^2 4 + 3(a^2)(4)^2 - 4^3$
$\equiv a^6 - 12a^4 + 48a^2 - 64$

EQUILATERAL TRIANGLE

◀ Plane shape ▶

EQUILIBRIUM

A body which is at rest is in equilibrium.

▶ *FORCES IN EQUILIBRIUM*

It is important to study systems of forces acting in a plane on a body which remains at rest. To start we consider coplanar forces acting on a particle.

A particle P is in equilibrium if and only if the vector sum (called the **resultant**) of the forces acting on it is the null vector.

Worked examples

1   Forces $(3i + 4j)N$, $(ai + 7j)N$ and $(-6i + bj)N$ act on a particle P which is in equilibrium. Find the values of a and b,

For equilibrium
$3i + 4j + ai + 7j - 6i + bj = 0$
$(3 + a - 6)i + (4 + 7 + b)j = 0$
The **i** components must be zero
$3 + a - 6 = 0 \Rightarrow a = 3$
The **j** component must also be zero
$4 + 7 + b = 0 \Rightarrow b = -11$

2   Forces $(5i - 9j)N$ and $(-2i + 5j)N$ act on a particle P and a third force $\mathbf{F}$ is applied to P which produces equilibrium. Calculate the magnitude of $\mathbf{F}$.

$\mathbf{F} + 5i - 9j - 2i + 5j = 0$
$\Rightarrow \mathbf{F} = -3i + 4j$
$|\mathbf{F}| = \sqrt{(3^2 + 4^2)} = 5$

The third force $\mathbf{F}$ has magnitude 5N

◀ Force, Moment of a force, Resultant of a set of forces,
Triangle (polygon) of forces ▶

▶ *RIGID BODIES*

Two new concepts are required in dealing with the equilibrium of a *rigid body*. When a rigid body is subjected to a system of coplanar forces, equilibrium occurs only if:

a) the vector sum of the forces acting on the body is zero,
b) there is no turning effect caused by the forces considered as a whole.

Condition a) can be fulfilled by showing that the sum of the resolved parts of the forces in two independent directions (often horizontal and vertical) are both zero. Condition b) requires us to define the **moment of a force**, because moments are used to measure the turning effect of a system of forces.

◀ Force, Resultant of a set of forces, Triangle (polygon) of forces ▶

EQUIVALENT (SYSTEMS OF FORCES)

Two systems of forces acting in a plane on a body are defined to be equivalent when *both* of the following conditions are satisfied:

a) the vector sum of the forces in the first system is equal to the vector sum of the forces in the second system,
b) the sum of the **moments of the forces** in the first system is equal to the sum of the moments of the forces in the second system *about every point in the plane*.

In general, two forces acting on a body may be replaced by a single force, called their **resultant**. Any system of forces may be reduced successively using this technique until the simplest equivalent system has been obtained. This simplest equivalent system may be a *single force* or a **couple**. In the special case when the system reduces to two equal and opposite forces acting in the same line, we have **equilibrium**.

◀ Couple, Equilibrium, Moment of a force, Resultant of a set of forces ▶

ESTIMATOR

An estimator for an unknown parameter θ based on a random sample X_1, X_2, ... X_n is a function of X_1, X_2, ... X_n (that is a statistic) suitable for estimating θ. The standard notation for an estimator is $\hat{\theta}$. The numerical value of $\hat{\theta}$ obtained from experimental data is called an estimate.

▶ *UNBIASED ESTIMATOR*

$\hat{\theta}$ is called *unbiased* if
  $E(\hat{\theta}) = \theta$

The precision of an estimator is measured by its variance – $Var(\hat{\theta})$. The standard deviation of $\hat{\theta}$ is normally called its *standard error*. Good estimators are characterised by a small standard error. The best of several unbiased estimators is the one with smallest standard error. The efficiency of one unbiased estimator $\hat{\theta}_1$ relative to another unbiased estimator $\hat{\theta}_2$, is defined by:

$$\text{Efficiency of } \hat{\theta}_1, \text{ relative to } \hat{\theta}_2 = \frac{\text{Var}(\hat{\theta}_2)}{\text{Var}(\hat{\theta}_1)}$$

▶ BIASED ESTIMATOR

An estimator $\hat{\theta}$ that is not unbiased is called *biased*. The bias is defined as $E(\hat{\theta}) - \theta$.

The precision of a biased estimator is measured by the **mean square error** (MSE), defined by

$$MSE = E[(\hat{\theta} - \theta)^2]$$
$$= \text{Var}(\hat{\theta}) + \text{Bias}^2$$

An estimator $\hat{\theta}_n$ based on a sample of size n is called *consistent* if

$$\lim E(\hat{\theta}_n) = \theta \text{ and } \lim \text{Var}(\hat{\theta}_n) = 0 \text{ as } n \to \infty$$

Note that it is not necessary for a consistent estimator to be unbiased, only asymptotically so.

EVEN FUNCTION

$f(x)$ is an even function if, for all x,
$$f(x) = f(-x)$$
For example,
$$f(x) = \sin^2 x$$
is an even function since
$$f(-x) = \sin^2(-x) = \{\sin(-x)\}^2$$
$$= (-\sin x)^2$$
$$= \sin^2 x = f(x)$$
However,
$$f(x) = x + \sin^2 x$$
is not an even function since
$$f(-x) = -x + \sin^2(-x)$$
$$= -x + \{\sin(-x)\}^2$$
$$= -x + \sin^2(x)$$
$$\neq f(x)$$

EVENT

An event is defined as a subset of the sample space of an experiment. For example, if 2 coins are tossed simultaneously, the sample space is

{HH, HT, TH, TT}

where the first letter denotes the first coin and the second letter the second coin (H = head, T = tail). The subset {HT, TH}, or in words 'one head and one tail', is an event.

◀ Probability ▶

EXPONENTIAL DISTRIBUTION

The continuous random variable X has the exponential distribution if its probability density function is given by

$f(x) = \lambda e^{-\lambda x}$ if $x \geqslant 0$
      $= 0$ otherwise

The graph of $f(x)$ is shown in Fig. E.2. The mean and variance are given by

$$E(x) = \frac{1}{\lambda}; \quad Var(x) = \frac{1}{\lambda^2}$$

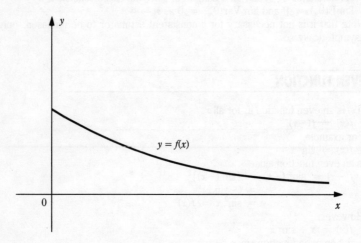

Fig. E.2

EXPONENTIAL FUNCTION

The exponential function $\exp(x)$ or e^x can be defined on the domain $(-\infty, \infty)$ in one of two ways.

▶ DEFINITION 1

$$e^x = 1 + x + \frac{x^2}{2!} + \frac{x^3}{3!} + \frac{x^4}{4!} + \dots$$

$$= \sum_{r=0}^{\infty} \frac{x^r}{r!} \qquad \qquad \text{(taking } 0! = 1)$$

▶ DEFINITION 2

$$e^x = \lim_{n \to \infty} \left(1 + \frac{x}{n}\right)^n$$

The graph of $y = e^x$ is shown in Fig. E.3. An important property of e^x is that its **derivative** is equal to itself, that is:

$$\frac{d}{dx}(e^x) = e^x$$

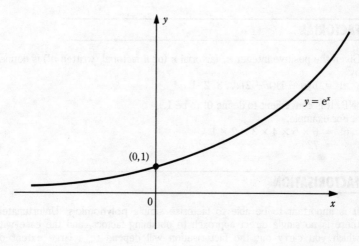

Fig. E.3

FACTORIAL

Given the positive integer n, factorial n (or n factorial, written $n!$) is defined by

$$n! = n(n - 1)(n - 2)\ldots 3.\, 2.\, 1$$

(NB. It is convenient to define $0!$ to be 1.)

For example,

$$6! = 6 \times 5 \times 4 \times 3 \times 2 \times 1$$
$$= 720$$

FACTORISATION

It is important to be able to factorise simple **polynomials**. Unfortunately there is no single direct approach to obtaining factors, and the ease with which you carry out the factorisation will depend to a large extent on experience, practice and familiarity with standard identities. However, you should find the following procedures helpful.

▶ COMMON MONOMIAL FACTOR

$\Rightarrow ab + ac \equiv a(b + c)$

Examples

$$2x^2y^2 + x^2y - 3xy^2 \equiv xy(2xy + x - 3y)$$
$$xy - 3x + 2y^2 - 6y \equiv x(y - 3) + 2y(y - 3) \equiv (y - 3)(x + 2y)$$

▶ DIFFERENCE OF TWO SQUARES

$\Rightarrow x^2 - y^2 \equiv (x - y)(x + y)$

Examples

$$9x^2 - 4y^2 = (3x)^2 - (2y)^2 \equiv (3x - 2y)(3x + 2y)$$

$$x^4 - y^4 \equiv (x^2)^2 - (y^2)^2 \equiv (x^2 - y^2)(x^2 + y^2)$$
$$\equiv (x - y)(x + y)(x^2 + y^2)$$

▶ PERFECT SQUARE TRINOMIALS

$$\Rightarrow x^2 + 2xy + y^2 \equiv (x + y)^2$$
$$x^2 - 2xy + y^2 \equiv (x - y)^2$$

Two terms are perfect squares. The third term is twice the product of the square roots of the other two terms.

Examples

$$4x^2 + 4x + 1 \Rightarrow (2x)^2 + 2.(2x).1 + 1^2 \equiv (2x + 1)^2$$

$$9x^2 - 48x + 64 \Rightarrow (3x)^2 - 2.(3x).8 + 8^2 \equiv (3x - 8)^2$$

▶ TRINOMIAL

$$\Rightarrow x^2 + (a + b)x + ab \equiv (x + a)(x + b)$$
Coefficient $x^2 = 1$, constant term = product of a and b,
coefficient x = sum of a and b, where a and b may be positive or negative.

Examples

$x^2 + 5x + 6,$ $6 = 2 \times 3, 5 = 2 + 3,$
$\Rightarrow (x + 2)(x + 3)$

$x^2 + x - 6$ $-6 = 3 \times (-2), 1 = 3 + (-2),$
$\Rightarrow (x + 3)(x - 2)$

$x^2 - 7x + 12,$ $12 = (-3) \times (-4), -3 + (-4) = -7,$
$\Rightarrow (x - 3)(x - 4)$

$$\Rightarrow acx^2 + (ad + bc)x + bd \equiv (ax + b)(cx + d)$$

Coefficient $x^2 = ac$, constant term = bd, and the coefficient of $x = ad + bc$, the sum of two numbers whose product is the same as the product of the constant term and the coefficient of the x^2 term, i.e. *abcd*. It is not always easy to find $ad + bc$, but the following examples may help.

Examples

$6x^2 + 17x + 12$ $\Rightarrow 6 \times 12 = 72 \Rightarrow$ need two numbers whose sum is 17 and whose product is 72. These are 8 and 9.
$6x^2 + 17x + 12 = 6x^2 + (8x + 9x) + 12 = 2x(3x + 4) + 3(3x + 4)$
$$= (2x + 3)(3x + 4)$$

$8x^2 + 6x - 27$ $\Rightarrow 8 \times (-27) = -216 \Rightarrow$ need two numbers whose sum is 6 and whose product is -216. These are 18 and -12.

$$8x^2 + 6x - 27 = 8x^2 + 12x + 18x - 27 = 4x(2x - 3) + 9(2x - 3)$$
$$= (4x + 9)(2x - 3)$$

$12x^2 - 23x + 10 \Rightarrow 12 \times 10 = 120 \Rightarrow$ need two numbers whose sum is -23 and whose product is 120. These are -8 and -15.
$$12x^2 - 23x + 10 = 12x^2 - 8x - 15x + 10 = 4x(3x - 2) - 5(3x - 2)$$
$$= (4x - 5)(3x - 2)$$

▶ SUM, DIFFERENCE OF TWO CUBES

$$x^3 + y^3 = (x + y)(x^2 - xy + y^2)$$
$$x^3 - y^3 = (x - y)(x^2 + xy + y^2)$$

(NB. In each case, the first bracket is the L.H.S. without the indices; and, in the second bracket, the xy term has the opposite sign to that in the first bracket.

Examples

$$8x^3 - 1 = (2x)^3 - 1^3 = (2x - 1)[(2x)^2 + 2x.1 + 1^2]$$
$$= (2x - 1)[4x^2 + 2x + 1]$$

$$x^{12} + y^{12} = (x^4)^3 + (y^4)^3 = (x^4 + y^4)(x^8 - x^4y^4 + y^8)$$

FACTOR THEOREM

This states that if $f(x)$ is a polynomial and $f(a) = 0$, then $x - a$ is a factor of $f(x)$. This result can be deduced from the **remainder theorem** by putting the remainder R equal to zero.

The following example shows how the factor theorem can be used to find integer roots of polynomial equations by trial and error.

Worked example

Find the roots of the cubic equation
$$x^3 - 2x^2 - 5x - 6 = 0$$

We find that
$$f(1) = -8$$
$$f(-1) = 0$$
$$f(2) = 0$$
$$f(-2) = 4$$
$$f(3) = 24$$
$$f(-3) = 0$$

It follows that $(x + 1)$, $(x - 2)$ and $(x + 3)$ are all factors so that
$$x^3 + 2x^2 - 5x - 6 \equiv (x + 1)(x - 2)(x + 3)$$
◀ Remainder theorem ▶

FISHER INDEX

FORCE

There are two distinct types of force. Forces of the first type are external to the body under consideration, the most important of these being *gravitational forces*. The gravitational force with which the earth attracts a body is called the *weight* of the body. When we are considering distances which are small compared with the radius of the earth, we use a constant vector **g** for the acceleration due to gravity and we take a value such as $9 \cdot 8\,\text{ms}^{-2}$ or $10\,\text{ms}^{-2}$ for the magnitude of **g** in numerical questions. It should be stressed, however, that the gravitational force of attraction is *not constant*, but is dependent on the bodies themselves and their surroundings as described by Newton's law of universal gravitation. If you need to use this law, the question will tell you how to do this.

The second type of force is related to the body or bodies under consideration. The most common are

a) forces exerted by one body on another body in contact with it, according to Newton's third law,
b) **frictional** forces,
c) the **tension** in a light string or the thrust in a light rod connected to the body,
d) specific forces applied to the body and described in a particular question.

In nearly every question set in examinations your solution will depend on a clear **space diagram** or **force diagram** (or diagrams) which displays all the forces acting on a body. A clear freehand sketch is sufficient unless you are drawing to scale for a graphical solution. After completing your sketch *always* read through a question again to make sure that you have included all the data and that you have not made any unjustified assumptions.

Worked example A

A force of magnitude 2N acts on a particle P of mass $0 \cdot 4\,$kg. Given that P moves through 2m from rest in time Ts in a straight line, find the magnitude of the acceleration of P and the value of T

$$\boxed{0 \cdot 4} \rightarrow 2\text{N}$$

Using $F = ma$ we have $\quad a = \dfrac{F}{m} = \dfrac{2}{0 \cdot 4}\,\text{ms}^{-2}$

$$\text{acceleration} = 5\,\text{ms}^{-2}$$

Using $s = ut + \dfrac{1}{2}at^2$ with $s = 2,\ t = T,\ a = 5,\ u = 0$

we have $2 = \dfrac{1}{2} \times 5 \times T^2 \Rightarrow T^2 = 0{\cdot}8$

and $\quad T = 0{\cdot}89$

Worked example B

A car is moving along a straight level road with constant speed. The engine of the car is producing a tractive force of magnitude 65N. Discuss the motion of the car.

Since the car is moving *with constant speed in a straight line*, we have, by Newton's first law, a total net force of zero acting on the car. We know also that the car has zero acceleration because it is moving with constant speed in a straight line. The car's engine is producing a constant force of magnitude 65N and this means that a second force equal in magnitude and opposite in direction to this must be acting on the car. This second force would be made up of various resistances like air resistance, friction etc. acting on the car, and opposing its motion.

Worked example C

At time ts, the velocity of a particle P, of mass $0{\cdot}3$kg, is $(3t\mathbf{i} + \mathrm{e}^t\mathbf{j} + t^2\mathbf{k})\mathrm{ms}^{-1}$ Find the magnitude of the force acting on P when $t = 2$

$$\mathbf{v} = 3t\mathbf{i} + \mathrm{e}^t\mathbf{j} + t^2\mathbf{k}$$

Acceleration $= \dfrac{\mathrm{d}\mathbf{v}}{\mathrm{d}t} = 3\mathbf{i} + \mathrm{e}^t\mathbf{j} + 2t\mathbf{k} \equiv \mathbf{a}$

Using $\quad \mathbf{F} = m\mathbf{a}$

$\qquad\quad \mathbf{F} = 0{\cdot}3\,(3\mathbf{i} + \mathrm{e}^t\mathbf{j} + 2t\mathbf{k})$

When $\quad t = 2,\ \mathbf{F} = 0{\cdot}3\,(3\mathbf{i} + \mathrm{e}^2\mathbf{j} + 4\mathbf{k})$

$\Rightarrow |\mathbf{F}| = \sqrt{(0{\cdot}9^2 + 0{\cdot}09\mathrm{e}^4 + 1{\cdot}2^2)}\,\mathrm{N} \approx 2{\cdot}68\mathrm{N}$

▶ FORCES AND CIRCULAR MOTION

We know that when a particle is moving in a circle, centre O and radius r, with constant speed v, the acceleration is of magnitude $\dfrac{v^2}{r}$ and is directed towards O.

Now we consider situations where circular motion occurs and we discuss the forces involved.

Worked example D

A particle P of mass M is attached to a fixed point O by means of a light inextensible string of length l. P moves in a horizontal circle at constant speed v. The centre of the circle is C, where C is at distance h vertically below O. Calculate the **tension** in the string and show that P completes one circular orbit in time $2\pi \sqrt{\dfrac{h}{l}}$ (see Fig. F.1).

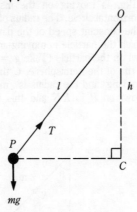

Fig. F.1

P has two forces acting on it; these are its weight mg and the tension in the string T. As P is moving in a *horizontal* circle, the vertical component of T is equal to mg. That is $T \cos \angle POC = mg$

$$\Rightarrow T\left(\frac{h}{l}\right) = mg \Rightarrow T = \frac{mgl}{h}$$

Applying Newton's second law horizontally, we have

$$T \cos \angle OPC = m\frac{v^2}{PC}$$

In $\triangle POC$, $\cos \angle OPC = \dfrac{PC}{l}$

and $PC^2 = l^2 - h^2$

$$\Rightarrow T\left(\frac{PC^2}{l}\right) = mv^2 \text{ and since } T = \frac{mgl}{h}$$

$$\Rightarrow \frac{mgl}{h}\left(\frac{PC^2}{l}\right) = mv^2 \Rightarrow v^2 = \frac{g(PC)^2}{h}$$

$$\Rightarrow v = PC\sqrt{\frac{g}{h}}$$

The circumference of the circular path of P is $2\pi PC$ and P will move around the circumference once in time

$$\frac{2\pi PC}{PC\sqrt{\dfrac{g}{h}}} = 2\pi \sqrt{\frac{h}{g}}$$

as required.

Worked example E

A particle, of mass 0·1kg, is moving on the inside surface of a fixed hemispherical bowl in a horizontal circle. The radius of the inner surface of the bowl is 2m. Given that the constant speed of the particle is 3ms^{-1}, find the radius of the circle in which the particle is moving and the magnitude of the force exerted by the bowl on the particle (Take $g = 10 \text{ms}^{-2}$)

O is the centre of the rim of the hemisphere, C the centre of the circle in which the particle P is moving, and the radius is rm. The magnitude of the force exerted by the bowl on P is R N and this force acts along PO – see Fig. F.2.

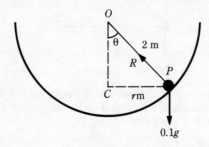

Fig. F.2

$\angle COP = \theta$

Resolving vertically $R \cos \theta = 0{\cdot}1g = 1$ (1)

Horizontally applying Newton's second law,

$$R \sin \theta = \frac{0{\cdot}1 \times 3^2}{r} = \frac{0{\cdot}9}{r} \tag{2}$$

Dividing (2) by (1) gives

$$\tan \theta = \frac{0{\cdot}9}{r} \tag{3}$$

In $\triangle OCP$, $\tan \theta = \dfrac{r}{OC} = \dfrac{r}{\sqrt{4 - r^2}}$ (4)

From (3) and (4) $= \dfrac{0{\cdot}9}{r} = \dfrac{r}{\sqrt{4 - r^2}}$

$$81(4 - r^2) = 100r^4$$
$$100r^4 + 81r^2 - 324 = 0$$
$$(25r^2 - 36)(4r^2 + 9) = 0$$
$$(5r - 6)(5r + 6)(4r^2 + 9) = 0$$

The only value of r applicable is $\dfrac{6}{5}$

The radius of the circle is 1·2m

$$\tan \theta = \frac{0 \cdot 9}{r} = \frac{0 \cdot 9}{1 \cdot 2} = \frac{3}{4}$$

So $\cos \theta = \frac{4}{5}$

and $R = \frac{1}{\cos \theta} = \frac{5}{4} = 1 \cdot 25$ [using (1)]

The force exerted by P on the bowl has magnitude $1 \cdot 25$N

▶ FORCES IN LIGHT ELASTIC STRINGS AND SPRINGS

Hooke's law states that if a light string is stretched in such a way that it assumes its *natural length* on release, then the **tension** is proportional to the extension. Similarly, if a spring is compressed, it is in **thrust**, and the thrust is proportional to the compression.

An elastic string, of natural length l, is stretched to a length $l + x$. In this case, the tension T in the string is given by

$$T = \lambda \left(\frac{x}{l} \right)$$

where λ is a constant for the string, called the *modulus of elasticity*. Suppose now that the string is stretched by a further small distance δx. The **work** done is approximately $T\delta x = \left(\frac{\lambda x}{l} \right) \delta x$.

Therefore, the work done on the string in stretching it from its natural length l to length $l + c$ is

$$\int_0^c \left(\frac{\lambda x}{l} \right) dx = \left[\frac{1}{2} \lambda \frac{x^2}{l} \right]_0^c = \frac{1}{2} \lambda \frac{c^2}{l}$$

We say that the **potential energy** stored in an elastic string (or spring) of natural length l and modulus of electricity λ, when it is extended (or contracted for a spring) by a length c is

$$\frac{1}{2} \lambda \frac{c^2}{l}$$

A light elastic string, of natural length l and modulus of elasticity $4mg$, has one end tied at a fixed point O. A particle P, of mass m, is tied at the other end of the string.

Find the distance OP when P hangs at rest vertically below O in equilibrium (see Fig. F.3).

Let T be the tension in the string. In equilibrium, as shown in Fig. F.3,

$$T = mg \tag{1}$$

and by Hooke's law

$$T = \frac{4mg(OP - l)}{l} \tag{2}$$

Fig. F.3

Eliminating T from (1) and (2) we have

$$\frac{4mg(OP - l)}{l} = mg \Rightarrow OP = \frac{5l}{4}$$

◀ Energy, Equilibrium, Friction, Impulse, Moment, Momentum, Newton's Laws of Motion, Parallel Forces, Power, Triangle (polygon) of forces, Work ▶

FREQUENCY DISTRIBUTION

Raw readings (or data) are condensed into a frequency distribution so that salient points can be easily seen and any underlying patterns more easily identified.

Worked example

A photographic competition is divided into a number of sections. In the wild-life section there are 84 entries and the judge awards marks for each entry as follows:

5	4	10	7	2	8	5	7	6	6
6	10	7	2	9	4	6	10	8	5
9	7	1	9	6	10	5	4	10	4
10	5	5	6	4	8	7	9	6	7
7	8	2	7	5	1	6	4	9	5
6	4	10	5	9	6	9	5	8	6
7	9	6	9	2	10	6	5	10	7
5	6	8	4	10	6	7	5	6	8
7	4	8	6						

Classify the data and give your results in tabular form.

Mark		Frequency	Mark		Frequency
1	II	2	6	LHT LHT LHT I	17
2	IIII	4	7	LHT LHT II	12
3		0	8	LHT III	8
4	LHT IIII	9	9	LHT IIII	9
5	LHT LHT III	13	10	LHT LHT	10
					84

◀ Histogram ▶

FREQUENCY POLYGON

◀ Histogram ▶

FRICTION

When two rough bodies are in contact, a force opposing motion is produced in the direction of the contact. If there is a normal reaction R between the bodies, the magnitude of the frictional force F cannot exceed μR where μ is a positive constant called the *coefficient of friction*.

▶ FRICTIONAL FORCE

Frictional forces are not considered when the surfaces of two bodies in contact are described as *smooth*. When the surfaces of two rough bodies are in contact, frictional forces need to be considered and the following three laws apply.

1 The magnitude of the limiting frictional force is proportional to the magnitude of the normal contact force exerted by one body on the other, and it acts at right-angles to the common normal in the opposite direction to that in which the body is moving or tending to move.

2 The coefficient of friction between the surfaces of two bodies in contact is the ratio of the magnitude of the limiting frictional force and the magnitude of the normal contact force. The value of the coefficient of friction depends only on the roughness of the contact surfaces and *not* on the areas of these surfaces.

3 When no movement takes place, the magnitude of the frictional force is just sufficient to prevent relative motion between the surfaces in contact and this magnitude will only take the limiting value when motion is on the point of occurring. Note that when motion occurs, the magnitude of the frictional force takes the limiting value and is

independent of the speed at which one body is sliding over the other.

The coefficient of friction is often denoted by μ. For a limiting frictional force of magnitude F and corresponding normal contact force of magnitude N, we write $F = \mu N$. In all other cases where we do not know that equilibrium is limiting, the frictional force of magnitude F and the corresponding normal contact force of magnitude N obey the relation

$$F < \mu N$$

and the magnitude of F is just sufficient to prevent movement.

In working exercises, it is very important to follow good practice by writing $F < \mu N$ unless you are told equilibrium is limiting when you may write $F = \mu N$.

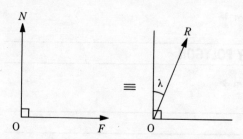

Fig. F.4

The diagrams in Fig. F.4 show two equivalent systems of forces acting at a point O where friction is limiting, the coefficient of friction being μ.

Since friction is limiting $F = \mu N$, so $\dfrac{F}{R} = \mu$

Resolving $\leftrightarrow F = R \sin \lambda$
$\quad\quad\quad\; \updownarrow N = R \cos \lambda$

Dividing $\dfrac{F}{N} = \dfrac{\sin \lambda}{\cos \lambda} = \tan \lambda = \mu$

and $F^2 + N^2 = R^2(\sin^2\lambda + \cos^2\lambda) = R^2$

The angle λ is called the *angle of friction* between the surfaces in contact. The magnitude of the resultant force (or total force) exerted by one body on the other in contact is R.

Worked example

An ice hockey puck moves across the ice in a straight line, moving with initial speed 12ms^{-1} and final speed 8ms^{-1}, while covering a distance of 20m. Calculate the coefficient of friction between the puck and the ice

The diagram (Fig. F.5) shows the forces acting on the puck.

$\updownarrow$ $N = mg$, where m kg is the mass of the puck, N newtons the magnitude of the normal contact force and F newtons the magnitude of the frictional force.

Since the puck is moving, $F = \mu N$

Also $F = ma$, where a ms^{-2} is the deceleration.

But using $v^2 = u^2 + 2as$

$$8^2 = 12^2 - 2a(20) \Rightarrow a = 2$$

$$\Rightarrow \mu mg = 2m$$

$$\Rightarrow \mu = \frac{2}{g} \approx 0\cdot2 \text{ (taking } g = 10\text{ms}^{-2})$$

Coefficient of friction between puck and ice is $0\cdot2$.

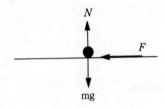

Fig. F.5

◀ Forces ▶

FUNCTION

A function f is a rule which associates each element of a set A with an element of a set B. Set A is called the **domain** of the function and set B the **range** of the function.

Given $x \epsilon A$, the image element in B is usually denoted by $f(x)$. The function is called one–one if the images of distinct elements of A under f are distinct elements of B. Alternatively, each element of B is the image of a unique element of A.

Functions which are not one–one are called many–one.

The following notations are commonly used:

$f: x \rightarrow 2x^2 + 1$

on (for example) the domain [0, 1];

$f(x) = 2x^2 + 1$

The range here is [1, 3].

Note that a function requires both a rule and a domain to be defined. If only the rule is given (for instance, $f(x) = \log_e(x - 1)$), then the domain is assumed to be the largest possible (say $x > 1$ for $f(x) = \log_e(x - 1)$)

▶ TEST FOR A ONE–ONE FUNCTION

If $f(x)$ is a continuous function throughout its domain, the simplest method of determining whether or not it is one–one is by finding the derivative $f'(x)$.

Then, if $f'(x)$ is either positive throughout the domain or negative throughout the domain, the function is one–one. We can also allow $f'(x)$ to equal zero at isolated points, but not over an interval.

Worked example

Show that the function f defined by

$$f(x) = \frac{x}{x - 1} \text{ for } x > 1$$

is one–one

Here,

$$f'(x) = \frac{x - 1 - x}{(x - 1)^2}$$

$$= \frac{-1}{(x - 1)^2} < 0 \text{ for } x > 1$$

Thus, the function is one–one.

▶ INVERSE FUNCTION

If the one–one function of f maps an element x in the domain to an element y in the range, then the inverse function f^{-1} maps y back to x. Clearly, the range of f is the domain of f^{-1} and the domain of f is the range of f^{-1}.

The following example shows how to find the inverse function.

Worked example

Find the inverse function of the function
$$f(x) = \log_e (x - 1) \text{ for } x > 1$$

Let
$$y = \log_e (x - 1)$$
So that
$$x - 1 = e^y$$
or
$$x = e^y + 1$$
Thus,
$$f^{-1}(x) = e^x + 1$$

We note that the range of f is $(-\infty, \infty)$. It follows that the domain of f^{-1} is $(-\infty, \infty)$ and its range is $(1, \infty)$.

A useful graphical point is that the graphs of $y = f(x)$ and $y = f^{-1}(x)$ are the mirror images of each other in the line $y = x$. The graphs of
$$f(x) = \log_e (x - 1) \text{ for } x > 1$$
and $f^{-1}(x) = e^x + 1$ for $-\infty < x < \infty$
are as shown in Fig. F.6.

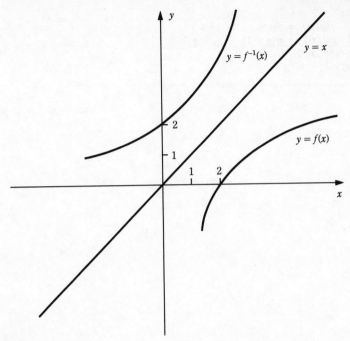

Fig. F.6

COMPOSITION OF FUNCTIONS

Suppose that the function f is defined on the domain D_f with range R_f. Suppose further that the function g is defined on the domain $D_g \subset R_f$ (that is contained in R_f) with range R_g.

Let the image under f of $x \epsilon D_f$ be $f(x)$. Then, since $f(x) \in D_g$, it has an image $g(f(x))$ under g. The function which maps $x \epsilon D_f$ to $g(f(x))$ is called the *composite function* of f and g, written gf or gof. Note the order here: gf means f then g.

The range of gf is not necessarily R_g, although it must be a subset of R_g.

The order of composition is important. In general, $gf \neq fg$; indeed fg will not even exist if $D_f \subset R_g$ since given $x \epsilon D_g$, the image under g of x (which is $g(x)$) may fall outside the domain of f and therefore have no image under f. This is illustrated by the following example.

Worked example

Given that
$$f(x) = x + 1 \text{ for } -\infty < x < \infty$$
and $g(x) = x^2 \quad \text{ for } -\infty < x < \infty$
Find expressions for $fg(x)$ and $gf(x)$

Here
$$f(g(x)) = f(x^2) = x^2 + 1$$
and $g(f(x)) = g(x + 1) = (x + 1)^2$
We note finally that
$$(gf)^{-1} = f^{-1}g^{-1}$$

GEOMETRIC SERIES

A geometric series is one in which the ratio of successive terms is constant.
The usual notation is

$a,\ ar,\ ar^2,\ ar^3$

where a = first term and r = common ratio.

If T_n denotes the nth term, then
$T_n = ar^{n-1}$

If S_n denotes the sum of the first n terms, then

$$S_n = \sum_{r=1}^{n} T_r$$

$$= \frac{a(1 - r^n)}{1 - r}$$

If $|r| < 1$, then S_n tends to a finite limit as $n \to \infty$. We write

$$S_\infty = \lim_{n \to \infty} S_n = \frac{a}{1 - r}$$

The formula for S_n is proved as follows:

$S_n = a + ar + ar^2 + \dots \qquad + ar^{n-2} + ar^{n-1}$

$rS_n = ar + ar^2 + ar^3 + \dots \qquad + ar^{n-2} + ar^{n-1} + ar^n$

$\Rightarrow S_n(1 - r) = a - ar^n \Leftrightarrow S_n = \dfrac{a(1 - r^n)}{1 - r}$

Worked example

A geometric series with first term 3 converges to sum 2. Find i) the
common ratio, ii) the 6th term, iii) the sum of the first 10 terms, giving
your answer to 3 decimal places.

Again, first interpret the information algebraically. 'The series converges to 2'
is simply another way of saying that 'the sum of the series to infinity is 2'.
Hence

$$a = 3, \quad S_\infty = \frac{a}{1 - r} = 2$$

$$\Rightarrow \frac{3}{1-r} = 2 \Leftrightarrow 2 - 2r = 3 \Leftrightarrow r = -\frac{1}{2}$$

$$T_n = ar^{n-1} \Rightarrow T_6 = 3\left(-\frac{1}{2}\right)^5 = -\frac{3}{32}$$

$$S_n = \frac{a(1-r^n)}{1-r} \Rightarrow S_{10} = \frac{3\left(1-\left(-\frac{1}{2}\right)^9\right)}{1-\left(-\frac{1}{2}\right)} = 2\cdot004$$

GEOMETRY

◀ Coordinate geometry ▶

GRAVITATIONAL POTENTIAL ENERGY

We define the gravitational potential energy of a particle situated at a point A to be the **work** which would be done by its weight if it were to move from A to a point B, placed at some fixed level. For example, if the point B is situated at height h above the level of A, the work required *against* gravity to move a particle, of mass m, from A to B is mgh and we should say that the potential energy of the particle at A with respect to the level of B is $-mgh$. Potential energy has no absolute value, but the difference between the potential energies of a particle at different levels can be determined absolutely.

◀ Work ▶

GROUP

A group is a set S of elements together with a binary operator o which operates on pairs of elements in S having the following four properties.

1 Closure
   For all $a, b \in S$, $a \circ b \in S$.
2 Associativity
   For all $a, b, c \in S$,
   $(a \circ b) \circ c = a \circ (b \circ c)$
3 Identity
   There exists an element $I \in S$ such that for all $a \in S$,
   $a \circ I = I \circ a = a$
4 Inverse
   For all $a \in S$, there exists an inverse a^{-1} such that
   $a \circ a^{-1} = a^{-1} \circ a = I$

If, further, the operator is commutative, that is to say, for all $a, b \in S$,
$$a \circ b = b \circ a$$
then the group is called *Abelian*.

If S contains a finite number of elements, then the properties of the group can be shown in the combination table.

Worked example

Write out the combination table for the group defined by the set
$S = \{1, 2, 3, 4\}$, and the binary operation 'multiplication modulo 5', i.e. given $a, b \in S$, $a \circ b$ is equal to the product ab minus that multiple of 5 necessary to reduce the product to an element of S.

The combination table is as shown. The table shows that 1 is the identity element.

o	1	2	3	4
1	1	2	3	4
2	2	4	1	3
3	3	1	4	2
4	4	3	2	1

We note that the table is a Latin Square, which is to say that each row and column contains each element just once. This is a characteristic of all group combination tables.

We can also note that this table is symmetric about the leading diagonal, indicating an Abelian group.

HIGHER DERIVATIVE

When $y = f(x)$ and $\dfrac{dy}{dx} = g(x)$, then $g(x)$ can be differentiated with respect

to x to give $\dfrac{d^2y}{dx^2}$, the second derivative of y with respect to x. You should

note the different positions of the 2 in the numerator and denominator.

$\dfrac{d^2y}{dx^2} = \dfrac{d}{dx}\left(\dfrac{dy}{dx}\right)$, read as 'differentiate $\dfrac{dy}{dx}$ with respect to x'.

Similarly, for higher derivatives $\dfrac{d^3y}{dx^3}$, $\dfrac{d^4y}{dx^4}$, ... $\dfrac{d^ny}{dx^n}$ the third, fourth, ... nth

derivatives respectively.

Alternative notations include:

$\quad f'(x), f''(x), f'''(x), \ldots f^{(n)}(x),$

or $\quad y'(x), y''(x), y'''(x), \ldots y^{(n)}(x),$

or $\quad y_1(x), y_2(x), y_3(x), \ldots y_n(x)$

Worked example A

Find $\dfrac{d^3y}{dx^3}$ when $y = \ln x$

$$\frac{dy}{dx} = \frac{1}{x}, \frac{d^2y}{dx^2} = -\frac{1}{x^2}, \frac{d^3y}{dx^3} = \frac{2}{x^3}$$

Worked example B

Given that $y = Ax^3 + B\ln x + C$ where A, B and C are constants, show that

$$\frac{d^3y}{dx^3} = \frac{2}{x^2}\frac{dy}{dx}$$

$$\frac{dy}{dx} = 3Ax^2 + \frac{B}{x}, \frac{d^2y}{dx^2} = 6Ax - \frac{B}{x^2}$$

$$\frac{d^3y}{dx^3} = 6A + \frac{2B}{x^3} = \frac{2}{x^2}\left[3Ax^2 + \frac{B}{x}\right] = \frac{2}{x^2}\frac{dy}{dx}$$

Worked example C

Given that $y = \sin 3x$ show that $\dfrac{dy}{dx} = 3 \sin\left(3x + \dfrac{\pi}{2}\right)$,

and deduce that $\dfrac{d^3y}{dx^3} = 3^3 \sin 3\left(x + \dfrac{\pi}{2}\right)$

$y = \sin 3x \Rightarrow \dfrac{dy}{dx} = 3 \cos 3x = 3 \sin\left(3x + \dfrac{\pi}{2}\right)$

Repeating the process $\dfrac{d^2y}{dx^2} = 3.3 \cos\left(3x + \dfrac{\pi}{2}\right) = 3^2\sin\left(3x + \dfrac{\pi}{2} + \dfrac{\pi}{2}\right)$

$$= 3^2\sin(3x + \pi)$$

$$\Rightarrow \frac{d^3y}{dx^3} = 3^2.3 \cos(3x + \pi)$$

$$= 3^3\sin\left(3x + \pi + \frac{\pi}{2}\right)$$

$$= 3^3\sin 3\left(x + \frac{\pi}{2}\right)$$

$$\Leftrightarrow \frac{d^2y}{dx^2} - 6\frac{dy}{dx} + 25y = e^{3x}[(24 \cos 4x - 7 \sin 4x)$$
$$- 6(3 \sin 4x + 4 \cos 4x) + 25 \sin 4x]$$
$$= e^{3x}[(24 - 24) \cos 4x + (-7 - 18 + 25) \sin 4x]$$
$$= 0$$

Alternatively $y = e^{3x} \sin 4x \Rightarrow ye^{-3x} = \sin 4x$

$$\Rightarrow \frac{dy}{dx}e^{-3x} - 3ye^{-3x} = 4 \cos 4x$$

$$\Rightarrow \left(\frac{d^2y}{dx^2}e^{-3x} - 3\frac{dy}{dx}e^{-3x}\right) - 3\left(\frac{dy}{dx}e^{-3x} - 3ye^{-3x}\right) = -16 \sin 4x$$
$$= -16ye^{-3x}$$

$$\Rightarrow \frac{d^2y}{dx^2} - 3\frac{dy}{dx} - 3\frac{dy}{dx} + 9y = -16y$$

or $\dfrac{d^2y}{dx^2} - 6\dfrac{dy}{dx} + 25y = 0$

◀ Derivative ▶

HISTOGRAM

A histogram is similar to a bar chart, but with the areas rather than the lengths of the bars representing the frequency. There should be no gaps between each bar in a histogram, as often happens with bar charts. The vertical axis is a **frequency density** and not frequency, so that the frequency is found by multiplying the width of the bar by the number on the frequency density axis.

For example, from the records at a garage it is found that 80 cars have been given a short-service in one week. The time, in minutes, to complete each service is recorded on the time-sheets and the following frequency distribution is prepared from these data.

Time (min)	45 –	50 –	55 –	60 –	65 –	70 –	75 –	80 –	85 –
Frequency	2	4	9	19	15	13	8	6	4

The notation 45 – means that the time in this interval is at least 45 minutes, but less than 50 minutes and in the last interval the time is at least 85 minutes, but less than 90 minutes.

A continuous variable such as time, which is illustrated here, requires us to choose class intervals with no gaps. The most widely used method of illustrating these data graphically is with a histogram in which the *areas* of the

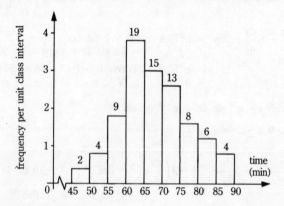

Fig. H.1

rectangles represent the frequencies, as shown in Fig. H.1. Several points are worth noting about the histogram:

   i) The actual frequency in each class interval is written over the top of the corresponding rectangle.

   ii) The height of the rectangle is obtained by dividing the length of class interval (5 min) by the area, which is of course, also the frequency or some constant factor times the frequency; for example, the height of the 55 – interval is $\dfrac{9}{5}$ units $= 1·8$ units,

iii) The same method can be used when a histogram with unequal class intervals needs to be drawn.

▶ FREQUENCY POLYGON

The data in this exercise could also be displayed using what is called a frequency polygon. The polygon is drawn by joining the mid-points of the tops of each rectangle in the histogram, as shown in Fig. H.2.

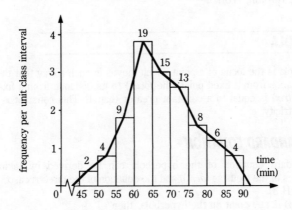

Fig. H.2

HOOKE'S LAW

Hooke's law states that the extension x produced in an elastic string by a **tension** T is proportional to T. The usual mathematical form of the law is

$$T = \frac{\lambda x}{l}$$

where l is the natural (unstretched) length of the string and λ the *modulus of elasticity*.

In the case of a string, both T and x must be positive. In the case of a spring, however, T and x can be negative, corresponding to a compression. If the string is extended by an amount x, then

$$\text{Stretch energy} = \frac{\lambda x^2}{2l}$$

This can be proved by noting that when the extension is y, the tension is $\lambda y/l$. Thus,

Work done on string in stretching an amount x $= \displaystyle\int_0^x T\mathrm{d}y$

$$= \int_0^x \frac{\lambda y}{l}\,\mathrm{d}y$$

$$= \frac{\lambda}{l}\left[\frac{y^2}{2}\right]_0^x$$

$$= \frac{\lambda x^2}{2l}$$

◀ Force, Tension, Work ▶

HYPERBOLA

A hyperbola is the locus of a point which moves in such a way that the ratio of its distance from a fixed point (the *focus*) to its distance from a fixed line (the *directrix*) is equal to a constant greater than 1. This constant is called the eccentricity, e.

▶ STANDARD EQUATION

The standard equation of the hyperbola can be derived by taking the coordinates of the focus as $(ae, 0)$ and the equation of the directrix as $x = a/e$ (see Fig. H.3).

If $P(x, y)$ is any point on the hyperbola, then

$$PF = \sqrt{(x - ae)^2 + y^2}$$

If D denotes the foot of the perpendicular from P the directrix, then

$$PD = x - \frac{a}{e}$$

Since $PF = ePD$, it follows that

$$\sqrt{(x - ae)^2 + y^2} = e\left(x - \frac{a}{e}\right) = ex - a$$

or, squaring,
$$(x - ae)^2 + y^2 = (ex - a)^2$$

that is,
$$x^2 - 2xae + a^2e^2 + y^2 = e^2x^2 - 2exa + a^2$$

which reduces to

$$\frac{x^2}{a^2} - \frac{y^2}{a^2(e^2 - 1)} = 1$$

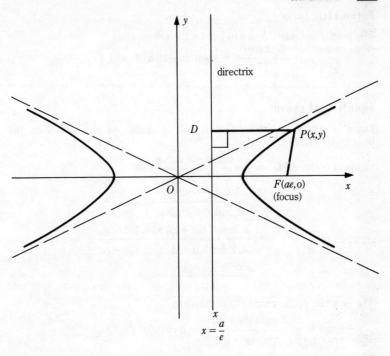

directrix

D

$P(x,y)$

O

$F(ae, 0)$
(focus)

$x = \dfrac{a}{e}$

Fig. H.3

or $\qquad \dfrac{x^2}{a^2} - \dfrac{y^2}{b^2} = 1$

where $b^2 = a^2(e^2 - 1)$

We note that, for large x and y,

$$\dfrac{x^2}{a^2} - \dfrac{y^2}{b^2} \approx 0$$

that is, $\qquad \left(\dfrac{x}{a} - \dfrac{y}{b}\right)\left(\dfrac{x}{a} + \dfrac{y}{b}\right) \approx 0$

This shows that

$$\dfrac{x}{a} - \dfrac{y}{b} = 0 \quad \text{and} \quad \dfrac{x}{a} + \dfrac{y}{b} = 0$$

that is, $\quad y = \pm \dfrac{bx}{a}$

are asymptotes to the hyperbola. These are shown on the graph in Fig. H.3.

Parametric form

The point $P(a\cosh\theta,\ b\sinh\theta)$ lies on the ellipse since
$$\frac{(a\cosh\theta)^2}{a^2} - \frac{(b\sinh\theta)^2}{b^2} = \cosh^2\theta - \sinh^2\theta = 1$$

Equation of chord

Let $P(a\cosh\theta,\ b\sinh\theta)$, $Q(a\cosh\phi,\ b\sinh\phi)$ be two points on the hyperbola. Then,

$$\begin{aligned}
\text{Gradient of chord } PQ &= \frac{b\sinh\theta - b\sinh\phi}{a\cosh\theta - a\cosh\phi}\\[2mm]
&= \frac{b(\sinh\theta - \sinh\phi)}{a(\cosh\theta - \cosh\phi)}\\[2mm]
&= \frac{b\,.\,2\cosh\tfrac{1}{2}(\theta+\phi)\sinh\tfrac{1}{2}(\theta-\phi)}{a\,.\,2\sinh\tfrac{1}{2}(\theta+\phi)\sinh\tfrac{1}{2}(\theta-\phi)}\\[2mm]
&= \frac{b\coth\tfrac{1}{2}(\theta+\phi)}{a}
\end{aligned}$$

The equation of the chord PQ is therefore
$$y - b\sinh\theta = \frac{b\coth\tfrac{1}{2}(\theta+\phi)}{a}(x - a\cosh\theta)$$

which reduces to
$$ay - ab\sinh\theta = bx\coth\tfrac{1}{2}(\theta+\phi) - ab\coth\tfrac{1}{2}(\theta+\phi)\cosh\theta$$

Equation of tangent

The equation of the tangent at $P(a\cosh\theta,\ b\sinh\theta)$ can be found by letting $Q\to P$, which means putting $\phi = \theta$ in the above equation. This gives
$$ay - ab\sinh\theta = bx\coth\theta - ab\coth\theta\cosh\theta$$
which reduces to
$$ay\sinh\theta - bx\cosh\theta = -ab$$
The equation of the tangent at P can be found using calculus in the following way.
$$x = a\cosh\theta; \quad y = b\sinh\theta$$
$$\frac{dx}{d\theta} = a\sinh\theta; \quad \frac{dy}{d\theta} = b\cosh\theta$$

Thus, the gradient of the tangent at P is given by
$$\begin{aligned}
\frac{dy}{dx} &= \frac{dy}{d\theta}\bigg/\frac{dx}{d\theta}\\[2mm]
&= \frac{b\coth\theta}{a}
\end{aligned}$$

The equation of the tangent at P is therefore

$$y - b \sinh\theta = \frac{b \coth\theta}{a} (x - a \cosh\theta)$$

that is,

$$ay \sinh\theta - bx \cosh\theta = -ab$$

Equation of normal

The gradient of the normal at $P(a \cosh\theta,\ b \sinh\theta)$ is given by

$$-1 \Big/ \frac{dy}{dx} = \frac{-a \tanh\theta}{b}$$

The equation of the normal at P is therefore

$$y - b \sinh\theta = \frac{-a \tanh\theta}{b} (x - a \cosh\theta)$$

or $\quad by \cosh\theta + ax \sinh\theta = (a^2 + b^2) \sinh\theta \cosh\theta$

▶ RECTANGULAR HYPERBOLA

A hyperbola with $e = \sqrt{2}$ is called a rectangular hyperbola. In this case,
$$\begin{aligned} b^2 &= a^2(e^2 - 1) \\ &= a^2 \end{aligned}$$
The equations of the asymptotes are therefore

$$y = \pm x$$

so that the asymptotes are perpendicular.

If the asymptotes are taken to be the coordinate axes, then the equation becomes $xy = c^2$. The graph is then as shown in Fig. H.4.

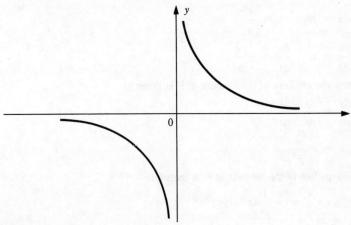

Fig. H.4

Parametric form

The point $(cp, c/p)$ lies on the rectangular hyperbola since

$$cp \cdot \frac{c}{p} = c^2$$

Equation of chord

Let $P(cp, c/p)$ and $Q(cq, c/q)$ be two points on the rectangular hyperbola. Then,

$$\text{Gradient of chord } PQ = \frac{\dfrac{c}{p} - \dfrac{c}{q}}{cp - cq}$$

$$= -\frac{1}{pq}$$

The equation of the chord PQ is therefore

$$y - \frac{c}{p} = -\frac{1}{pq}(x - cp)$$

or $\quad pqy + x = c(p + q)$

Equation of tangent

The equation of the tangent at $P(cp, c/p)$ can be found by letting $Q \rightarrow P$, which means putting $q = p$ in the above equation. This gives

$$p^2 y + x = 2cp$$

The equation of the tangent at P can be found using calculus in the following way.

$$x = cp; \qquad y = \frac{c}{p}$$

$$\frac{dx}{dp} = c; \qquad \frac{dy}{dp} = -\frac{c}{p^2}$$

Thus, the gradient of the tangent at P is given by

$$\frac{dy}{dx} = \frac{dy}{dp} \Big/ \frac{dx}{dp}$$

$$= -\frac{1}{p^2}$$

The equation of the tangent at P is therefore

$$y - \frac{c}{p} = -\frac{1}{p^2}(x - cp)$$

or $\quad p^2 y + x = 2cp$

Equation of normal

The gradient of the normal at $P(cp, c/p)$ is

$$-1 \left/ \frac{dy}{dx} \right. = p^2$$

The equation of the normal at P is therefore

$$y - \frac{c}{p} = p^2(x - cp)$$

or $\quad py - p^3 x = c(1 - p^4)$

◀ Inverse hyperbolic function ▶

HYPERBOLIC FUNCTION

The basic hyperbolic functions $\sinh x$ and $\cosh x$ are defined on the domain $(-\infty, \infty)$ by

$$\sinh x = \tfrac{1}{2}(e^x - e^{-x})$$
$$\text{and} \quad \cosh x = \tfrac{1}{2}(e^x + e^{-x})$$

Four further functions are defined as follows.

$$\tanh x = \frac{\sinh x}{\cosh x}$$

$$\coth x = \frac{\cosh x}{\sinh x} \quad (x \neq 0)$$

$$\text{sech}\, x = \frac{1}{\cosh x}$$

$$\text{cosech}\, x = \frac{1}{\sinh x} \quad (x \neq 0)$$

The graphs of these functions are as shown in Figs. H.5, H.6, H.7 and H.8.

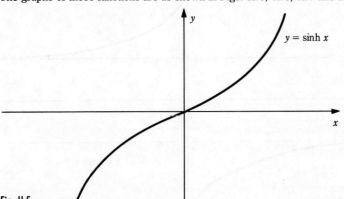

Fig. H.5

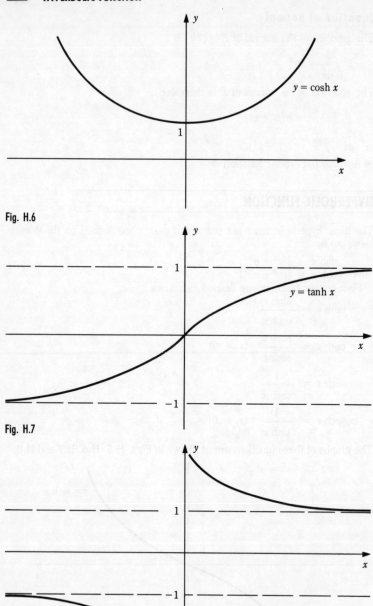

Fig. H.6

Fig. H.7

Fig. H.8

HYPOTHESIS (STATISTICAL)

A statistical hypothesis is an assertion concerning the probability distribution of one or more random variables. The hypothesis is *simple* if it completely specifies the distributions involved. The hypothesis is *composite* if it does not completely specify the distributions involved.

For example, the following statements are hypotheses:

a) The wingspans of a certain type of bird are normally distributed with mean $1 \cdot 2$ m and standard deviation $0 \cdot 3$ m (*simple*)
b) A coin is unfair in that it falls 'heads' and 'tails' with different probabilities (*composite, since the probability is not specified*).
c) The mean lifetime of a certain brand of electric light bulb is equal to 1,200 hours (*composite, since the actual distribution is not specified*).

It is customary in statistics to set up two hypotheses:

H_0 (the *null hypothesis*), which is usually simple and often represents the 'status quo'; and

H_1 (the *alternative hypothesis*), which is usually composite, representing a change from the status quo.

The usual procedure is to take a random sample of observations $X_1, X_2, \ldots X_n$ and to define a test statistic that is a function of these observations. The possible values of this test statistic are divided into two disjoint sets, the critical region C in which H_1 is accepted and its complement C' in which H_0 is accepted.

For example, suppose we are dealing with a random variable X that is normally distributed with parameters μ, σ^2 (σ^2 known) and

$$H_0: \mu = \mu_0$$
versus $H_1: \mu \neq \mu_0$

Then a suitable test statistic is $\bar{X} = \sum_{i=1}^{n} X_i/n$, and it would be appropriate to take

$$C = \{\bar{X} \text{ such that } |\bar{X} - \mu_0| > k\}$$
and $C' = \{\bar{X} \text{ such that } |\bar{X} - \mu_0| \leq k\}$

for some constant k, that is, accept H_0 if $\bar{X}$ is close to μ_0 and H_1 otherwise.

When carrying out a hypothesis test, it is possible to make two different types of error: a *Type 1* error, which is the acceptance of H_1 when H_0 is true; and a *Type 2* error, which is the acceptance of H_0 when H_1 is true. The probability of making a *Type 1* error, often denoted by α, is called the significance level of the test. The probability of making a *Type 2* error is usually denoted by β.

It is, of course, desirable to choose a critical region which gives small values of α, β. For a fixed sample size, however, any attempt to modify the critical region C to reduce α will cause an increase in β. The final choice of C is therefore a compromise.

Worked example

A seed merchant sells two mixtures of wallflower seeds, mixture A and mixture B. Mixture A contains an equal number of 'yellow' seeds (seeds which will produce plants with yellow flowers) and 'red' seeds. Mixture B contains 25 per cent 'yellow' seeds and 75 per cent 'red' seeds. He finds an unlabelled bag of wallflower seeds and wishing to know whether it is mixture A or B, he decides to plant 30 seeds and to observe the colour of the resulting flowers. What decision procedure should he adopt?

Let X denote the number of yellow flowering plants obtained out of 30. Then X is binomially distributed with parameters 30, p, that is B(30, p), and we take

$$H_0: p = \frac{1}{2} \qquad \text{(Mixture } A\text{)}$$

and $\quad H_1: p = \dfrac{1}{4} \qquad \text{(Mixture } B\text{)}$

Now under H_0, the expected number of yellow flowering plants is 15; under H_1 it is 7·5. We therefore take as critical region

$C: X \leqslant k$

where k is clearly going to be somewhere between 7·5 and 15, and so near to 11.

Taking $k = 11$

α = Prob (Type 1 error)

= P(Accept $H_1 | H_0$ true)

= P($X \leqslant 11 | X$ is B(30, $\frac{1}{2}$))

= 0·1002 (using binomial tables)

Also

β = Prob (Type 2 error)

= P(Accept $H_0 | H_1$ true)

= P($X \geqslant 12 | X$ is B(30, $\frac{1}{4}$))

= 1 − P($X \leqslant 11 | X$ is B(30, $\frac{1}{4}$))

= 1 − 0·9493 = 0·0507

Repeating these calculations with other values of k we obtain the following table:

k	9	10	11	12
α	0·0214	0·0494	0·1002	0·1808
β	0·1966	0·1057	0·0507	0·0216

This table illustrates that as we vary k, α increases as β decreases (and vice versa). Clearly $k = 10$ and $k = 11$ give the most balanced critical regions, although it is a pity that there is no intermediate possibility.

You could argue that $k = 11$ is slightly preferable to $k = 10$ since it i) minimises $\alpha + \beta$; and ii) is the minimax value since it minimises the larger of α, β. The choice would also, however, depend on the relative importance of Type 1 and Type 2 errors.

◀ Correlation co-efficients ▶

IDENTITY

◀ Equations and identities ▶

IMPACT (DIRECT)

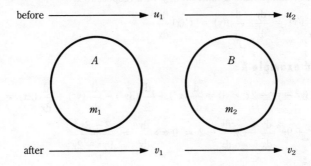

before ──────────▶ u_1 ──────────▶ u_2

A B

m_1 m_2

after ──────────▶ v_1 ──────────▶ v_2

Fig. I.1

Suppose that two bodies A, B of respective masses m_1, m_2 travelling in the same line collide. Let the velocities before and after the impact be u_1, u_2, v_1, v_2 as shown in Fig. I.1. Then the velocities after the impact can be found in terms of the velocities before the impact and the **coefficient of restitution** (e) by using i) the conservation of **momentum** and ii) **Newton's experimental law**.

Using i)
$$m_1 v_1 + m_2 v_2 = m_1 u_1 + m_2 u_2 \tag{1}$$
Using ii)
$$v_2 - v_1 = e(u_1 - u_2) \tag{2}$$

Solving these equations,
$$v_1 = \frac{(m_1 - em_2)}{m_1 + m_2} u_1 + \frac{m_2(1 + e)}{m_1 + m_2} u_2$$

IMPLICIT FUNCTION

and $v_2 = \dfrac{m_1(1-e)}{m_1+m_2} u_1 + \dfrac{(m_2-em_1)}{m_1+m_2} u_2$

If the bodies are not moving initially in the same line, a similar approach can still be used. The motion in the line of the impact can be analysed as above; the motion perpendicular to this line is unaffected by the impact.

◄ Coefficient of restitution, Momentum, Newton's experimental law ►

IMPLICIT FUNCTION

A relationship which cannot be arranged in the explicit form $y = f(x)$, such as $x^3 - 3y^3 - y^2 - 2x = 0$, is said to define an implicit function y of x.

▶ *DERIVATIVE*

The **derivative** of such a function with respect to x is found by applying the normal rules for derivatives, but it should be noted that the chain rule is required to differentiate a function of y with respect to x.

Thus $\dfrac{\mathrm{d}}{\mathrm{d}x} f(y) = \dfrac{\mathrm{d}y}{\mathrm{d}x} \cdot \dfrac{\mathrm{d}}{\mathrm{d}y} f(y) = f'(x) \dfrac{\mathrm{d}y}{\mathrm{d}x}$

Worked example A

$x^3 + 3y^3 - y^2 - 2x = 0 \Rightarrow \dfrac{\mathrm{d}}{\mathrm{d}x}(x^3) + \dfrac{\mathrm{d}}{\mathrm{d}x}(3y^3) - \dfrac{\mathrm{d}}{\mathrm{d}x}(y^2) - \dfrac{\mathrm{d}}{\mathrm{d}x}(2x) = 0$

$\Rightarrow 3x^2 + 9y^2 \dfrac{\mathrm{d}y}{\mathrm{d}x} - 2y \dfrac{\mathrm{d}y}{\mathrm{d}x} - 2 = 0 \Leftrightarrow \dfrac{\mathrm{d}y}{\mathrm{d}x} = \dfrac{2 - 3x^2}{9y^2 - 2y}$

Worked example B

Find $\dfrac{\mathrm{d}y}{\mathrm{d}x}$ in terms of x and y when  $\ln y = y\ln x,\ (x > 0,\ y > 0)$

$\dfrac{\mathrm{d}}{\mathrm{d}x}(\ln y) = \dfrac{\mathrm{d}}{\mathrm{d}x}(y\ln x) \Rightarrow \dfrac{1}{y}\dfrac{\mathrm{d}y}{\mathrm{d}x} = \dfrac{\mathrm{d}y}{\mathrm{d}x}\ln x + \dfrac{y}{x}$

$\Rightarrow \left(\dfrac{1}{y} - \ln x\right)\dfrac{\mathrm{d}y}{\mathrm{d}x} = \dfrac{y}{x} \Rightarrow \dfrac{\mathrm{d}y}{\mathrm{d}x} = \dfrac{y^2}{x(1 - y\ln x)}$

IMPULSE

The impulse imparted to a body (say by a sudden jerk) is equal to its change in **momentum**. For example, Fig. I.2 shows two masses connected by a string passing over a pulley. When the string becomes taut, the 3 kg mass is moving downwards with speed $10\,\mathrm{ms}^{-1}$. In order to calculate i) the speed

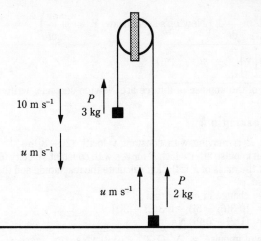

Fig. 1.2

with which the 2 kg mass starts to move upwards; ii) the impulsive tension in the string, we proceed as follows.

Let P (kg ms^{-1}) denote the impulsive tension when the 2 kg mass is jerked upwards, and let the masses move with speed u immediately after the jerk. Then, since the impulsive tension measures change in momentum, it follows that:

for 2 kg mass: $P = 2u$

for 3 kg mass: $P = 3(10-u)$

Equating these

$$2u = 30 - 3u$$

whence $u = 6$

Substituting

$$P = 2u = 12$$

▶ IMPULSE OF A FORCE

The impulse of a **force** is a vector quantity, let us call it **J**, and if the velocity of a particle P changes from $\mathbf{v}_1$ to $\mathbf{v}_2$ in a time interval t, then we define $\mathbf{J} = m\mathbf{v}_2 - m\mathbf{v}_1$, where m is the mass of P. That is, the impulse of a force acting on a particle over an interval of time is the change in momentum produced by the force.

If the force **F** is constant, then we have $\mathbf{v}_2 = \mathbf{v}_1 + \mathbf{a}t$

where **a** is the acceleration of the particle.

Also $\mathbf{F} = m\mathbf{a}$ (Newton's second law). Combining these two equations by eliminating **a** gives

$$\mathbf{F}t = m(\mathbf{v}_2 - \mathbf{v}_1) = \mathbf{J}$$

If the force **F** is variable, we write

$$\mathbf{J} = \int_0^t \mathbf{F}\,dt$$

$$= \int_0^t m \frac{d\mathbf{v}}{dt} \, dt \left(\text{Newton's second law, } \mathbf{F} = m \frac{d\mathbf{v}}{dt} \right)$$

$$= m\left[\mathbf{v}\right]_{\mathbf{v}_1}^{\mathbf{v}_2} = m(\mathbf{v}_2 - \mathbf{v}_1)$$

The units of the impulse of a force are Newton-seconds, written N s.

Worked example A

A particle P is moving with constant velocity $(2\mathbf{i} - 3\mathbf{j})\text{ms}^{-1}$. The particle receives an impulse after which P moves with constant velocity $(6\mathbf{i} - 6\mathbf{j})\text{ms}^{-1}$. Given that the mass of P is 0.3kg, calculate the magnitude and the direction of the impulse

Impulse = change in momentum
$$= [0.3(6\mathbf{i} - 6\mathbf{j}) - 0.3(2\mathbf{i} - 3\mathbf{j})]\,\text{N s}$$
$$= (1.2\mathbf{i} - 0.9\mathbf{j})\,\text{N s}$$

Magnitude of impulse $= \sqrt{[(1.2)^2 + (0.9)^2]}\,\text{N s}$
$$= 1.5\,\text{N s}$$

The direction of the impulse is directed along the vector $4\mathbf{i} - 3\mathbf{j}$

Worked example B

A particle P, of mass 0.2kg, falls freely from rest at a height of 10m above a horizontal floor. P bounces back from the floor with speed 4ms^{-1}. Calculate the impulse of the force exerted by P on the floor. (Take $g = 9.8\text{ms}^{-2}$.)

Using $v^2 = u^2 + 2as$ with $u = 0$, $a = 9.8$ and $s = 10$ we have
$v^2 = 2 \times 9.8 \times 10 = 196 \Rightarrow v = 14$
P strikes the floor with speed 14ms^{-1} and rebounds with speed 4ms^{-1}

Impulse = change in momentum
$$= 0.2[14 - (-4)]\,\text{N s}$$
$$= 3.6\,\text{N s}$$

◀ Coefficient of restitution, Force, Momentum ▶

INCREMENT

The derivative of y with respect to x is given by

$$\frac{dy}{dx} = \lim_{\delta x \to 0} \frac{\delta y}{\delta x}$$

For small δx, it follows that

$$\frac{dy}{dx} \approx \frac{\delta y}{\delta x}$$

or

$$\delta y \approx \frac{dy}{dx} \cdot \delta x$$

This result enables us to calculate the increment in y resulting from an increment in x. The following example gives an illustration of this.

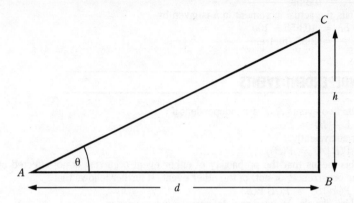

Fig. 1.3

Worked example

BC represents a flagpole of unknown height h m. To estimate h, the angle of elevation θ of the top of the flagpole is measured from A which is distance d m from the bottom of the flagpole. Show that if θ is overestimated by an amount $\delta\theta$, the height is overestimated by an amount δh where

$$\delta h \approx d \sec^2 \theta \, \delta\theta$$

Calculate an approximation to δh given $d = 100$, $\theta = 45°$ and $\delta\theta = 1°$. Here

$$h = d \tan \theta$$

so that

$$\frac{dh}{d\theta} = d \sec^2 \theta$$

Now

$$\delta h = \frac{dh}{d\theta} . \delta\theta$$

$$= d \sec^2 \theta \, \delta\theta$$

We are given that $\delta\theta = 1°$, but we must convert to radians since the standard results for differentiating trigonometric functions are valid only for radian measure. Now

$$1° = \frac{\pi}{180} \text{ radians}$$

and $\sec 45° = \sqrt{2}$, so that

$$\delta h \approx 100 \times 2 \times \frac{\pi}{180} = 3 \cdot 49 \text{ (m)}$$

NB. We can check this result by calculating the true height when $\theta = 46°$:
$$h = 100 \tan 46°$$
$$= 103\cdot55$$
Thus the actual increment in h is given by
$$\delta h = 103\cdot55 - 100$$
$$= 3\cdot55 \text{ (metres)}$$

INDEPENDENT EVENTS

The two events A, B are independent if
$$P(A|B) = P(A)$$
or equivalently
$$P(B|A) = P(B)$$
This means that the probability of either event occurring is not affected by the occurrence, or not, of the other event. It further follows that
$$P(A \cap B) = P(A) \, P(B)$$
which can also be used as a definition of independence.

The notion of independence of three or more events is more complex. For example, given the three events A, B, C, these are *pairwise independent* if
$$P(A \cap B) = P(A) \, P(B)$$
$$P(A \cap C) = P(A) \, P(C)$$
$$P(B \cap C) = P(B) \, P(C)$$
The three events are *totally independent* if, in addition,
$$P(A \cap B \cap C) = P(A) \, P(B) \, P(C)$$
The following example shows that pairwise independence does not imply total independence.

Worked example

A fair coin is tossed three times. Let A = event that first toss produced a 'head'; B = event that second toss produced a 'head'; C = event that two successive tosses produce the same outcome. Show that A, B, C, are pairwise independent but not totally independent.

Here the sample space is
{HHH, HHT, HTH, HTT, THH, THT, TTH, TTT}
and each outcome is equally likely ('equi-likely'). We see that

$$P(A) = P(B) = \frac{1}{2}; \quad P(C) = \frac{3}{4}$$

$$P(A \cap B) = \frac{1}{4}; \quad P(A \cap C) = P(B \cap C) = \frac{3}{8}$$

Thus

$$P(A \cap B) = P(A) \, P(B)$$
$$P(A \cap C) = P(A) \, P(C)$$
$$P(B \cap C) = P(B) \, P(C)$$
establishing pairwise independence.

However,

$$P(A \cap B \cap C) = \frac{1}{8}$$

whereas

$$P(A)\,P(B)\,P(C) = \frac{1}{2} \times \frac{1}{2} \times \frac{3}{4} = \frac{3}{16}$$

so that

$$P(A \cap B \cap C) \neq P(A)\,P(B)\,P(C)$$

so that the events are not totally independent.

◀ Probability ▶

INDEX

The figure indicating the **power** is known as the index – x^3, index 3; $7y^6$, index 6

INDEX NUMBERS

You may already be familiar with the *retail price index*, which measures the change in the cost of certain household commodities each month, and in particular the cost now compared with the cost some few years ago (the base cost), when the exercise first started. A simple example will show how the calculations are undertaken and the difference between the three main indices, the Paasche index, the Laspeyres index and the Fisher index.

Generally n basic terms are considered, the average quantity of each item purchased, both in the base year and in the year under consideration, together with the prices of each item in the two years.

▶ PAASCHE INDEX

$$\sum_{\text{all items}} \text{(Present price)}\,.\,\text{(Average quantity now consumed)}$$

$$\sum_{\text{all items}} \text{(Base year price)}\,.\,\text{(Average quantity consumed in baseyear)}$$

▶ LASPEYRES INDEX

$$\sum_{\text{all items}} \text{(Present price)}\,.\,\text{(Average quantity consumed in base year)}$$

$$\sum_{\text{all items}} \text{(Base year price)}\,.\,\text{(Average quantity consumed in base year)}$$

▶ FISHER INDEX

The Fisher index is then the geometric mean of the Paasche and Laspeyres indices, i.e.

Fisher index $= \sqrt{[(\text{Paasche index})(\text{Laspeyres index})]}$

Worked example

The table shows the average price in pence per kilogram of seven staple food items for the years 1984 and 1989, together with the average weight in kilograms consumed by a family of four in those years. Calculate the following indices: a) Paasche, b) Laspeyres, c) Fisher.

Item	Price (pkg⁻¹)	Weight (kg)	Price (pkg⁻¹)	Weight (kg)
Bread	55	200	62	192
Butter	192	64	208	50
Margarine	96	56	116	78
Potatoes	28	248	30	260
Sugar	52	80	58	76
Tea	140	59	154	54
Coffee	1260	10	1490	16

Paasche index

$$= \frac{62 \times 192 + 208 \times 50 + 116 \times 78 + 30 \times 260 + 58 \times 76 + 154 \times 54 + 1490 \times 16}{55 \times 200 + 192 \times 64 + 96 \times 56 + 28 \times 248 + 52 \times 80 + 140 \times 59 + 1260 \times 10}$$

$$= \frac{75716}{60628} = 1 \cdot 249$$

Laspeyres index

$$= \frac{62 \times 200 + 208 \times 64 + 116 \times 56 + 30 \times 248 + 58 \times 80 + 154 \times 59 + 1490 \times 10}{60628}$$

$$= \frac{68274}{60628} = 1 \cdot 126$$

Fisher index

$= \sqrt{(1 \cdot 249 \times 1 \cdot 126)}$

$= 1 \cdot 186$

Thus, taking 1984 as 100 per cent, the 1989 price index is:
Paasche $\approx$ 125 per cent, Laspeyres $\approx$ 113 per cent, Fisher $\approx$ 119 per cent
The figures may appear quite disparate, but to a large extent this is due to a 60 per cent increase in the consumption of coffee between 1984 and 1989. The Paasche index shows this more clearly by taking into account the increase in the consumption of coffee, the Laspeyres index does not take it into account, whilst the Fisher index attempts to balance the two.

INDICES

i) $a.a.a...$ (m times) $= a^m$

ii) $a^m.a^n = a^{m+n}$

iii) $\dfrac{a^m}{a^n} = a^{m-n}$

iv) $(a^m)^n = a^{mn}$

v) $a^0 = 1$

vi) $a^{-m} = \dfrac{1}{a^m}$

◀ Power ▶

INDUCTION

Mathematical induction is a method of proving an assertion which is claimed to be true for integer values of a parameter n. The method involves assuming the result true for $n = k$, and then proving it true for $n = k + 1$. It then remains to show that the result is true for $n = 1$. For if this is the case, then it must be true for $n = 2$ and therefore $n = 3$ and so on. The method is commonly used to prove sums of series, but it can also be used in a variety of other contexts.

Worked example A

Prove that $\displaystyle\sum_{r=1}^{n} r^2 = \frac{n(n + 1)(2n + 1)}{6}$

Assume the result true for $n = k$, which means

$$\sum_{r=1}^{k} r^2 = \frac{k(k + 1)(2k + 1)}{6}$$

Consider $\displaystyle\sum_{r=1}^{k+1} r^2 = \sum_{r=1}^{k} r^2 + (k + 1)^2$

$$= \frac{k(k + 1)(2k + 1)}{6} + (k + 1)^2$$

$$= \frac{(k + 1)}{6} \left\{ k(2k + 1) + 6(k + 1) \right\}$$

$$= \frac{(k + 1)}{6} \left\{ 2k^2 + k + 6k + 6 \right\}$$

$$= \frac{(k + 1)(k + 2)(2k + 3)}{6}$$

This is actually the assumed result with $k + 1$ replacing k. Thus, if it is true for $n = k$, then it is also true for $n = k + 1$.

Now, putting $n = 1$ in the given formula gives 1, which is correct. Thus the result is proved by mathematical induction.

Worked example B

Prove that $5^n - 4n + 3$ is divisible by 4 for all positive integral values of n.
Assume the assertion is true for $n = k$, that is, $5^k - 4k + 3$ is divisible by 4.
Then consider

$$5^{k+1} - 4(k + 1) + 3 - (5^k - 4k + 3)$$
$$= 5^k(5 - 1) - 4$$
$$= 4(5^k - 1)$$

This difference is divisible by 4. Thus if the assertion is true for $n = k$, then it is true for $n = k + 1$.

Putting $n = 1$, $5 - 4n + 3 = 4$, which is divisible by 4. Thus the result is proved by mathematical induction.

INEQUALITIES

◀ Inequations ▶

INEQUATIONS (INEQUALITIES)

Expression of the form $x > b$, $2x^2 - x + 3 > 0$, $\dfrac{x + 1}{x - 2} > 2$ are known as inequations or inequalities. Their solutions consist of a range or ranges of values of the variable concerned. The solution(s) may be represented on a number line as follows.

$x > 2$ ────────⊕────▶ the hollow circle showing $x = 2$ is excluded
         0 1 2

$x \geqslant 2$ ────────●────▶ the solid circle showing $x = 2$ is included.
         0 1 2

$-1 > x \cup x \geqslant 2$ ◀────⊕──┼──●────▶
                        -1 0 1 2

You should note when dealing with an inequation that if a and b are positive constants then $x > y$ implies:

   i) $x \pm a > y \pm a$ i.e. can add or subtract a constant to each side,
   ii) $ax > ay$ i.e. can multiply each side by a *positive* constant,
   iii) $ax \pm b > ay \pm b$ i.e. can combine i) and ii),
   iv) $-x < -y$ i.e. can multiply each side by a minus sign, but the inequality sign must be reversed

You are advised *never* to cross-multiply when solving an inequation, but to proceed as shown in worked example A.

Worked example A

Solve $\dfrac{x}{x+1} < \dfrac{x+2}{x+3}$

$\dfrac{x+2}{x+3} - \dfrac{x}{x+1} > 0$ i.e. take all terms to one side

$\dfrac{(x+2)(x+1) - x(x+3)}{(x+3)(x+1)} > 0 \Rightarrow \dfrac{2}{(x+3)(x+1)} > 0$

A *tabular display* can now be used to complete the solution.

Value of x	$x < -3$	$-3 < x < -1$	$x > -1$
Sign of $(x+1)$	$-$ve	$-$ve	$+$ve
Sign of $(x+3)$	$-$ve	$+$ve	$+$ve
Sign of $\dfrac{2}{(x+3)(x+1)}$	$+$ve	$-$ve	$+$ve

$\Rightarrow$ Solution is $x < -3 \cup x > -1$

▶ INEQUATIONS INVOLVING MODULUS SIGN

The notation $|x| < 2$ means $-2 < x < 2$, i.e. the numerical value of x is less than 2.

Worked example B

Solve $|2x - 3| < 5$
This means $-5 < 2x - 3 < 5$ so it is necessary to consider two inequalities,
$-5 < 2x - 3$ and $2x - 3 < 5$.
Now $-5 < 2x - 3 \Rightarrow 2x > -2,\ x > -1$
and $2x - 3 < 5 \Rightarrow 2x < 8,\ x < 4$
The complete solution is therefore $-1 < x < 4$
Shown on a number line as

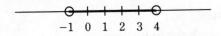

Worked example C

Solve $x^2 - |x| - 6 < 0$
Rearranging $|x| > (x^2 - 6)$ or for $x \geqslant 0 \Rightarrow x^2 - x - 6 < 0$
that is $(x - 3)(x + 2) < 0$

Value of x	$0 \leqslant x < 3$	$x > 3$
Sign of $(x - 3)$	$-$ve	$+$ve
Sign of $(x + 2)$	$+$ve	$+$ve
Sign of $(x - 3)(x + 2)$	$-$ve	$+$ve

$\Rightarrow 0 \leqslant x < 3$

For $x \leqslant 0 \ -(x^2 - 6) > x \Rightarrow x^2 + x - 6 < 0 \Leftrightarrow (x + 3)(x - 2) < 0$

Value of x	$x < -3$	$-3 < x \leqslant 0$
Sign of $(x + 3)$	$-$ve	$+$ve
Sign of $(x - 2)$	$-$ve	$-$ve
Sign of $(x + 3)(x - 2)$	$+$ve	$-$ve

$\Rightarrow -3 < x \leqslant 0$

Hence the range of x including *both* signs is $-3 < x < 3$.

INFLEXION (POINTS OF)

The graph of $y = f(x)$ has a point of inflexion at $x = x_0$ if and only if the signs of $f''(x)$ on either side of x_0 are different. Graphically, this means that

i) The graph of $y = f(x)$ is convex on one side of the point of inflexion and concave on the other.
ii) The tangent at a point of inflexion passes through the curve, that is, points on the curve on either side of the point of inflexion are on opposite sides of the tangent.

Graphically this is represented as shown in Fig. I.4. If $f''(x)$ is continuous, the above definition implies that $f''(x) = 0$ at a point of inflexion. This condition is not, however, sufficient to ensure a point of inflexion. It must be shown further that $f''(x)$ has opposite signs on either side of the point.

Worked example

Find the points of inflexion on the curve
$y = f(x) = x^3 - 6x^2 + 10x - 3$
Here
$f'(x) = 3x^2 - 12x + 10$
$f''(x) = 6x - 12$
Now,
$f''(x) = 0$ when $x = 2$

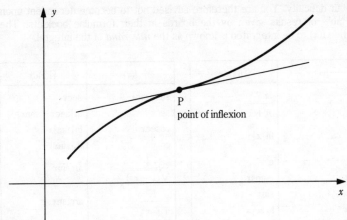

Fig. I.4

Furthermore,

$$f''(1\cdot9) = 6 \times 1\cdot9 - 12 = -0\cdot6 < 0$$

and $f''(2\cdot1) = 6 \times 2\cdot1 - 12 = 0\cdot6 > 0$

The opposite signs confirm that a point of inflexion occurs where $x = 2$, which is at $(2, 1)$.

INTEGRAL

◀ Integration ▶

INTEGRAL TERM

An integral term is one consisting of the product of a number of letters and/ or numbers, so that only multiplication, and neither addition nor subtraction nor division, occurs.

$6xy^2$, $-3x^{10}$, $\sqrt{2}yz$, 7

INTEGRAND

◀ Integration ▶

INTEGRATION

Under the entry **Derivative** are listed the basic results for the derivatives of standard functions. Listing those results in reverse order, it is possible to obtain a table of basic results for the *integrals* of standard functions. As with differentiation, it is essential that you know the results and can apply them without difficulty. You are therefore advised not to become dependent upon the table of results given by the boards in their formulae booklets. The function f(x) to be integrated is known as the *integrand* of the integral.

f(x)	$\int f(x)dx$
$x^n, n \neq -1$	$\dfrac{x^{n+1}}{n+1}$
$\dfrac{1}{x}$	$\ln|x|$
e^x	e^x
$\sin x$	$-\cos x$
$\cos x$	$\sin x$
$\tan x$	$\ln \sec x$
$\sec^2 x$	$\tan x$
$\text{cosec}^2 x$	$-\cot x$

f(x)	$\int f(x)dx$
$\sec x \tan x$	$\sec x$
$\sec x$	$\ln|\sec x + \tan x|$
$\text{cosec} x$	$\ln|\tan \frac{1}{2}x|$
$\cot x$	$\ln|\sin x|$
$\dfrac{1}{\sqrt{(1-x^2)}}$	$\arcsin x$
$\dfrac{1}{1+x^2}$	$\arctan x$

You should remember that the results given in the right-hand column are not unique since, strictly speaking, each should be associated with an arbitrary constant C, say, the constant of integration. That is, for $n \neq -1$,

$$\int x^n dx = \frac{x^{n+1}}{n+1} + C$$

For convenience we shall drop the arbitrary constant and introduce it only when it is essential to the problem in question, but in any indefinite integral it must be implicit that a *constant of integration* is required. It is advisable to check the results of any integration by differentiating back.

▶ FOUR BASIC RULES OF INTEGRATION

Rule 1 $\int cf(x)dx = c\int f(x)dx$ where c is a constant
Rule 2 $\int [f(x) \pm g(x)]dx = \int f(x)dx \pm \int g(x)dx$

Worked examples for rules 1 and 2

Rule 1: $\int 7\sin xdx = 7\int \sin xdx = -7\cos x$

Rule 2: $\int (7x^2 - 3e^x)dx = 7\int x^2 dx - 3\int e^x dx = \frac{7}{3}x^3 - 3e^x$

Rule 3   If $\int f(x)dx = F(x)$ then $\int f(x + a)dx = F(x + a)$, where a is any constant; i.e. the addition of a constant to the variable makes no difference to the *form* of the integral

Worked examples for rule 3

$$\int x^2 dx = \frac{x^3}{3} \Rightarrow \int (x+4)^2 dx = \frac{(x+4)^3}{3}$$

$$\int \frac{1}{x} dx = \ln|x| \Rightarrow \int \frac{1}{x-3} dx = \ln|x-3|$$

You must exercise care in using this rule. It only applies when x is replaced by $(x+a)$ and does not cover the case when the expression inside the brackets is not linear, i.e. the first degree in x.

Thus $\int (x^2+3)^2 dx \neq \dfrac{(x^2+3)^3}{3}$

Rule 4 If $\int f(x) dx = F(x)$ then $\int f(bx+a) dx = \dfrac{1}{b} F(bx+a)$, where a and b are constants

That is, if x is replaced by $bx + a$ then the form of the integral remains the same, but the answer must be divided by b, the coefficient of x.

Worked example for rule 4

$$\int \sqrt{x}\, dx = \frac{2}{3} x^{\frac{3}{2}} \Rightarrow \int \sqrt{(2x-3)}\, dx = \frac{1}{2} \cdot \frac{2}{3} (2x-3)^{\frac{3}{2}} = \frac{1}{3}(2x-3)^{\frac{3}{2}}$$

$$\int \cos x\, dx = \sin x \Rightarrow \int \cos 4x\, dx = \frac{1}{4}\sin 4x$$

$$\int e^x\, dx = e^x \Rightarrow \int e^{2x}\, dx = \frac{1}{2} e^{2x}$$

$$\int \frac{1}{x} dx = \ln|x| \Rightarrow \int \frac{1}{4-3x} dx = \frac{1}{(-3)} \ln|4-3x|$$

$$\int \frac{1}{1+x^2} dx = \arctan x = \int \frac{1}{9+x^2} dx = \frac{1}{9} \int \frac{1}{1+\left(\dfrac{x}{3}\right)^2} dx$$

$$= 3 \cdot \frac{1}{9}\arctan\left(\frac{x}{3}\right)$$

Again you are reminded that rule 4 only applies when x is replaced by $bx + a$ and does not apply to integrals of the form

$$\int \frac{1}{\sqrt{(4+3x^2)}} dx$$

You are also warned to look out for the constant b being $|-1|$. A very common mistake is to forget to divide by b when it happens to be -1.

Thus $\int \dfrac{1}{1-x}\, dx = -\ln|1-x|$, not $\ln|1-x|$.

Remember also that to each of the above worked examples should be added a constant of integration.

 ## INTEGRATION BY SUBSTITUTION

You are often *given* the required substitution. If you are not, and you find the integral difficult, look to see if one part of the integrand is, apart from a constant factor, the derivative of all or part of the rest of the integrand.

For instance:

$\int x^2(2 + 3x^3)^4 dx$, x^2 is the derivative of $2 + 3x^3$ divided by 9

$\int \sin^4 x \cos x \, dx$, $\cos x$ is the derivative of $\sin x$

$\int \dfrac{1}{x} \ln x \, dx$, $\dfrac{1}{x}$ is the derivative of $\ln x$

$\int \dfrac{e^{2x}}{1 + 3e^{2x}} dx$, e^{2x} is the derivative of $1 + 3e^{2x}$ divided by 6

Worked example

$\int x^2(2 + 3x^3)^4 dx$, x^2 is part of the derivative of $2 + 3x^3$

Let $t = 2 + 3x^3$, $\dfrac{dt}{dx} = 9x^2 \Rightarrow x^2 dx \equiv \dfrac{1}{9} dt$

$$\Rightarrow \int x^2(2 + 3x^3)^4 dx = \int (2 + 3x^3)^4 . x^2 dx = \int t^4 . \dfrac{1}{9} dt$$

$$= \dfrac{1}{9} . \dfrac{t^5}{5} = \dfrac{(2 + 3x^3)^5}{45}$$

 ## INTEGRATION INVOLVING TRIGONOMETRIC FUNCTIONS

When considering integrals involving trigonometric functions, it is sometimes necessary to seek the aid of the trigonometric identities.

Worked examples

$$\int \sin 3x \cos x \, dx = \int \dfrac{1}{2} (\sin 4x + \sin 2x) dx$$

$$= \dfrac{1}{2} \left(-\dfrac{1}{4} \cos 4x - \dfrac{1}{2} \cos 2x \right) = -\dfrac{1}{8} (\cos 4x + 2\cos 2x)$$

The product of two sines or two cosines or a sine and a cosine can all be integrated by this method.

$$\int \cos^2 3x \, dx = \int \frac{1}{2}(\cos 6x + 1)dx = \frac{1}{12}\sin 6x + \frac{x}{2}$$

Here we have used the double-angle formula $\cos 2A \equiv 2\cos^2 A - 1$

▶ INTEGRATION OF RATIONAL ALGEBRAIC FRACTIONS

Fractions in which the numerator and denominator contain only constants and positive integral powers of the variable can often be integrated using partial fractions and the integral

$$\int \frac{1}{ax + b} \, dx = \frac{1}{a}\ln|ax + b|$$

If the denominator is of the first degree, then of course, partial fractions are unnecessary; division by the denominator is all that is required.

Worked examples

$$\int \frac{6x^2}{3x + 1} \, dx = \int \left(2x - \frac{2}{3} + \frac{2}{3}\frac{1}{3x + 1}\right) dx = x^2 - \frac{2}{3}x + \frac{2}{9}\ln|3x + 1|$$

$$\int \frac{2x + 1}{x^2 - 3x + 2} \, dx = \int \frac{2x + 1}{(x - 1)(x - 2)} \, dx = \int \left(\frac{5}{x - 2} - \frac{3}{x - 1}\right) dx$$

$$= 5\ln|x - 2| - 3\ln|x - 1|$$

▶ DEFINITE INTEGRALS

Given that $\int f(x)dx = F(x)$ then an integral of the form

$$\int_a^b f(x)dx = \left[F(x)\right]_a^b = F(b) - F(a)$$

is known as a *definite integral*; a and b are called the limits of the integral.

Worked example

$$\int_1^2 (x^2 - 1)dx = \left[\frac{1}{3}x^3 - x\right]_1^2 = \left[\frac{1}{3}2^3 - 2\right] - \left[\frac{1}{3}1^3 - 1\right]$$

$$= \frac{8}{3} - 2 - \frac{1}{3} + 1 = 1\frac{1}{3}$$

When the integral is a definite integral, care must be taken to ensure that should a change of variable be necessary in order to integrate, then either

i) the limits must be changed to accommodate the new variable; or

ii) the integral must be treated as an indefinite integral and the limits inserted at the end of the integration after the function has been expressed in terms of the original variable.

◀ Approximate integration, Parts (integration by), Substitution (integration by) ▶

INTERMEDIATE VALUE THEOREM

This theorem states that if the function f is continuous in the interval $[a, b]$ and $f(a)$, $f(b)$ have different signs, then the equation $f(x) = 0$ has at least one root in the interval (a, b). If the interval is sufficiently small, the equation will have only one root in the interval.

This result can be used to locate the roots of an equation, which can then be pinpointed more accurately using an **iterative method**. Consider the cubic equation

$$f(x) = x^3 - 2x^2 - 5x + 7 = 0$$

We find that

$$f(-3) = -23$$
$$f(-2) = 1$$
$$f(-1) = 9$$
$$f(0) = 7$$
$$f(1) = 1$$
$$f(2) = -3$$
$$f(3) = 1$$

The sign changes show that there are roots in the intervals $(-3, -2)$, $(1, 2)$ and $(2, 3)$. Since every cubic equation has 3 roots (some of which may, of course, be complex), we know that there are no other roots.

INVERSE

◀ Function, Inverse trigonometric function, Mapping ▶

INVERSE HYPERBOLIC FUNCTION

Consider the function $f(x) = \sinh x$
defined on the domain $(-\infty, \infty)$ with range $(-\infty, \infty)$. Since f is a $1:1$ function, it has an inverse called the inverse sinh function and written $f^{-1}(x) = \sinh^{-1} x$.

This inverse also has domain $(-\infty, \infty)$ and range $(-\infty, \infty)$. There is a logarithmic form for the inverse, obtained as follows.
Let $y = \sinh^{-1} x$
so that

$$x = \sinh y = \frac{e^y - e^{-y}}{2}$$

Thus,

$$2x = e^y - e^{-y}$$

or

$$e^{2y} - 2xe^y - 1 = 0$$

Solving this quadratic equation in e^y,

$$e^y = \frac{2x \pm \sqrt{4x^2 + 4}}{2}$$

$$= x \pm \sqrt{x^2 + 1}$$

Since $e^y > 0$ for all, we must take the + sign so that

$$e^y = x + \sqrt{x^2 + 1}$$

and

$$y = \sinh^{-1}x = \ln(x + \sqrt{x^2 + 1})$$

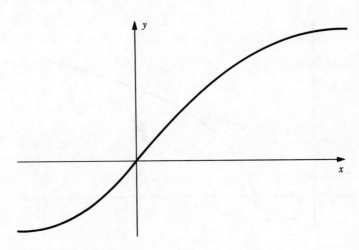

Fig. I.5

The graph of $\sinh^{-1}x$ is shown in Fig. I.5.

Now consider the function $f(x) = \cosh x$
defined on the domain $(-\infty, \infty)$ with range $(1, \infty)$. Unfortunately, f is not
1:1 since for all x, $\cosh x = \cosh(-x)$. Thus in order to enable us to define
an inverse function, we must restrict the domain to $(0, \infty)$. If we do this,
then the resulting inverse is called the inverse cosh function, written

$$f^{-1}(x) = \cosh^{-1}x$$

This inverse has domain $(1, \infty)$ and range $(0, \infty)$. There is also a logarithmic
form for this inverse. Let

$$y = \cosh^{-1}x$$

so that

$$x = \cosh y = \frac{e^y + e^{-y}}{2}$$

Thus,
$$2x = e^y + e^{-y}$$
or
$$e^{2y} - 2xe^y + 1 = 0$$
Solving,
$$e^y = \frac{2x \pm \sqrt{4x^2 - 4}}{2}$$
$$= x \pm \sqrt{x^2 - 1}$$
so that $y = \ln(x + \sqrt{x^2 - 1})$

The negative sign results in a negative value for y so we conclude that
$$\cosh^{-1}x = \ln(x + \sqrt{x^2 - 1})$$

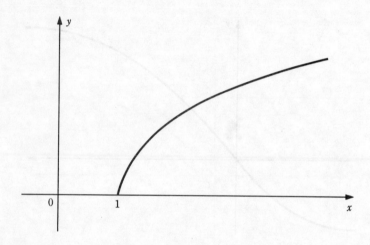

Fig. I.6

The graph of $\cosh^{-1}$ is shown in Fig. I.6.

Finally, consider the function
$$f(x) = \tanh x$$
defined on the domain $(-\infty, \infty)$ with range $(-1, 1)$. This time f is a $1:1$ function with an inverse. This is called the inverse tanh function, written
$$f^{-1}(x) = \tanh^{-1}x$$
This inverse has domain $(-1, 1)$ and range $(-\infty, \infty)$. It also has a logarithmic form, obtained as follows. Let
$$y = \tanh^{-1}x$$
so that
$$x = \tanh y = \frac{e^y - e^{-y}}{e^y + e^{-y}}$$

Thus,
$$xe^y + xe^{-y} = e^y - e^{-y}$$
whence
$$e^y(1 - x) = e^{-y}(1 + x)$$
or
$$e^{2y} = \frac{1 + x}{1 - x}$$

It follows that
$$2y = \ln\left(\frac{1 + x}{1 - x}\right)$$
or $y = \tanh^{-1}x = \frac{1}{2}\ln\left(\frac{1 + x}{1 - x}\right)$

The graph of $\tanh^{-1}x$ is shown in Fig. I.7.

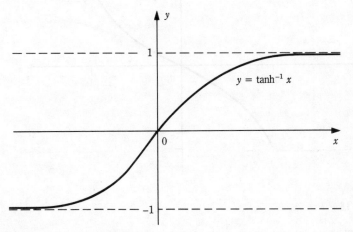

$y = \tanh^{-1} x$

Fig. I.7

INVERSE TRIGONOMETRIC FUNCTION

Consider the function $f(x) = \sin x$ defined on the domain $(-\infty, \infty)$. Now f is a many:1 function, which means that many values of x give the same value of $\sin x$. For example, working in radians,

$$\sin\frac{\pi}{4} = \sin\frac{9\pi}{4} = \sin\frac{17\pi}{4} = \frac{1}{\sqrt{2}}$$

It follows that f has no inverse function. The only way to ensure the existence of an inverse function is to restrict the domain to make f a 1:1 function.

This can be done by defining
$$f(x) = \sin x$$

on the domain $\left[-\dfrac{\pi}{2}, \dfrac{\pi}{2}\right]$; the range of f is $[-1, +1]$. The inverse of f is

called the inverse sine function, written
$$f^{-1}(x) = \sin^{-1}x$$

with domain $[-1, +1]$; the range of f^{-1} is $\left[-\dfrac{\pi}{2}, \dfrac{\pi}{2}\right]$. This value is sometimes

called the *principal value* of $\sin^{-1}x$. The graph of $\sin^{-1}x$ is shown in Fig. I.8.

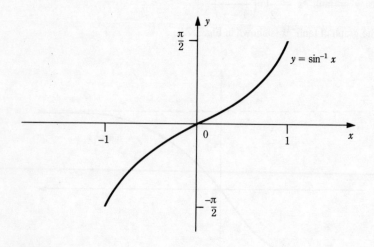

Fig. I.8

Similarly, if $f(x) = \cos x$ is defined with domain $[0, \pi]$ and range $[-1, +1]$, then the inverse of f is called the principal value of
$$f^{-1}(x) = \cos^{-1}x$$
with domain $[-1, +1]$ and range $[0, \pi]$. The graph of $\cos^{-1} x$ is shown in Fig. I.9.

Finally, if $f(x) = \tan x$ is defined with domain $\left(-\dfrac{\pi}{2}, \dfrac{\pi}{2}\right)$ and range

$(-\infty, \infty)$, then the inverse of f is called the principal value of
$$f^{-1}(x) = \tan^{-1}x$$

with domain $(-\infty, \infty)$ and range $\left(-\dfrac{\pi}{2}, \dfrac{\pi}{2}\right)$. The graph of $\tan^{-1}x$ is shown in

Fig. I.10.

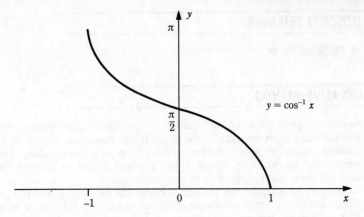

Fig. I.9

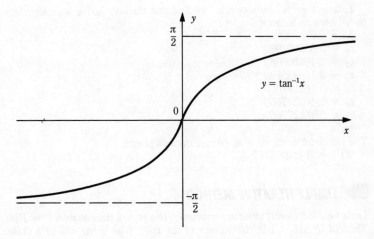

Fig. I.10

IRRATIONAL TERM

An irrational term is one in which one or more of the indices of the letters are irrational:

$x^{\sqrt{2}}, x^2 y^{\sqrt{5}}$

◄ Rational term ►

ISOSCELES TRIANGLE

◀ Plane shape ▶

ITERATIVE METHOD

An iterative method for solving a mathematical problem is one which starts with an initial approximation to the solution and then uses a formula to calculate successive approximations which converge to the solution. The problem can therefore be solved to any required degree of accuracy by repeating the process as many times as necessary.

Consider, for example, the problem of calculating the positive square root of a, where $a > 0$, using only simple arithmetic operations. This can be done using the iterative formula

$$x_{n+1} = \frac{1}{2}\left(x_n + \frac{a}{x_n}\right)$$

with $x_0 = 1$

Taking $a = 10$, for example, we find that the successive approximations to $\sqrt{10}$ are as follows:

$x_1 = 5 \cdot 5$
$x_2 = 3 \cdot 659090909$
$x_3 = 3 \cdot 196005082$
$x_4 = 3 \cdot 162455623$
$x_5 = 3 \cdot 162277665$
$x_6 = 3 \cdot 162277660$
$x_7 = 3 \cdot 162277660$
etc.

The calculator confirms that, to nine decimal places,

$\sqrt{10} = 3 \cdot 162277660$

▶ SIMPLE ITERATIVE METHOD

Let α be a sufficiently close approximation to a root of the equation $x = F(x)$. Then, if $|F'(x)| < 1$ in the vicinity of the root, $\beta = F(\alpha)$ will be a closer approximation to the root. This result can be illustrated graphically as shown in Fig. I.11. The result leads to the iterative formula

$x_{n+1} = F(x_n)$

with x_0 a suitably chosen initial approximation

This will converge to the root provided that $|F'(x)| < 1$ in the vicinity of the root. If this condition is not satisfied, then the process will diverge.

The easiest way to determine whether or not a particular iterative process is convergent is to try it and see. We can illustrate by means of an example which shows that, in some cases, there may be two (or more) ways of rearranging an equation into the appropriate form, some leading to a convergent iteration and others to a divergent iteration.

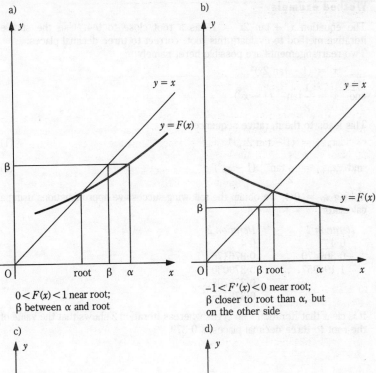

a)

$0 < F(x) < 1$ near root;
β between α and root

b)

$-1 < F'(x) < 0$ near root;
β closer to root than α, but
on the other side

c)

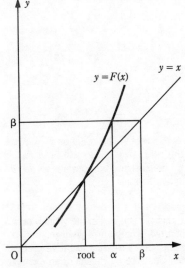

$F'(x) > 1$ near root;
α between β and root

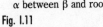
Fig. I.11

d)

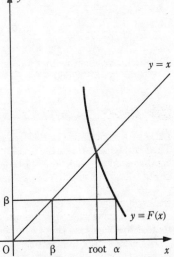

$F'(x) < -1$ near root;
β further away from root than α,
but on the other side

Worked example

The equation $x^3 + \tan 2x = 1$ has a root close to $0 \cdot 4$. Use the simple iterative method to evaluate this root, correct to three decimal places.

Two rearrangements are possible here, namely

$$x = (1 - \tan 2x)^{\frac{1}{3}}$$

and $\quad x = \dfrac{1}{2} \tan^{-1} (1 - x^3)$

This leads to the iterative sequences

$$x_{n+1} = (1 - \tan 2x_n)^{\frac{1}{3}} \tag{1}$$

and $\quad x_{n+1} = \dfrac{1}{2} \tan^{-1} (1 - x_n{}^3) \tag{2}$

Taking $x_0 = 0 \cdot 4$, we obtain the following successive approximations using a calculator:

Iteration 1	*Iteration 2*
$0 \cdot 4$	$0 \cdot 4$
$-0 \cdot 309470 \ldots$	$0 \cdot 376176 \ldots$
$1 \cdot 196357 \ldots$	$0 \cdot 379030 \ldots$
	$0 \cdot 378708 \ldots$
	$0 \cdot 378745$

It is clear that Iteration 1 diverges whereas Iteration 2 shows that the value of the root to three decimal places is $0 \cdot 379$.

KENDALL'S CORRELATION COEFFICIENT

◀ Correlation coefficient (Kendall's τ) ▶

KINEMATICS

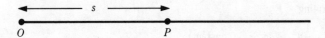

Fig. K.1

Kinematics is the study of moving particles. We consider one-dimensional motion, that is, motion on a straight line (see Fig. K.1). Let a particle P be at a distance s from O at time t. Then, the **velocity** v is defined by

$$v = \frac{ds}{dt} = \dot{s}$$

The **acceleration** a is defined by

$$a = \frac{dv}{dt} = \dot{v}$$

Alternative forms for a are

$$a = v\frac{dv}{ds} = \ddot{s}$$

▶ CONSTANT ACCELERATION EQUATIONS

Suppose that a is constant. Then, since $\dfrac{dv}{dt} = a$

it follows by **integration** that $v = at + A$ (constant). Suppose that $v = u$ when $t = 0$. Then, substituting

$$u = 0 + A$$

so that $v = u + at$ (1)

Consider this equation in the form

$$\frac{ds}{dt} = u + at$$

Integrating

$$s = ut + \frac{1}{2}at^2 + B \text{ (constant)}$$

Assuming that $s = 0$ when $t = 0$, it follows that

$$0 = 0 + 0 + B$$

whence

$$s = ut + \frac{1}{2}at^2$$ (2)

Alternatively

$$v\frac{dv}{ds} = a$$

or $\int v dv = a\int ds$

Integrating

$$\frac{1}{2}v^2 = as + C \text{ (constant)}$$

Since $v = u$ when $s = 0$, it follows that

$$\frac{1}{2}u^2 = C$$

whence $v^2 = u^2 + 2as$ (3)

Which of equations (1), (2) and (3) is used in any particular context depends upon exactly what is required. If the acceleration is not constant, then more complicated **differential equations** have to be solved.

DIAGRAMMATIC METHODS

An alternative approach is to use a diagrammatic method. Consider, for example, a graph of velocity against time, as shown in Fig. K.2.

Velocity–time diagram

From this graph

$$a = \frac{dv}{dt} = \text{gradient of curve}$$

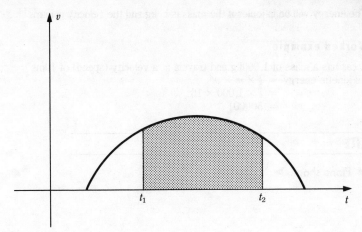

Fig. K.2

Distance travelled in $[t_1, t_2]$ = $\displaystyle\int_{t_1}^{t_2} v\,\mathrm{d}t$ = shaded area

Distance–time diagram

Here the velocity is obtained as the gradient of the graph.

Acceleration–time diagram

Here the velocity increase during any interval is the area under the curve between the appropriate times.

Velocity–distance diagram

Here the acceleration is given by $v\,\dfrac{\mathrm{d}v}{\mathrm{d}s}$

that is, the ordinate times the gradient.

KINETIC ENERGY

Kinetic energy (K.E.) is **energy** that a body has because it is moving. The energy will depend on the mass (m) of the body and on its speed (v).

$$\text{K.E.} = \frac{1}{2}mv^2$$

The energy will be in joules if the mass is in kg and the velocity is in ms^{-1}

Worked example

A car has a mass of 1,000kg and travels at a velocity (speed) of $10ms^{-1}$
Its kinetic energy $= \frac{1}{2} \times m \times v^2$
$= \frac{1}{2} \times 1,000 \times 10^2$
$= 50000J$

KITE

◀ Plane shape ▶

LASPEYRES INDEX

◀ Index numbers ▶

LAWS (DETERMINATION OF)

Variables x, y are often related by a non-linear equation, such as $y = x^n$. In order to verify such relationships and to estimate the parameters (here n), it is useful to transform the variables to make the relationship linear. We could, for example, take natural logarithms of both sides, in which case the relationship becomes

$$\ln y = n\ln x$$
or
$$Y = nX$$
where Y $\ln y$ and $X = \ln x$

If we plot values of $Y = \ln y$ against values of $X = \ln x$, then we should obtain a straight line of gradient n passing through the origin. If we do not, then the assumed relationship is incorrect. The value of n can then be estimated as the gradient of the line through the plotted points.

The table gives some more relationships which can be 'linearised' by suitable transformations.

Given relationship	rearrangement	plot
$y = \dfrac{1}{ax + b}$	$\dfrac{1}{y} = ax + b$	$Y = \dfrac{1}{y}$ against $X = x$
$y = ax^b$	$\ln y = \ln a + b\ln x$	$Y = \ln y$ against $X = \ln x$
$y = ab^x$	$\ln y = \ln a + x\ln b$	$Y = \ln y$ against $X = x$
$y = ae^{bx}$	$\ln y = \ln a + bx$	$Y = \ln y$ against $X = x$
$y = ax + bx^2$	$\dfrac{y}{x} = a + bx$	$Y = \dfrac{y}{x}$ against $X = x$

Worked example

The variables x, y are believed to be related by the equation
$$y = ab^x$$

where a, b are unknown constants. Observations on x, y produce the following results

x	1·2	2·4	3·6	4·8	6·0
y	3·87	7·05	12·86	23·46	42·78

   i) Confirm this relationship by plotting ln$y$ against x.
  ii) Estimate a, b.

Taking natural logs,
    $\ln y = \ln a + x \ln b$
Thus, a plot of $Y = \ln y$ against x should give a straight line with a gradient ln$b$ and intercept ln$a$ on the Y axis. Using a calculator, we find the following values:

x	1·2	2·4	3·6	4·8	6·0
ln$y$	1·35	1·95	2·55	3·16	3·76

The graph (Fig. L.1) shows that the values of ln$y$ plotted against x do lie on a straight line, confirming the relationship. We see that

$$\ln a = \text{intercept on ln}y \text{ axis}$$
$$= 0·75$$
whence $a = e^{0·75} \approx 2·12$
and $\ln b = \text{gradient of line}$
$$= \frac{3·76 - 0·75}{6}$$
$$= 0·502$$
whence $b = e^{0·502} \approx 1·65$

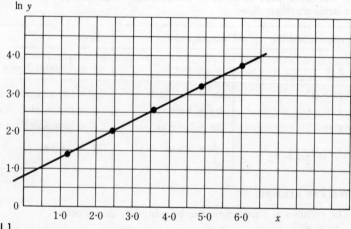

Fig. L.1

L'HÔPITAL'S RULE

Let $f(x)$, $g(x)$ be two functions such that $f(x) = g(a) = 0$.
Then l'Hôpital's rule states that

$$\lim_{x \to a} \frac{f(x)}{g(x)} = \frac{f'(a)}{g'(a)}$$

provided that $f'(a)$ and $g'(a)$ are not both zero. If they are,

$$\lim_{x \to a} \frac{f(x)}{g(x)} = \frac{f''(a)}{g''(a)}$$

provided that $f''(a)$ and $g''(a)$ are not both zero. If they are, this process of differentiation continues until derivatives $f^{(n)}(a)$, $g^{(n)}(a)$ which are not both zero are found. Then,

$$\lim_{x \to a} \frac{f(x)}{g(x)} = \frac{f^{(n)}(a)}{g^{(n)}(a)}$$

Worked example

Evaluate

$$\lim_{x \to 0} \frac{1 - \cos x}{x^2}$$

Here
$$f(x) = 1 - \cos x \quad \text{and} \quad g(x) = x^2$$
$$f'(x) = \sin x \quad \text{and} \quad g'(x) = 2x$$
Since $f'(0) = g'(0) = 0$, we must differentiate again.
$$f''(x) = \cos x \quad \text{and} \quad g''(x) = 2$$
so that $f''(0) = 1$ and $g''(0) = 2$
Thus,

$$\lim_{x \to 0} \frac{1 - \cos x}{x^2} = \frac{1}{2}$$

LINE (COORDINATE GEOMETRY OF STRAIGHT)

Let P_1 (x_1, y_1) and P_2 (x_2, x_2) be two distinct points (Fig. L.2). Then the gradient m of the line $P_1 P_2$ is defined by

$$m = \tan \theta = \frac{P_2 Q}{P_1 Q} = \frac{y_2 - y_1}{x_2 - x_1}$$

To find the equation of this line, consider a general point $P(x, y)$ on it. Then

since $\dfrac{PR}{P_1R} = \dfrac{P_2Q}{P_1Q}$ (both $= \tan \theta$)

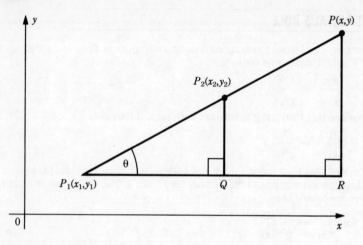

Fig. L.2

it follows that $\dfrac{y - y_1}{x - x_1} = \dfrac{y_2 - y_1}{x_2 - x_1}$

This is the equation of the line. Since the right-hand side is equal to m, an alternative form is

$$\frac{y - y_1}{x - x_1} = m$$

or $\quad y - y_1 = m(x - x_1)$

which gives the equation of the line with gradient m passing through the point (x_1, y_1)

The equation is of the form

$y = mx + c$ (where $c = y_1 - mx_1$)

which is the *general equation* of a straight line. We note that $y = c$ when $x = 0$, so that c is the intercept on the y-axis. Two lines

$$y = m_1 x + c_1$$

and $\quad y = m_2 x + c_2$

are perpendicular if $\quad m_1 m_2 = -1$

and parallel if $\quad m_1 = m_2$

The point of intersection of these two lines can be found by solving the two equations simultaneously. A unique point of intersection exists if $m_1 \neq m_2$

Worked example

Find the equation of the line l_1 joining the points $(2, 1)$ and $(3, 3)$. Write down the equation of the line l_2 which is perpendicular to l_1 and passes through the point $(1, 9)$.

Find the point of intersection of l_1 and l_2 and deduce the perpendicular distance from the point $(1, 9)$ to l_1

The gradient m_1 of l_1 is

$$m_1 = \frac{3-1}{3-2} = 2$$

The equation of l_1 is therefore

$$y - 1 = 2(x - 2)$$
$$\text{or} \quad y = 2x - 3 \tag{1}$$

The gradient m_2 of l_2 is equal to $-\dfrac{1}{m_1}$, i.e. $-\dfrac{1}{2}$.

The equation of l_2 is therefore

$$y - 9 = -\frac{1}{2}(x - 1)$$

$$\text{or} \quad y = -\frac{1}{2}x + \frac{19}{2} \tag{2}$$

To find the point of intersection of l_1 and l_2, we solve (1) and (2) simultaneously.

Thus,

$$2x - 3 = -\frac{1}{2}x + \frac{19}{2}$$

$$\text{or} \quad \frac{5}{2}x = \frac{25}{2}$$

$$x = 5$$

Substituting,

$$y = -\frac{1}{2}.5 + \frac{19}{2} = 7$$

The point of intersection is therefore $(5, 7)$.

Perpendicular distance $=$ Distance between $(1, 9)$ and $(5, 7)$
$$= \sqrt{(7 - 9)^2 + (5 - 1)^2} = \sqrt{20} = 2\sqrt{5}$$

LINEAR

Linear has to do with being straight; so a **line** that is linear is straight. The general equation of a linear line is $y = mx + c$ where m is the gradient of the straight line and c is the y-axis intercept. This **equation** is called a *linear equation*.

▶ *SOLUTIONS TO STRAIGHT-LINE QUESTIONS*

In solving questions on the straight line it is usually advisable to draw a reasonably accurate diagram. Diagrams often indicate the way forward.

Worked example A

A variable line passes through the fixed point $(6, 3)$ and meets the x-axis at A and the y-axis at B. Find the equation of the locus of N, the mid-point of AB.

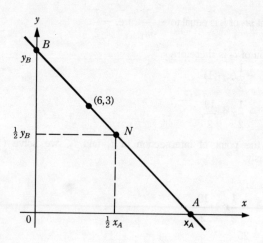

Fig. L.3

Draw the diagram as in Fig. L.3. The equation of AB is $y - 3 = m(x - 6)$ where m is the gradient

At A, $y = 0 \Rightarrow x_A = \dfrac{1}{m}(6m - 3)$

At B, $x = 0 \Rightarrow y_B = 3 - 6m$

Let the coordinates of the mid-point of AB be (X, Y)

$$\Rightarrow X = \frac{1}{2m}(6m - 3) \text{ and } Y = \frac{1}{2}(3 - 6m)$$

The gradient m of the line is variable and, in order to obtain the locus of N, it is necessary to eliminate m between the two equations for X and Y

$$Y = \frac{1}{2}(3 - 6m) \Rightarrow m = \frac{1}{6}(3 - 2Y)$$

Substituting in $X = \dfrac{1}{2m}(6m - 3) \Rightarrow X = \dfrac{(3 - 2Y - 3)}{\left(\dfrac{3 - 2Y}{3}\right)}$

$\Rightarrow X = \dfrac{6Y}{2Y - 3}$

$\Rightarrow$ locus of mid-point of AB is the curve with equation
$x(2y - 3) = 6y$

Worked example B

Prove that the points $A(-3, 4)$; $B(1, -4)$; and $C(3, 7)$ in Fig. L.4 are the vertices of a right-angled triangle. Find the equation of the line passing through the mid-point of the hypotenuse and perpendicular to the hypotenuse

$\left.\begin{array}{llll} AB^2 = [-3 - 1]^2 + [4 - (-4)]^2 & = 16 + 64 & = 80 \\ BC^2 = [1 - 3]^2 + [-4 - 7]^2 & = 4 + 121 & = 125 \\ CA^2 = [3 - (-3)^2)] + [7 - 4]^2 & = 36 + 9 & = 45 \end{array}\right\} BC^2 = AB^2 + CA^2$

$\Rightarrow \triangle ABC$ is right-angled at A

Mid-point of $BC = \left[\dfrac{1}{2}(3 + 1), \dfrac{1}{2}(7 - 4)\right] = \left(2, \dfrac{3}{2}\right)$

Gradient of $BC = m_1 = \dfrac{7 - (-4)}{3 - 1} = \dfrac{11}{2}$

$\Rightarrow$ gradient of line perpendicular to BC is m_2 where $\dfrac{11}{2} \cdot m_2 = -1$

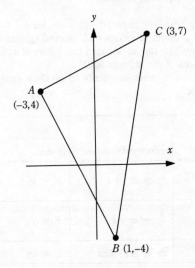

Fig. L.4

$$\Rightarrow m_2 = -\frac{2}{11}$$

$\Rightarrow$ equation of straight line passing through the mid-point of BC and perpendicular to BC is $\left(y - \frac{3}{2}\right) = -\frac{2}{11}\left(x - 2\right)$

$$\Rightarrow 22y + 4x - 41 = 0$$

▶ REDUCTION OF EQUATION TO LINEAR FORM

The equation $y = mx + c$ is that of a straight line whose gradient is m and whose intercept on the y-axis is c. Many equations which would normally produce curves (i.e. not straight lines) when values of y are plotted against values of x can be rearranged and new variables chosen so that a straight-line graph can be obtained. This exercise is a particularly useful one when it is required to check an experimental law.

Consider the equation $y = ax + bx^2$, where a and b are constants. If a curve is sketched for given values of a and b it would be parabolic. If, however, the equation is rearranged in the form

$$\frac{y}{x} = a + bx$$

and a new variable Y, where

$$Y = \frac{y}{x}$$

is chosen then the equation becomes

$$Y = a + bx$$

This equation can now be compared with $y = mx + c \Rightarrow Y \equiv y$, $x \equiv x$.

Consequently, a graph of values of Y plotted against values of x yields a straight line from which can be deduced the values of a, (intercept on Y-axis) and b, (the gradient of the straight line).

Further examples of rearrangements to produce straight line graphs are shown in the table.

given equation	rearranged equation	axes	
		y-axis	x-axis
$y = ax + \dfrac{b}{x}$	$xy = ax^2 + b$	$Y = xy$	$X = x^2$
$y = \dfrac{1}{ax + b}$	$\dfrac{1}{y} = ax + b$	$Y = \dfrac{1}{y}$	$X = x$
$y = ax^b$	$\ln y = \ln a + b \ln x$	$Y = \ln y$	$X = \ln x$

given equation	rearranged equation	axes	
		y-axis	*x-axis*
$y = ab^x$	$\ln y = \ln a + x\ln b$	$Y = \ln y$	$X = x$
$y = ae^{bx}$	$\ln y = \ln a + bx$	$Y = \ln y$	$X = x$
$yx^a = b$	$\ln y = \ln b - a\ln x$	$Y = \ln y$	$X = \ln x$
$y = a(x-2)^b$	$\ln y = \ln a + b\ln(x-2)$	$Y = \ln y$	$X = \ln(x-2)$

Worked example C

The variables x and y below are believed to be related by a law of the form $y = \ln(ax^2 + bx)$ where a and b are constants. By drawing a suitable straight-line graph, show that this is so and from your graph estimate values of a and b

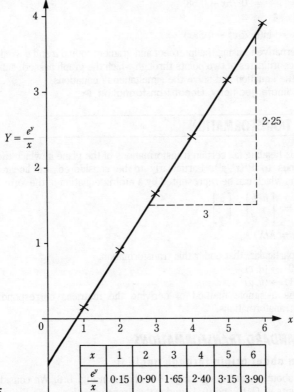

x	1	2	3	4	5	6
$\dfrac{e^y}{x}$	0·15	0·90	1·65	2·40	3·15	3·90

Fig. L.5

x	1	2	3	4	5	6
y	$-1\cdot897$	$0\cdot588$	$1\cdot599$	$2\cdot262$	$2\cdot757$	$3\cdot153$

$$y = \ln(ax^2 + bx) \Rightarrow e^y = ax^2 + bx \Rightarrow \frac{e^y}{x} = ax + b$$

Letting $Y = \dfrac{e^y}{x}$, $\Rightarrow Y = ax + b$ which is of straight-line form, a being the

gradient and b being the intercept on the Y-axis. Hence plot

$$Y = \frac{e^y}{x} \text{ against } x \text{ (Fig. L.5)}$$

Intercept on Y-axis $\Rightarrow b = -0\cdot575 \approx -0\cdot58$

Gradient $= a = \dfrac{2\cdot25}{3} = 0\cdot75$

$$\Rightarrow Y = \frac{e^y}{x} = 0\cdot75x - 0\cdot58$$

$$\Rightarrow y = \ln(0\cdot75x^2 - 0\cdot58x)$$

An alternative to using the intercept and gradient to find a and b would be to take the coordinates of two points through which the graph passed, substitute them in the equation and solve the simultaneous equations.

◀ Coordinate geometry, Linear transformation ▶

LINEAR TRANSFORMATION

Under this heading fall certain transformations of the plane in which the point $P(x, y)$ goes to $P'(x', y')$. Particularly to be considered are linear transformations which can be represented by a **matrix** equation of the form

$$\begin{bmatrix} x' \\ y' \end{bmatrix} = \begin{bmatrix} a & b \\ c & d \end{bmatrix} \begin{bmatrix} x \\ y \end{bmatrix}$$
(or $X' = MX$)

Note, in particular, that under this transformation,

$(1, 0) \rightarrow (a, c)$

and $(0, 1) \rightarrow (b, d)$

This gives a simple method of deriving the matrices corresponding to standard transformations.

▶ STANDARD TRANSFORMATIONS

Rotation about origin through angle θ

Rotation about origin through angle θ is shown in Fig. L.6. We consider the image points of $(1, 0)$ and $(0, 1)$ under this transformation – see Fig. L.7.

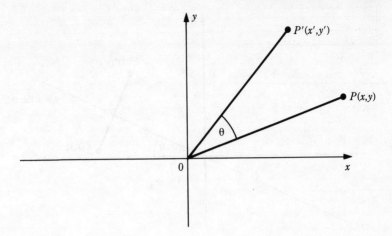

Fig. L.6

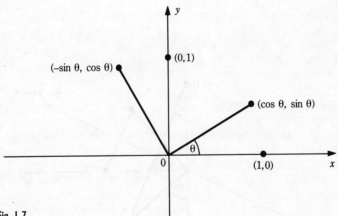

Fig. L.7

We see that
$(1, 0) \rightarrow (\cos \theta, \sin \theta) = (a, c)$ and $(0, 1) \rightarrow (-\sin \theta, \cos \theta) = (b, d)$
Thus

$$\text{Rotation matrix} = \begin{bmatrix} \cos \theta & -\sin \theta \\ \sin \theta & \cos \theta \end{bmatrix}$$

Reflection in the line $y = x\tan \theta$

Reflection in the line $y = x\tan \theta$ is shown in Fig. L.8. We again consider the image points of $(1, 0)$ and $(0, 1)$ under the transformation – see Fig. L.9.

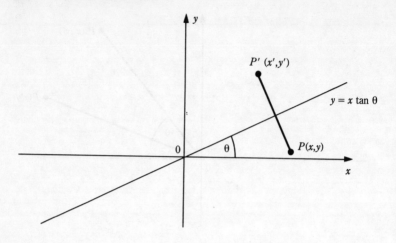

Fig. L.8

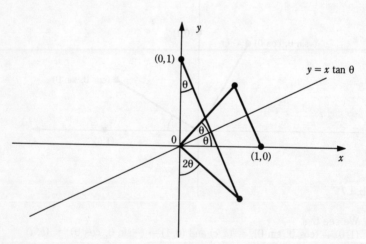

Fig. L.9

We see that
$(1, 0) \rightarrow (\cos 2\theta, \sin 2\theta) = (a, c)$ and $(0, 1) \rightarrow (\sin 2\theta, -\cos 2\theta) = (b, d)$
Thus,

$$\text{Rotation matrix} = \begin{bmatrix} \cos 2\theta & \sin 2\theta \\ \sin 2\theta & -\cos 2\theta \end{bmatrix}$$

▶ *COMBINATION OF TRANSFORMATIONS*

Suppose that two transformations are applied successively, having matrices $\mathbf{M_1}$, $\mathbf{M_2}$. Suppose that under these, $\mathbf{X} \to \mathbf{X'} \to \mathbf{X''}$.

Since $\mathbf{X'} = \mathbf{M_1 X}$
and $\mathbf{X''} = \mathbf{M_2 X'}$
it follows that
$$\mathbf{X''} = \mathbf{M_2 M_1 X}$$
so that the matrix of the combined transformation is $\mathbf{M_2 M_1}$ (note the order: this denotes $\mathbf{M_1}$ then $\mathbf{M_2}$).

▶ *TRANSLATION*

Consider now the translation in which
$$(x, y) \to (x + h, y + k) = (x', y')$$
We have to introduce (3×3) transformation matrices to deal with this, and we write
$$\begin{bmatrix} x' \\ y' \\ 1 \end{bmatrix} = \begin{bmatrix} 1 & 0 & h \\ 0 & 1 & k \\ 0 & 0 & 1 \end{bmatrix} \begin{bmatrix} x \\ y \\ 1 \end{bmatrix}$$

It is possible also to express rotations and reflections within this framework – for instance:
$$\text{Rotation matrix} = \begin{bmatrix} \cos\theta & -\sin\theta & 0 \\ \sin\theta & \cos\theta & 0 \\ 0 & 0 & 1 \end{bmatrix}$$
$$\text{Reflection matrix} = \begin{bmatrix} \cos 2\theta & \sin 2\theta & 0 \\ \sin 2\theta & -\cos 2\theta & 0 \\ 0 & 0 & 1 \end{bmatrix}$$

◀ Matrix/matrices ▶

LOGARITHMS

If $a^b = c$, where a, $c > 0$, then b is called the logarithm (or log) of c to base a, written $b = \log_a c$

For example,
$$3^4 = 81$$
So that
$$4 = \log_3 81$$
Logarithms have the following properties:

i) $\log_a 1 = 0$ for all $a > 0$
ii) $\log_a(bc) = \log_a b + \log_a c$
iii) $\log_a(b^c) = c \log_a b$
iv) $\log_a\left(\dfrac{1}{b}\right) = -\log_a b$

v) $\log_a\left(\dfrac{b}{c}\right) = \log_a b - \log_a c$

vi) $\log_a c = \log_b c \times \log_a b$

These results enabled logarithms (to base 10) to be used to facilitate arithmetical calculations, a method now totally redundant owing to the arrival of cheap calculators.

▶ PROOF OF LOGARITHM LAWS

The 'laws' of logarithms above are proved by using the definition of a logarithm and the rules for indices.

Worked example A

Prove $\log_a x - \log_a y = \log_a\left(\dfrac{x}{y}\right)$

Let $\log_a x = A$ and $\log_a y = B$

$\Rightarrow a^A = x$ and $a^B = y$

$\Rightarrow \dfrac{x}{y} = \dfrac{a^A}{b^B} = a^{A-B} \Rightarrow \log_a\left(\dfrac{x}{y}\right) = A - B = \log_a x - \log_a y$

Worked example B

Prove the change of base formula $\log_a x = \dfrac{\log_b x}{\log_b a}$

Hence solve $3\log_8 x - \log_x 8 = 2$

Let $\log_a x = y \Rightarrow x = a^y \Rightarrow \log_b x = \log_b(a^y)$

$\Rightarrow \log_b x = y \log_b a$ or $y = \log_a x = \dfrac{\log_b x}{\log_b a}$

$3\log_8 x - \log_x 8 = 2 \Rightarrow 3\log_8 x - \dfrac{\log_8 8}{\log_8 x} = 2$

or $\quad 3(\log_8 x)^2 - 2(\log_8 x) - 1 = 0$

$\qquad (3\log_8 x + 1)(\log_8 x - 1) = 0 \Rightarrow \log_8 x = -\dfrac{1}{3}$ or 1

$\Rightarrow x = 8^{-\frac{1}{3}} = \dfrac{1}{2}$ or $8^1 = 8$

Worked example C

Given that $\log_2(x + 1) - 1 = 2\log_2 y$ and $\log_2(x - 5y + 4) = 0$ find x and y

$$\log_2(x - 5y + 4) = 0 \Rightarrow x - 5y + 4 = 2^0 = 1 \Rightarrow x = 5y - 3$$
$$\Rightarrow \log_2(x + 1) - 1 = 2\log_2 y \Rightarrow \log(5y - 2) - 2\log_2 y = 1$$

$$\Rightarrow \log_2 \frac{5y - 2}{y^2} = 1 \Rightarrow \frac{5y - 2}{y^2} = 2$$

$$\Rightarrow 2y - 5y + 2 = 0 \Leftrightarrow (2y - 1)(y - 2) = 0 \Rightarrow y = \frac{1}{2} \text{ or } 2$$

When $y = \frac{1}{2}$, $x = -\frac{1}{2}$, when $y = 2$, $x = 7$

Worked example D

Solve for x, correct to three significant figures
$$4^{2x+1} \cdot 5^{x-2} = 6^{1-x}$$

Equations such as this where the unknown variable occurs in the index and where there are no plus or minus signs other than those in the index can usually be solved by the use of logarithms. However, you must always be careful to ensure that you do not fall into the trap of taking logarithms through a plus or minus sign. For example: $2^x + 3^{2x-1} = 4$. It is not correct to say $\log 2^x + \log 3^{2x-1} = \log 4$. The correct statement is $\log(2^x + 3^{2x-1}) = \log 4$ and this will not lead anywhere. Returning to our example,
$$4^{2x+1} \cdot 5^{x-2} = 6^{1-x} \Rightarrow \log(4^{2x+1} \cdot 5^{x-2}) = \log 6^{1-x}$$
$$\Rightarrow \log 4^{2x+1} + \log 5^{x-2} = \log 6^{1-x} \Rightarrow (2x + 1)\log 4 + (x - 2)\log 5$$
$$= (1 - x)\log 6$$

Using logarithms to the base $10 \Rightarrow 2{\cdot}6814x = 1{\cdot}5741$ or $x = 0{\cdot}587$

▶ NATURAL LOGARITHMS

Logarithms to base e are called *natural logarithms* so that if, for $x > 0$,
$$e^y = x$$
then
$$y = \log_e x \text{ or } \ln(x)$$
The function $\ln(x)$ is defined on the domain $(0, \infty)$ and its graph is shown in Fig. L.10.

An important property of $\ln(x)$ is that

$$\frac{d}{dx}(\ln(x)) = \frac{1}{x}$$

or, alternatively, omitting the arbitrary constant,

$$\ln(x) = \int \frac{dx}{x}$$

In particular,

$$\ln(z) = \int_1^z \frac{dx}{x}$$

This enables $\ln(z)$ to be defined as equal to the shaded area in the graph shown in Fig. L.11.

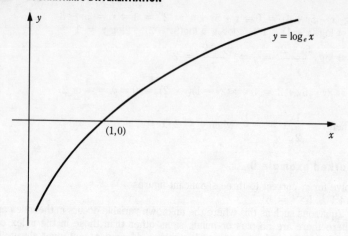

Fig. L.10

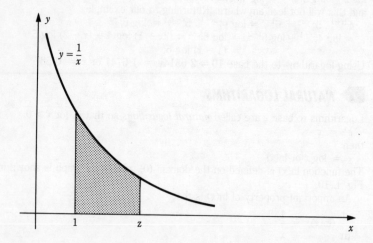

Fig. L.11

LOGARITHMIC DIFFERENTIATION

When the independent variable, say x, occurs in the index of any function other than the exponential function (e^x), then it is necessary to use logarithmic differentiation, that is, to take logarithms of the function before differentiating.

Worked example A

Differentiate $y = a^x$, where a is a constant

$$y = a^x \Rightarrow \ln y = \ln a^x = x \ln a$$

$$\Rightarrow \frac{d}{dx}(\ln y) = \frac{d}{dx}(x \ln a) \Leftrightarrow \frac{1}{y}\frac{dy}{dx} = 1 . \ln a$$

$$\Rightarrow \frac{dy}{dx} = y \ln a = a^x \ln a$$

Worked example B

Differentiate $y = (x + 2)^{x+1}$

$$\Rightarrow \ln y = \ln(x + 2)^{x+1} = (x + 1)\ln(x + 2)$$

$$\Rightarrow \frac{1}{y}\frac{dy}{dx} = \ln(x + 2) + \frac{x + 1}{x + 2}$$

$$\Rightarrow \frac{dy}{dx} = y\left[\ln(x + 2) + \frac{x + 1}{x + 2}\right] = \left[\ln(x + 2) + \frac{x + 1}{x + 2}\right](x + 2)^{x+1}$$

Logarithmic differentiation is also useful when required to find the derivatives of functions which involve products or quotients

Worked example C

Find $\dfrac{dy}{dx}$ given that $y = \dfrac{e^{2x} \sin 3x}{\sqrt{(1 - x^2)}}$

$$y = \frac{e^{2x} \sin 3x}{\sqrt{(1 - x^2)}} \Rightarrow \ln y = \ln\left[\frac{e^{2x} \sin 3x}{(1 - x^2)^{\frac{1}{2}}}\right] = \ln e^{2x} + \ln \sin 3x - \ln(1 - x^2)^{\frac{1}{2}}$$

$$\ln y = 2x + \ln \sin 3x - \tfrac{1}{2}\ln(1 - x^2)$$

$$\Leftrightarrow \frac{1}{y}\frac{dy}{dx} = 2 + \frac{3 \cos 3x}{\sin 3x} - \frac{1}{2} . \frac{(-2x)}{1 - x^2}$$

$$\Leftrightarrow \frac{dy}{dx} = \left[2 + \frac{3 \cos 3x}{\sin 3x} + \frac{x}{1 - x^2}\right]\frac{e^{2x} \sin 3x}{\sqrt{(1 - x^2)}}$$

◀ Derivative, Logarithm ▶

LOGARITHMIC FUNCTION

The **exponential function** $f : x \mapsto e^x$, $x \in \mathbb{R}$ is a one–one **mapping** and so possesses an **inverse**. Its inverse is the logarithmic function

$$y = e^x \Rightarrow \text{for the inverse } x = e^y$$

$$\Rightarrow \log_e x = \log_e e^y \Rightarrow y\log_e e = y \Rightarrow y = \log_e x = \ln x$$

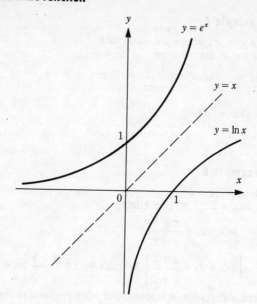

Fig. L.12

The graphs of the exponential function and the logarithmic function are as shown in Fig. L.12, each being the reflection of the other in the line $y = x$. You should note that no part of the curve with equation $y = \ln x$ lies in the 2nd or 3rd quadrant – that is, $\ln x$ does not exist for $x < 0$.

◀ Exponential function, Function, Logarithm ▶

McLAURIN SERIES

The McLaurin series is a power series containing powers of x for a function $f(x)$, and is a special case of the **Taylor series**. The result is

$$f(x) = f(0) + xf'(0) + \frac{x^2}{2!}f''(0) + \ldots + \frac{x^r}{r!}f^{(r)}(0) + \ldots$$

or alternatively

$$f(x) = \sum_{r=0}^{\infty} \frac{x^r f^{(r)}(0)}{r!}$$

To prove this result, let
$$f(x) = a_0 + a_1x + a_2x^2 + a_3x^3 + a_4x^4 + \ldots + a_rx^r + \ldots$$

By successive differentiation,
$$f'(x) = a_1 + 2a_2x + 3a_3x^2 + 4a_4x^3 + \ldots + ra_rx^{r-1} + \ldots$$
$$f''(x) = 2a_2 + 6a_3x^2 + 12a_4x^2 + \ldots + r(r-1)a_rx^{r-2} + \ldots$$

and in general,
$$f^{(r)}(x) = r!a_r + \text{terms involving powers of } x.$$

Putting $x = 0$,
$$a_0 = f(0)$$
$$a_1 = f'(0)$$
$$a_2 = \frac{f''(0)}{2}$$

and in general
$$a_r = \frac{f^{(r)}(0)}{r!}$$

The question of *convergence* is outside the A-level and AS-level curriculum. Suffice it here to say that some series are convergent for all x, some only for restricted values of x (often $|x| < 1$).

Some common McLaurin series, which can be derived by differentiating as above, are given below.

$$\exp(x) = 1 + x + \frac{x^2}{2} + \frac{x^3}{6} + \ldots$$

$$= \sum_{r=0}^{\infty} \frac{x^r}{r!}$$

$$\ln(1 + x) = x - \frac{x^2}{2} + \frac{x^3}{3} - \frac{x^4}{4} + \ldots$$

$$= \sum_{r=0}^{\infty} \frac{(-1)^{r+1} x^r}{r}$$

$$\sin x = x - \frac{x^3}{6} + \frac{x^5}{120} - \frac{x^7}{5040} + \ldots$$

$$= \sum_{r=0}^{\infty} \frac{(-1)^r x^{2r+1}}{(2r + 1)!}$$

$$\cos x = 1 - \frac{x^2}{2} + \frac{x^4}{24} - \frac{x^6}{720} + \ldots$$

$$= \sum_{r=0}^{\infty} \frac{(-1)^r x^{2r}}{(2r)!}$$

$$\tan^{-1} x = x - \frac{x^3}{3} + \frac{x^5}{5} - \frac{x^7}{7} + \ldots$$

$$= \sum_{r=0}^{\infty} \frac{(-1)^r x^{2r+1}}{(2r + 1)}$$

◄ Taylor series ►

MAPPING

A relation in which each element of the **domain** is associated with one and only one element of the range is called a **function** or mapping – see Fig. M.1.

NB. A one–many mapping is not a function. Functions are normally denoted by a single letter, say f, g, F, G, and so on, and consequently a notation frequently used for a function f, say, is $f : x \mapsto$

Thus for $y = f(x) = 3x + 2$, we write $f : x \mapsto 3x + 2$

Often we loosely refer to 'the function $f(x) = 3x + 2$' but strictly speaking $f(x)$ is not the function, but rather the value of the function at x.

► INVERSE

If a function f is such that it is one–one and maps an element x_n in the domain to an element y_n in the range then the function which maps the element y_n back to x_n is said to be the *inverse* of the function f and is denoted by f^{-1}. You must note that the function f has to be one–one, (one–many relations are not functions) and that the domain of f is then identical with the range of its inverse function f^{-1} and the range of f is identical with the domain of f^{-1}.

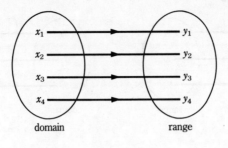

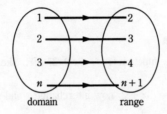

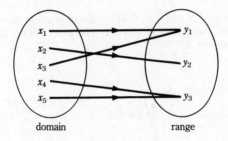

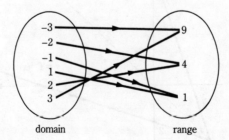

Fig. M.1

To obtain the inverse function f^{-1}, simply interchange the x and y in the equation of the function and then rearrange the equation to make y the subject – see Fig. M.2.

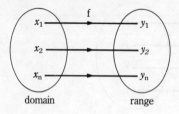 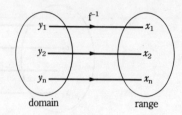

Fig. M.2

Worked example A

Find the inverse of the function $f: x \mapsto 3x + 2$, $x \in \mathbb{R}$. Sketch the graphs of the functions f and f^{-1}

$f: x \mapsto 3x + 2 \Rightarrow y = 3x + 2$; now interchange x and y

$\Rightarrow x = 3y + 2 \Rightarrow y = \frac{1}{3}(x - 2) \Rightarrow f^{-1}: x \mapsto \frac{1}{3}(x - 2)$, $x \in \mathbb{R}$

The graphs of $y = f(x)$ and $y = f^{-1}(x)$ in this case are as shown in Fig. M.3. You should note thate these graphs are reflections (mirror images) of each other in the line $y = x$.

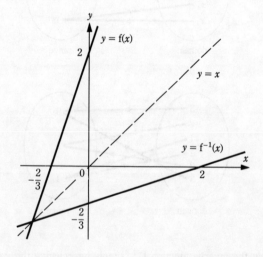

Fig. M.3

Worked example B

The function f is defined by $f: x \mapsto x^2 - 6x + 2$, $0 \leqslant x \leqslant 7$

a) Find the minimum value of $f(x)$
b) Sketch the function and state its range
c) State, with reasons, whether f^{-1} exists or not

$$y = f(x) = x^2 - 6x + 2$$

$$\Rightarrow \frac{dy}{dx} = 2x - 6 \Rightarrow \frac{dy}{dx} = 0 \text{ when } x = 3$$

$$\frac{d^2y}{dx^2} = 2 = \text{positive} \Rightarrow y \text{ has a minimum value of } -7 \text{ when } x = 3$$

When $x = 0$, $y = 2$, when $x = 7$, $y = 9$, hence the graph of the function is as shown in Fig. M.4. The range of f is therefore $[-7, 9]$. The function is not a one–one mapping for $0 \leqslant x \leqslant 6$, hence f^{-1} does not exist.

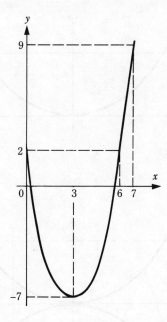

Fig. M.4

NB. The end points of the domain do not necessarily give the end points of the range. The straight line $y = c$, $-7 < c \leqslant 2$ cuts the graph of the function in two distinct points, showing that the function is not a one–one mapping and hence does not have an inverse for $0 \leqslant x \leqslant 6$. This is a good test as to whether a function possesses an inverse – graph the function and then if, and only if, all straight lines parallel to the x-axis meet the graph of f in at most one point the function will have an inverse.

Worked example C

State which of the following relations are functions and determine the inverse function in those cases where one exists

i) $R_1 = \{(x,y), y = x^2, x \in \mathbb{R}, x \neq 0\}$
ii) $R_2 = \{(x,y), y = \pm x^2, x \in \mathbb{R}, x \neq 0\}$
iii) $R_3 = \{(x,y), y = x^2, x \in \mathbb{R}^+\}$

i) $y = x^2, x \in \mathbb{R}, x \neq 0$ (Fig. M.5)
Relation is a two–one mapping $\Rightarrow$ relation is a function, but does not have an inverse.

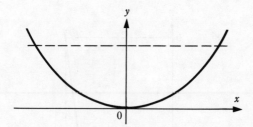

Fig. M.5

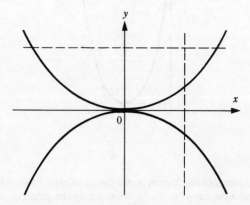

Fig. M.6

ii) $y = \pm x^2$, $x \in \mathbb{R}$, $x \neq 0$ (Fig. M.6)
Relation is a two–two mapping $\Rightarrow$ relation is not a function.

iii) $y = x^2$, $x \in \mathbb{R}$, $x \neq 0$ (Fig. M.7)
Relation is a one–one mapping $\Rightarrow$ relation is a function which has an inverse.
$y = x^2$, $x \in \mathbb{R}^+ \Rightarrow x = +\sqrt{y} \Rightarrow y = +\sqrt{x}$, $x \in \mathbb{R}^+$
$\Rightarrow f^{-1} = \{(x,y), y = +\sqrt{x}, x \in \mathbb{R}^+\}$

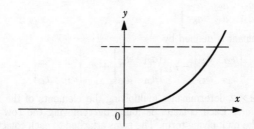

Fig. M.7

MATRIX/MATRICES

A matrix is a rectangular array of numbers satisfying certain rules. The usual notation for a matrix with m rows and n columns (called a matrix of order $m \times n$) is

$$\mathbf{A} = \begin{bmatrix} a_{11} & a_{12} \ldots a_{1n} \\ a_{21} & a_{22} \ldots a_{2n} \\ a_{m1} & a_{m2} \ldots a_{mn} \end{bmatrix}$$

Here, a_{ij} denotes the element in the ith row and jth column. The transpose of $\mathbf{A}$, written $\mathbf{A}'$, is formed by interchanging the rows and columns of $\mathbf{A}$. $\mathbf{A}'$ is a matrix of order $(n \times m)$ and

$$\mathbf{A}' = \begin{bmatrix} a_{11} & a_{21} \ldots a_{m1} \\ a_{12} & a_{22} \ldots a_{m2} \\ a_{1n} & a_{2n} \ldots a_{mn} \end{bmatrix}$$

The matrix is called *square* if $m = n$.

▶ DETERMINANT

An important characteristic of a square matrix is its *determinant*. Although it is possible to write down a general definition for the determinant of a $(n \times n)$ matrix, it is easier to start with a 2×2 matrix as follows.

Given the 2×2 matrix

$$\mathbf{A} = \begin{bmatrix} a_{11} & a_{12} \\ a_{21} & a_{22} \end{bmatrix}$$

the determinant of $\mathbf{A}$ is defined by

$$\det \mathbf{A} = |\mathbf{A}| = a_{11} a_{22} - a_{12} a_{21}$$

Given the 3×3 matrix

$$\mathbf{A} = \begin{bmatrix} a_{11} & a_{12} & a_{13} \\ a_{21} & a_{22} & a_{23} \\ a_{31} & a_{32} & a_{33} \end{bmatrix}$$

The determinant is defined by

$$|\mathbf{A}| = a_{11} \begin{vmatrix} a_{22} & a_{23} \\ a_{32} & a_{33} \end{vmatrix} - a_{12} \begin{vmatrix} a_{21} & a_{23} \\ a_{31} & a_{33} \end{vmatrix} + a_{13} \begin{vmatrix} a_{21} & a_{22} \\ a_{31} & a_{32} \end{vmatrix}$$

Here, the 2×2 determinants multiplying the elements of the top row are called *cofactors*. Each cofactor is found by removing the row and column containing the multiplying term. The signs attached to each cofactor alternate $+ - + \dots$.

Note that the determinant can actually be expanded about any row or any column. The sign to be attached to each factor is shown in the array:

$$\begin{bmatrix} + & - & + \\ - & + & - \\ + & - & + \end{bmatrix}$$

For example, if the determinant is expanded about the second column, then

$$|\mathbf{A}| = - a_{12} \begin{vmatrix} a_{21} & a_{23} \\ a_{31} & a_{33} \end{vmatrix} + a_{22} \begin{vmatrix} a_{11} & a_{13} \\ a_{31} & a_{33} \end{vmatrix} - a_{32} \begin{vmatrix} a_{11} & a_{13} \\ a_{21} & a_{23} \end{vmatrix}$$

This definition is easily extended to $n \times n$ matrices, for example $n = 4$. If

$$\mathbf{A} = \begin{bmatrix} a_{11} & a_{12} & a_{13} & a_{14} \\ a_{21} & a_{22} & a_{23} & a_{24} \\ a_{31} & a_{32} & a_{33} & a_{34} \\ a_{41} & a_{42} & a_{43} & a_{44} \end{bmatrix}$$

then

$$|\mathbf{A}| = a_{11} \begin{vmatrix} a_{22} & a_{23} & a_{24} \\ a_{32} & a_{33} & a_{34} \\ a_{42} & a_{43} & a_{44} \end{vmatrix} - a_{12} \begin{vmatrix} a_{21} & a_{23} & a_{24} \\ a_{31} & a_{33} & a_{34} \\ a_{41} & a_{43} & a_{44} \end{vmatrix}$$

$$+ a_{13} \begin{vmatrix} a_{21} & a_{22} & a_{24} \\ a_{31} & a_{32} & a_{34} \\ a_{41} & a_{42} & a_{44} \end{vmatrix} - a_{14} \begin{vmatrix} a_{21} & a_{22} & a_{23} \\ a_{31} & a_{32} & a_{33} \\ a_{41} & a_{42} & a_{43} \end{vmatrix}$$

A square matrix having zero determinant is called *singular*; otherwise, the matrix is *non-singular*.

▶ UNIT (OR IDENTITY) MATRIX

The $(n \times n)$ matrix for which $a_{ij} = 1$ if $i = j$ and $a_{ij} = 0$ if $i \neq j$ is called the unit (or identity) matrix $\mathbf{I}$. For example, if $n = 3$,

$$\mathbf{I} = \begin{bmatrix} 1 & 0 & 0 \\ 0 & 1 & 0 \\ 0 & 0 & 1 \end{bmatrix}$$

NB. Elements for which $i = j$ are called *diagonal elements*.

▶ MATRIX MULTIPLICATION

The matrices $\mathbf{A}$ of order $(p \times q)$ and $\mathbf{B}$ of order $(r \times s)$ can be multiplied to give $\mathbf{C} = \mathbf{AB}$ if $q = r$, i.e. the number of columns in $\mathbf{A}$ is equal to the number of rows in $\mathbf{B}$. The terms of the product matrix $\mathbf{C}$ are given by

$$c_{ij} = \sum_{k=1}^{q} a_{ik}b_{kj}$$

that is, the (i, j) term of $\mathbf{C}$ is found by multiplying the ith row of $\mathbf{A}$ into the jth column of $\mathbf{B}$.

The fact that the product $\mathbf{AB}$ can be formed does not mean that the product $\mathbf{BA}$ can be formed (this requires that $p = s$). Even if it can be formed, it does not follow that $\mathbf{AB} = \mathbf{BA}$. Matrix multiplication is not commutative.

Matrix multiplication is, however, associative in the sense that

$(\mathbf{AB})\mathbf{C} = \mathbf{A}(\mathbf{BC})$

In view of this, the brackets may be removed and $\mathbf{ABC}$ is unambiguous.

▶ INVERSE OF A

Given the non-singular square matrix $\mathbf{A}$, the inverse matrix $\mathbf{A}^{-1}$ satisfies the equations

$\mathbf{AA}^{-1} = \mathbf{A}^{-1}\mathbf{A} = \mathbf{I}$

The inverse matrix can be found by the following steps.

Step 1   Find the cofactor matrix of $\mathbf{A}$, that is, the matrix whose elements are the cofactors of the elements of $\mathbf{A}$. These are found by evaluating the determinant formed by eliminating the row and column containing the element and applying the appropriate sign.

Step 2   Transpose the cofactor matrix to the adjoint matrix, adj $\mathbf{A}$.

Step 3   Divide throughout by the determinant of $\mathbf{A}$.

The process can be summed up by the equation

$$\mathbf{A}^{-1} = \frac{\text{adj } \mathbf{A}}{|\mathbf{A}|}$$

Worked example

Find the inverse of

$$\begin{bmatrix} 1 & 2 & 4 \\ 2 & 3 & 6 \\ 3 & 5 & 8 \end{bmatrix}$$

We find that

$$\text{cofactor matrix} = \begin{bmatrix} -6 & 2 & 1 \\ 4 & -4 & 1 \\ 0 & 2 & -1 \end{bmatrix}$$

as, for example

$$\text{cofactor of } 6 = -\begin{vmatrix} 1 & 2 \\ 3 & 5 \end{vmatrix} = 1$$

Thus,

$$\text{adj } \mathbf{A} = \begin{bmatrix} -6 & 4 & 0 \\ 2 & -4 & 2 \\ 1 & 1 & -1 \end{bmatrix}$$

Also, expanding about the top row,

$$|\mathbf{A}| = 1 \times (3 \times 8 - 5 \times 6) - 2(2 \times 8 - 3 \times 6) + 4(2 \times 5 - 3 \times 3) = 2$$

Thus,

$$\mathbf{A}^{-1} = \frac{\text{adj } \mathbf{A}}{|\mathbf{A}|}$$

$$= \begin{bmatrix} -3 & 2 & 0 \\ 1 & -2 & 1 \\ \frac{1}{2} & \frac{1}{2} & -\frac{1}{2} \end{bmatrix}$$

It is easily verified that $\mathbf{AA}^{-1} = \mathbf{I}$

An alternative method is based on row or column operations. The idea is to modify rows (or columns) of $\mathbf{A}$ and $\mathbf{I}$ simultaneously by adding or subtracting multiples of other rows (or columns) to change $\mathbf{A}$ into $\mathbf{I}$. This process will change $\mathbf{I}$ into $\mathbf{A}^{-1}$. We rework the above example, concentrating on rows.

$$\begin{bmatrix} 1 & 2 & 4 \\ 2 & 3 & 6 \\ 3 & 5 & 8 \end{bmatrix} ; \quad \begin{bmatrix} 1 & 0 & 0 \\ 0 & 1 & 0 \\ 0 & 0 & 1 \end{bmatrix}$$

(second row becomes second row minus $2 \times$ first row)

$$\begin{bmatrix} 1 & 2 & 4 \\ 0 & -1 & -2 \\ 3 & 5 & 8 \end{bmatrix} ; \quad \begin{bmatrix} 1 & 0 & 0 \\ -2 & 1 & 0 \\ 0 & 0 & 1 \end{bmatrix}$$

(third row becomes third row minus $3 \times$ first row)

$$\begin{bmatrix} 1 & 2 & 4 \\ 0 & -1 & -2 \\ 0 & -1 & -4 \end{bmatrix} ; \quad \begin{bmatrix} 1 & 0 & 0 \\ -2 & 1 & 0 \\ -3 & 0 & 1 \end{bmatrix}$$

(third row becomes third row minus second row)

$$\begin{bmatrix} 1 & 2 & 4 \\ 0 & -1 & -2 \\ 0 & 0 & -2 \end{bmatrix} ; \quad \begin{bmatrix} 1 & 0 & 0 \\ -2 & 1 & 0 \\ -1 & -1 & 1 \end{bmatrix}$$

(first row becomes first row plus 2 × second row)

$$\begin{bmatrix} 1 & 0 & 0 \\ 0 & -1 & -2 \\ 0 & 0 & -2 \end{bmatrix} ; \quad \begin{bmatrix} -3 & 2 & 0 \\ -2 & 1 & 0 \\ -1 & -1 & 1 \end{bmatrix}$$

(second row becomes second row minus third row)

$$\begin{bmatrix} 1 & 0 & 0 \\ 0 & -1 & 0 \\ 0 & 0 & -2 \end{bmatrix} ; \quad \begin{bmatrix} -3 & 2 & 0 \\ -1 & 2 & -1 \\ -1 & -1 & 1 \end{bmatrix}$$

Since all off-diagonal terms on the left are zero, we can now do the final steps in one operation. Change the signs of the second and third rows and divide the third row by 2

$$\begin{bmatrix} 1 & 0 & 0 \\ 0 & 1 & 0 \\ 0 & 0 & 1 \end{bmatrix} ; \quad \begin{bmatrix} -3 & 2 & 0 \\ -1 & 2 & -1 \\ \frac{1}{2} & \frac{1}{2} & -\frac{1}{2} \end{bmatrix}$$

The right-hand matrix is A^{-1}.

MAXIMUM AND MINIMUM

The function $f(x)$ has a *local maximum* at $x = x_0$ if $f(x)$ has a larger value at x_0 than at points immediately on either side of it. The function $f(x)$ has a *local minimum* at $x = x_0$ if $f(x)$ has a smaller value at x_0 than at points immediately on either side of it.

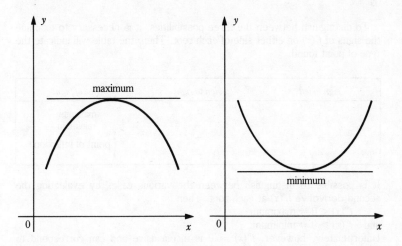

Fig. M.8

At a maximum or minimum, $f'(x) = 0$ (see Fig. M.8). Local maxima and minima are called *turning points*.

Using the above result, turning points can be located by solving the equation $f'(x) = 0$. Each root of this equation corresponds to either   i) a maximum; or   ii) a minimum; or   iii) neither a maximum nor a minimum. Possibility iii) is illustrated in Fig. M.9, and it corresponds to a point of inflexion.

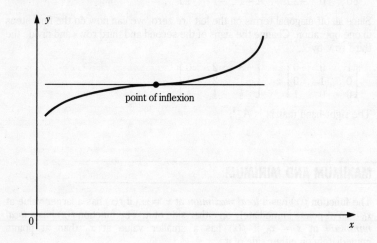

point of inflexion

Fig. M.9

To distinguish between the three possibilities, it is necessary to examine the signs of $f'(x)$ on either side of each root. Then, the table will indicate the type of point found.

sign to left	sign to right	type of point
+	−	maximum
−	+	minimum
+	+	$\left.\begin{array}{l} \\ \end{array}\right\}$ point of inflexion
−	−	

It is possible to distinguish between the various cases by evaluating the second **derivative** $f''(x)$ at each root. Then

$\quad f''(x) < 0 \Rightarrow$ maximum

and $f''(x) > 0 \Rightarrow$ minimum

Unfortunately, however, $f''(x) = 0$ is inconclusive and can correspond to any one of the three possibilities. Higher **derivatives** have to be evaluated to distinguish between them.

MEAN

The term mean usually refers to the *arithmetic mean*, which is the most common type of average. In fact it is usually what people are referring to when they talk about the 'average'.

The mean of a set of numeric data is the sum of all the data divided by the total frequency of the data. In other words, it is the sum of all the numbers divided by how many numbers there are. For example, to find the mean of 4, 6, 3, 2, 7, 12, 8, 5, 13 and 9, you add up all the numbers to give you 69. Then divide by the number of numbers, which is 10, to give a mean of 6·9.

ESTIMATED MEAN

An estimated mean is found from a *grouped* frequency distribution where we do not know all the individual items of data. We only know how many items of data are between certain limits. For example, consider the grouped frequency in table i). This shows the number of candidates obtaining various ranges of marks in an examination. To estimate the mean, we assume that each candidate scored the middle mark in each range. We then estimate the total marks for that group by multiplying the middle mark by the frequency.

We can now add up all these estimates to find how many the total data adds up to. Then divide this by the total frequency to obtain our estimated mean.

The second table ii) shows how we have done this in this example. Here we estimate the mean as $892 \div 37 = 24$.

Marks	Frequency
0–10	3
11–20	7
21–30	19
31–40	8

i)

Marks	Midway x	Frequency f	fx
0–10	5	3	15
11–20	15·5	7	108·5
21–30	25·5	19	484·5
31–40	35·5	8	284
total		37	892

ii)

$$\text{Mean} = \frac{\Sigma fx}{\Sigma f} = \frac{892}{37} = 24.1$$

MEAN OF A DISTRIBUTION

The population mean μ of a continuous distribution with **probability density function** $f(x)$ is defined by

$$\mu = E(X)$$

$$= \int_{-\infty}^{\infty} xf(x)\,\mathrm{d}x$$

MEAN SQUARE ERROR (MSE)

The population mean of a discrete distribution with probability function p_x is defined by

$$\mu = E(X) = \sum_x x p_x$$

 **SAMPLE MEAN**

The sample mean $\bar{X}$ of the random sample $X_1, X_2, \ldots X_n$ is defined by

$$\bar{X} = \sum_{i=1}^{n} \frac{X_i}{n}$$

◀ Median, Mode ▶

MEAN SQUARE ERROR (MSE)

◀ Estimator ▶

MEASUREMENTS OF CENTRAL TENDENCY

◀ Mean, Median, Mode ▶

MECHANICAL ENERGY (CONSERVATION OF)

The principle of conservation of mechanical energy states that, for bodies in motion under the action of a *conservative system of forces*, the sum of the kinetic and the potential energies of the bodies is constant. If the work done by a force on a particle which is moved from a point A to a point B is independent of the path joining A and B, the force is said to be conservative. In particular, the uniform gravitational field is a conservative field of force.

We include two simple examples to illustrate the main difference between a *conservative* system and a *non-conservative* system of forces.

First, consider two points A and B, where B is at vertical height h above A, and suppose a particle of mass m is moved from A to B and then from B to A. The total work done in this complete operation $= -mgh + mgh = 0$, thus agreeing with the contention that the work done $=$ force $\times$ distance, and in this case, the distance is zero.

Consider now the points A and B at a distance h apart on a rough horizontal table. The particle of mass m is moved along the table from A to B and then from B to A. Let us suppose that the frictional force opposing the movement of the particle on the surface of the table is proportional to the weight of the particle in magnitude and equal to kmg, where k is a numerical constant. As the particle is moved from A to B the frictional force acts in the direction $\overrightarrow{BA}$ and the work required against friction to move the particle directly from A to B is $kmgh$. As the particle returns to A from B a further amount of work equal to *kmgh* is required to achieve this because the frictional force acts in the direction $\overrightarrow{AB}$. In all, the total work required is 2*kmgh* and none of this is 'recoverable' as in the first example because it is transferred into other forms of energy, for instance, heat because of the friction. Frictional forces are non-conservative, as this example illustrates.

Often a particle is subjected to both conservative and non-conservative forces simultaneously and in such cases only part of the work is recoverable. We may, however, extend the principle of conservation of mechanical energy when frictional forces are involved and the following statement is often called the *work–energy principle*.

increase in mechanical energy = work done by – work done
                                               external forces   against friction

We may need to adjust the signs in this equation when work is done against external forces, rather than by them, and there may be an overall decrease in the total initial mechanical energy in these cases.

MEDIAN

The median is a type of average. It is the middle item of data, once that data has been sorted into ascending order. If there are two items of data in the middle, as there will be with an even number of items, then we add them together and divide by 2 to calculate the median. In general, if there are N numbers in a frequency distribution, then the middle item is the $\dfrac{(N+1)}{2}$ th.

For example, here are 15 test results.

(81, 63, 59, 71, 36, 99, 56, 31, 5, 65, 46, 83, 71, 53, 15)

To calculate the median score, put the marks into ascending order (5, 15, 31, 36, 46, 53, 56, 59, 63, 65, 71, 71, 81, 83, 99). Now find the middle one, which is 59. So the median score is 59.

▶ SAMPLE MEDIAN

Let x_1, x_2, ... x_n denote a **random sample** from some distribution and let y_1, y_2, ... y_n denote the same values rearranged in ascending order.

Then, for odd *n*,

Sample median = $y_{\frac{1}{2}(n+1)}$

and for even *n*,

Sample median = $\frac{1}{2}\{y_{\frac{1}{2}n} + y_{\frac{1}{2}n+1}\}$

Worked example

Find the medians of the following samples

i) 2·3, 3·6, 1·9, 2·4, 1·8

ii) 2·3, 3·6, 1·9, 2·4, 1·8, 2·0

i) Arranging in ascending order, we obtain
  1·8, 1·9, 2·3, 2·4, 3·6
  Since $n = 5$,
  Sample median $= y_{\frac{1}{2}(5+1)}$
$$= y_3 = 2·3$$
  We note that this is the 'middle' value in the sample.

ii) Rearranging, we obtain
  1.8, 1.9, 2.0, 2.3, 2.4, 3.6
  Since $n = 6$,
  Sample median $= \frac{1}{2}\{y_{\frac{1}{2}n} + y_{\frac{1}{2}n+1}\}$
$$= \frac{1}{2}(y_3 + y_4)$$
$$= \frac{1}{2}(2·0 + 2·3)$$
$$= 2·15$$

▶ POPULATION MEDIAN

The population median m of a continuous distribution having **probability density function** $f(x)$ is defined by

$$\int_{-\infty}^{m} f(x)dx = \int_{m}^{\infty} f(x)dx = \frac{1}{2}$$

This shows that the median divides the area below the probability density function into two equal halves.

MODE

The mode is a type of average; it can be defined as 'what most people have'. The mode is the value occurring most times in a particular frequency distribution. The number 1 hit single each week is the record that has sold more copies than any other record that week; it is therefore the modal record.

In a *bar chart*, the mode is always the data represented by the longest bar.

In a **histogram**, the modal class will be the data represented by the bar of greatest area.

In a **pie chart**, the mode will be the data represented by the largest sector (the largest angle).

▶ ESTIMATION OF MODE FROM HISTOGRAM

For this we can use the histogram drawn to display the data about short-service times, which is also shown in Fig. H.1. The technique for estimating the mode, which is depicted in Fig. M.10, can be explained as follows. The class interval – 60 – contains the largest number of members, and all class intervals are of the same length. This is called the *modal class*. The rectangles

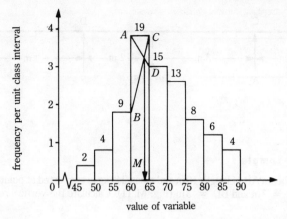

Fig. M.10

on either side of the modal class are also considered and the lines AD and BC are joined. The estimate of the mode is then taken as the horizontal axis coordinate of the intersection of these lines. The estimate of the mode is therefore 63·6.

MODULUS

If P represents the **complex number** $z = x + iy$ (see Fig. A.13) then the length of OP, usually denoted by r, $|z|$ or $|x + iy|$, is called the modulus of z. Clearly $|z| = r = \sqrt{(x^2 + y^2)}$, $r > 0 \Rightarrow$ the modulus of a complex number can always be found by multiplying the number by its conjugate, since if $z = x + iy$, $zz^* = (x + iy)(x - iy) = x^2 + y^2 = |z|^2$.

◀ Argument, Complex number, Polar form ▶

MODULUS OF ELASTICITY

◀ Force ▶

MOMENT OF A FORCE

The moment of a **force** of magnitude P about an axis is equal to the product of the force and the perpendicular distance (h) of its line of action from the axis (moment = Ph). Most A-level questions on this topic are two-dimensional, in which case a moment is either clockwise or anticlockwise.

The theory of moments can be used to calculate reactions, as shown in the following example.

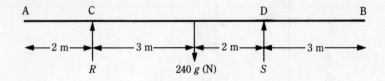

Fig. M.11

Worked example

A uniform beam AB of length 10 m and mass 240 kg is supported at points C, D where AC = 2 m and BD = 3 m (Fig. M.11). Calculate the vertical reaction at C, D.

Let the vertical reaction at C, D be R, S (N) respectively. Then, considering the vertical equilibrium of the beam,

$$R + S = 240g \tag{1}$$

Furthermore, taking moments about C (or rather an axis through C perpendicular to the beam and to R),

$$3 \times 240g = 5S$$

or

$$5S = 720g \tag{2}$$

It follows from (2) that

$$S = 144g$$

and thence from (1) that

$$R = 96g$$

MOMENT OF INERTIA

Consider first a number of discrete masses located at various points, as shown, for example, in Fig. M.12. Let a mass m_i be located at the point (x_i, y_i) $(i = 1, 2, \ldots n)$. Then,

Moment of inertia about x-axis $= \displaystyle\sum_{i=1}^{n} m_i y_i^2$

and

Moment of inertia about y-axis $= \displaystyle\sum_{i=1}^{n} m_i x_i^2$

Consider now a uniform lamina bounded by the curve $y = f(x)$, the ordinates $x = a$ and $x = b$ and the x-axis, as shown in Fig. M.13. Let the density of the lamina be ρ/unit area. Consider a thin strip as shown. Then,

2nd moment of strip about y-axis $= x^2 \cdot \rho y \delta x$

It follows that

Moment of intertia of lamina about y-axis $= \rho \int_a^b x^2 y \, dx$

Furthermore, assuming that the moment of inertia of a uniform rod of mass m and length l about an axis through an end perpendicular to the rod is $\frac{1}{3}ml^2$,

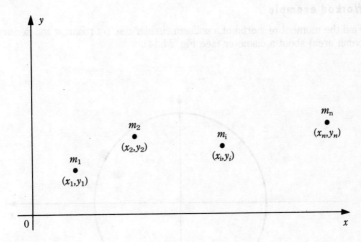

Fig. M.12

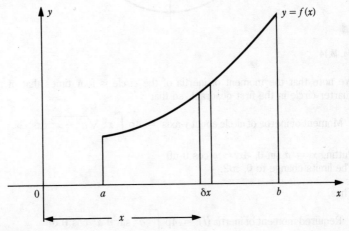

Fig. M.13

2nd moment of strip about x-axis $= \dfrac{1}{3}\rho y \delta x . y^2$

so that

Moment of inertia of lamina about x-axis $= \dfrac{1}{3}\rho \displaystyle\int_a^b y^3 \mathrm{d}x$

Worked example

Find the moment of inertia of a uniform circular disc (of radius a and density ρ/unit area) about a diameter (see Fig. M.14).

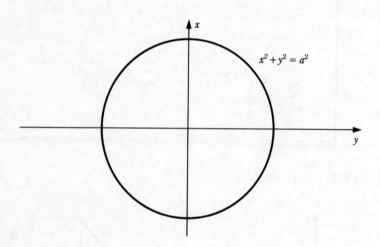

Fig. M.14

We note that the moment of inertia of the circle is four times that of the quarter-circle in the first quadrant, so that

Moment of inertia of circle about y-axis $= 4\rho \displaystyle\int_0^a x^2 \sqrt{a^2 - x^2}\ \mathrm{d}x$

Putting $x = a \sin \theta$, $\mathrm{d}x = a \cos \theta\ \mathrm{d}\theta$
The limits change to 0, $\pi/2$.

Thus,

Required moment of inertia $(I) = 4\rho \displaystyle\int_0^{\frac{\pi}{2}} a^2 \sin^2\theta\ a^2 \cos^2\theta\ \mathrm{d}\theta$

$$= 4\rho a^4 \int_0^{\frac{\pi}{2}} \sin^2\theta \, \cos^2\theta \, d\theta$$

$$= \rho a^4 \int_0^{\frac{\pi}{2}} \sin^2 2\theta d\theta$$

$$= \frac{\rho a^4}{2} \int_0^{\frac{\pi}{2}} (1 - \cos 4\theta) d\theta$$

$$= \frac{\rho a^4}{2} \left[\theta - \frac{1}{4} \sin 4\theta \right]_0^{\frac{\pi}{2}}$$

$$= \frac{\pi \rho a^4}{4}$$

If M denotes the mass of the circle,

$$M = \rho . \pi a^2$$

or $\rho = \dfrac{M}{\pi a^2}$

Thus,

$$\mathbf{I} = \frac{\pi a^4}{4} \cdot \frac{M}{\pi a^2} = \frac{1}{4} M a^2$$

There are two useful theorems which can be used to evaluate further moments of inertia.

▶ PARALLEL AXES THEOREM

If the moment of inertia of a body of mass M about an axis through the centre of mass is I, then the moment of inertia about a parallel axis distant h from the first is $I + Mh^2$.

▶ PERPENDICULAR AXES THEOREM

If the moments of inertia of a lamina about two perpendicular axes intersecting at O in its plane are I_x, I_y, then the moment of inertia about the axis through O perpendicular to the plane is $I_x + I_y$.

Worked examples using the two theorems

Find the moments of inertia of a circular disc of radius a and mass M about   i) a tangent in its plane; and   ii) an axis through its centre perpendicular to its plane.

i) Draw a diagram as in Fig. M.15. We have shown earlier that

Moment of inertia of disc about diameter $= \dfrac{1}{4} M a^2$

Thus, using the parallel axes theorem,

Moment of inertia of disc about tangent $= \dfrac{1}{4}Ma^2 + Ma^2$

$$= \dfrac{5}{4}Ma^2$$

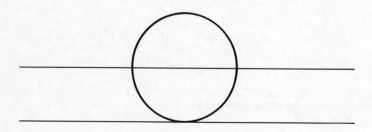

Fig. M.15

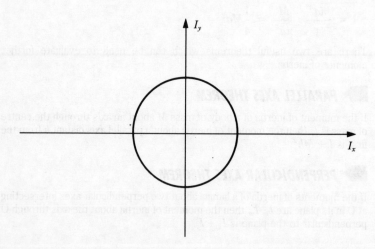

Fig. M.16

ii) Draw a diagram as in Fig. M.16. If I_x, I_y denote the moments of inertia about the two diameters shown, then

$$I_x = I_y = \dfrac{1}{4}Ma^2$$

Using the perpendicular axes theorem,
Moment of inertia of disc about perpendicular axis through centre

$$= \frac{1}{4}Ma^2 + \frac{1}{4}Ma^2$$

$$= \frac{1}{2}Ma^2$$

◄ Centre of mass ►

MOMENTUM

The momentum of a particle of mass m moving with velocity $\mathbf{v}$ is equal to $m\mathbf{v}$. It is a **vector**. The units of momentum are kgm/s. *Newton's Second Law* shows the connection between **force** and the change in momentum.

► CONSERVATION OF MOMENTUM

In a collision, momentum is *conserved*, that is, the total momentum after the collision is equal to the total momentum before the collision.

Worked example

Two particles P_1, P_2 of masses m_1, m_2 respectively moving in opposite directions in a straight line collide and stick together. Their speeds before collision are v_1, v_2 respectively. Calculate the speed of the combined particle. Deduce the condition for this speed to be zero (Fig. M.17).

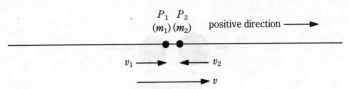

Fig. M.17

Let v denote the speed of the combined particle after the collision. Then,
Initial momentum $= m_2v_2 - m_1v_1$
Final momentum $= (m_1 + m_2)v$
Then, using conservation of momentum,
$(m_1 + m_2)v = m_2v_2 - m_1v_1$

Whence $\quad v = \dfrac{m_2v_2 - m_1v_1}{m_1 + m_2}$

Clearly $\quad v = 0$ if $m_2v_2 = m_1v_1$

► *IMPULSE AND MOMENTUM*

Consider two particles, A and B of mass m_A and m_B, moving initially with velocity $\mathbf{u}_A$ and $\mathbf{u}_B$. The particle A is acted on by an external force $\mathbf{F}_A$ and the particle B is acted on by an external force $\mathbf{F}_B$. In addition, there is a force of interaction between A and B, $\mathbf{T}$ on A and $-\mathbf{T}$ on B, according to Newton's third law. The final velocities of A and B are $\mathbf{v}_A$ and $\mathbf{v}_B$.

Using the impulse–momentum equation on each particle in turn we have for this system

$A:\ \int(\mathbf{F}_A + \mathbf{T})\mathrm{d}t\ =\ m_A\mathbf{v}_A - m_A\mathbf{u}_A$
$B:\ \int(\mathbf{F}_B - \mathbf{T})\mathrm{d}t\ =\ m_B\mathbf{v}_B - m_B\mathbf{u}_B$

By adding these equations we have

$$\int\mathbf{F}_A\mathrm{d}t + \int\mathbf{F}_B\mathrm{d}t\ =\ (m_A\mathbf{v}_A + m_B\mathbf{v}_B) - (m_A\mathbf{u}_A + m_B\mathbf{u}_B)$$

In words, this result shows that the sum of the impulses of the external forces on a pair of particles is equal to their total change in momentum. When no external forces are acting, we see that the total momentum remains unchanged. This important result is called *the principle of conservation of momentum* and it can clearly be extended to systems containing three or more particles. The total momentum in a given direction of all the bodies in a system is not changed by any interaction between them.

Worked example

Two particles, of mass $3m$ and $2m$, move in opposite directions in a straight line with speed $4u$ and $2u$ respectively. The particles collide and coalesce to form a single particle P of mass $5m$. Calculate the speed of P in terms of u.

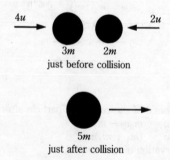

just before collision

just after collision

Fig. M.18

Fig. M.18 shows the situation just before and just after the collision in the sense shown.

By the conservation of momentum principle

$$12mu - 4mu = 5mv$$

$$v = \frac{8u}{5}$$

The speed of P after the collision is $\dfrac{8u}{5}$

◀ Coefficient of restitution, Impulse ▶

MONOMIAL

An algebraic expression consisting of only one term:

$$7x, \; 8x^2, \; 9ab, \; \frac{-2x}{\sqrt{y}}$$

MUTUALLY EXCLUSIVE EVENTS

The events A, B are mutually exclusive if $A \cap B = \phi$, the null event. This means that they cannot occur together.

NATURAL LOGARITHMS

◀ e, Logarithm ▶

NEWTON–RAPHSON FORMULA

◀ Newton's method ▶

NEWTON'S EXPERIMENTAL LAW

This states that, when two bodies collide, the relative velocity in the direction of the impact after the impact is equal to $-e$ times the relative velocity before the impact, where e is a constant between 0 and 1 called the **coefficient of restitution**.

The collision is called *inelastic* if $e = 0$, in which case the bodies stick together on impact.

◀ Coefficient of restitution, Impact, Impulse, Momentum ▶

NEWTON'S LAWS OF MOTION

First law Every body will remain at rest or continue to move in a straight line at constant speed unless acted on by an external force.

Second law The rate of change of momentum of a moving body is proportional to the external force acting on it, and is in the direction of that force.

Third law Action and reaction are equal and opposite – that is, when two bodies are in contact, the force exerted by one on the other is minus the force exerted by the other on the first.

The second law in mathematical form states, in the usual notation, that

$$\frac{\mathrm{d}}{\mathrm{d}t}(mv) \propto F$$

If m is constant, then

$$\frac{\mathrm{d}}{\mathrm{d}t}(mv) = m\frac{\mathrm{d}v}{\mathrm{d}t}$$

and $\quad m\dfrac{\mathrm{d}v}{\mathrm{d}t} \propto F$

or $\quad F = kma$

where k is a constant of proportionality and $a = $ acceleration.

The unit of force (1 Newton) is chosen so that $F = 1$ when $m = 1$ (kg) and $a = 1$ (ms^{-2}). Thus,

$F = ma$

◀ Coefficient of restitution, Impact, Impulse, Momentum ▶

NEWTON'S METHOD (NEWTON–RAPHSON METHOD)

Newton's method for solving the equation
$f(x) = 0$
is an iterative method based on the following result. If α is a sufficiently close approximation to a root of the equation
$f(x) = 0$
then a closer approximation β is, in general, given by

$$\beta = \alpha - \frac{f(\alpha)}{f'(\alpha)}$$

This result can be illustrated as shown in Fig. N.1.

Let P be the point $(\alpha, f(\alpha))$. Then the gradient of the tangent at P to the curve $y = f(x)$ is $f'(\alpha)$, that is $\tan \theta = f'(\alpha)$. Referring to the figure,

$$\tan \theta = \frac{\mathrm{PA}}{\mathrm{BA}}$$

whence

$$\mathrm{BA} = \frac{\mathrm{PA}}{\tan \theta} = \frac{f(\alpha)}{f'(\alpha)}$$

Now the true value of the root of $f(x) = 0$ is the x value corresponding to C. Fig. N.1 shows that B (with x value β) is closer to C than A (with value α). Thus

$$\beta = \alpha - \mathrm{BA} = \alpha - \frac{f(\alpha)}{f'(\alpha)}$$

is closer to the root than α.

This leads to the iterative formula

$$x_{n+1} = x_n - \frac{f(x_n)}{f'(x_n)}$$

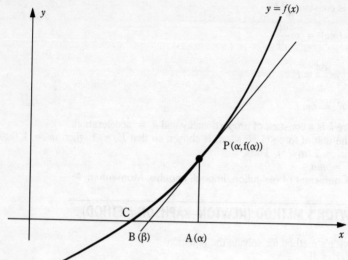

Fig. N.1

with x_0 a suitable chosen initial approximation.

Consider, for example, the equation

$$\sin x = \frac{1}{2}x$$

which has a root in the vicinity of $\frac{2\pi}{3}$. We rewrite the equation in the form

$$f(x) = 2 \sin x - x = 0$$

so that

$$f'(x) = 2 \cos x - 1$$

The appropriate iterative formula is therefore

$$x_{n+1} = x_n - \left(\frac{2 \sin x_n - x_n}{2 \cos x_n - 1} \right)$$

with $x_0 = \frac{2\pi}{3}$. We find using a calculator that

$$x_1 = 1 \cdot 913222955$$
$$x_2 = 1 \cdot 895671752$$
$$x_3 = 1 \cdot 895494285$$
$$x_4 = 1 \cdot 895494267$$

It is clear from these successive approximations that, for example, the value of the root is $1 \cdot 8955$ correct to four decimal places.

NON-UNIFORM CIRCULAR MOTION

A few syllabuses require students to extend their work on uniform circular motion to consider cases where the speed v varies. The motion of a particle moving in a vertical circle under gravity is a typical case.

The formulae derived for uniform circular motion require amendment in these cases to the following. At a particular instant for speed v we have:

Velocity of particle is of magnitude v directed along the tangent to the circle.

Acceleration of particle has components:

$\dfrac{dv}{dt}$ directed along the tangent to the circle

$\dfrac{v^2}{a}$ directed towards the centre O of the circle

At this instant also, $v = aw$, but it must be appreciated that w is now the angular speed at this instant only.

Worked example

A particle moves in a circular path, centre O and radius 2m, starting with angular speed 10 rad s^{-1} at time $t = 0$. At time ts, the angular speed w of the particle is $(10 - 2t) \text{ rad s}^{-1}$. Calculate, at the instant when $t = 3$

a) the linear speed of the particle
b) the resultant acceleration of the particle

At the instant when $t = 3$

a) Angular speed $= 4 \text{ rad s}^{-1}$
   So linear speed $= aw = 2 \times 4\text{ms}^{-1} = 8\text{ms}^{-1}$

b) Acceleration component along tangent $= \dfrac{dv}{dt}$

$$= a\frac{dw}{dt}$$

$$= 2 \times (-2)\text{ms}^{-2}$$
$$= -4\text{ms}^{-2}$$

Acceleration component directed towards centre
$$= \frac{v^2}{a} = \frac{8^2}{2} = 32\text{ms}^{-2}$$

Resultant acceleration of magnitude $\sqrt{4^2 + 32^2}\text{ms}^{-2}$
$$\approx 32{\cdot}25\text{ms}^{-2}$$

At this instant the direction of the acceleration is $\arctan\left(\dfrac{4}{32}\right)$ with the

radius of the circle, which is $7\cdot1°$ approximately.

◀ Circular motion ▶

NORMAL

The normal to a curve at a point P on the curve is a straight line through P perpendicular to the tangent to the curve at P. This is shown diagrammatically in Fig. N.2. The following example shows how to find the equation of a normal.

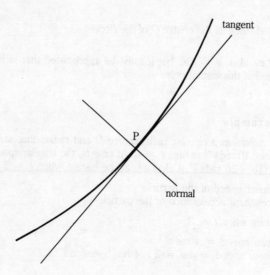

Fig. N.2

Worked example

Find the equation of the normal to the parabola $y^2 = 4x$ at the point $(4, 4)$.

Since $y^2 = 4x$ it follows, differentiating with respect to x, that

$$2y\,\frac{dy}{dx} = 4$$

So that $\dfrac{dy}{dx} = \dfrac{4}{2y} = \dfrac{1}{2}$

where $y = 4$.

The gradient of the tangent at the point $(4, 4)$ is therefore $\frac{1}{2}$ so that the gradient of the normal is $-1/\frac{1}{2} = -2$. Its equation is therefore

$$y - 4 = -2(x - 4)$$

or $\quad y = -2x + 12$

NORMAL DISTRIBUTION

The continuous random variable X has the normal distribution with parameters μ, σ^2 (abbreviated to N(μ, σ^2)), if its probability density function is given by

$$f(x) = \frac{1}{\sigma\sqrt{2\pi}} e^{-\frac{(x-\mu)^2}{2\sigma^2}} \quad \text{all } x$$

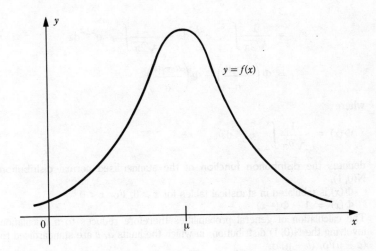

Fig. N.3

The graph of $f(x)$ is as shown in Fig. N.3. The mean and variance are given by

$$E(X) = \mu; \quad \text{Var}(X) = \sigma^2$$

To evaluate normal probabilities, consider

$$P(a < X < b) = \int_a^b f(x)\mathrm{d}x$$

$$= \frac{1}{\sigma\sqrt{2\pi}} \int_a^b e^{-\frac{(x-\mu)^2}{2\sigma^2}} \, \mathrm{d}x$$

This integral cannot be evaluated analytically. We therefore put

$$z = \frac{(x - \mu)}{\sigma}$$

so that $\quad dz = \dfrac{dx}{\sigma}$

The limits become $\dfrac{(b - \mu)}{\sigma}$ and $\dfrac{(a - \mu)}{\sigma}$ so that

$$P(a < X < b) = \frac{1}{\sigma\sqrt{2\pi}} \int_{\frac{(a-\mu)}{\sigma}}^{\frac{(b-\mu)}{\sigma}} e^{-\frac{1}{2}z^2} \sigma dz$$

$$= \frac{1}{\sqrt{2\pi}} \int_{\frac{(a-\mu)}{\sigma}}^{\frac{(b-\mu)}{\sigma}} e^{-\frac{1}{2}z^2} dz$$

$$= \frac{1}{\sqrt{2\pi}} \int_{-\infty}^{\frac{(b-\mu)}{\sigma}} e^{-\frac{1}{2}z^2} dz - \frac{1}{\sqrt{2\pi}} \int_{-\infty}^{\frac{(a-\mu)}{\sigma}} e^{-\frac{1}{2}z^2} dz$$

$$= \Phi\left(\frac{b - \mu}{\sigma}\right) - \Phi\left(\frac{a - \mu}{\sigma}\right)$$

where

$$\Phi(x) = \frac{1}{\sqrt{2\pi}} \int_{-\infty}^{x} e^{-\frac{1}{2}z^2} dz$$

denotes the **distribution function** of the standardised normal distribution N(0, 1).

$\Phi(x)$ is tabulated in statistical tables for $x \geqslant 0$. For $x < 0$,

$\Phi(x) = 1 - \Phi(-x)$

The calculation of general probabilities therefore reduces to a calculation involving the N(0, 1) distribution, in which the limits a, b are standardised to $(a - \mu)/\sigma$, $(b - \mu)/\sigma$.

Worked example

The wingspans of a certain bird species have the normal distribution N(1·2, 0·2²), where measurements are in metres. Calculate the probability that the wingspan of a randomly chosen bird of the species lies between 1·0 m and 1·5 m.

We require

$$P(1·0 < X < 1·5) = \Phi\left(\frac{1·5 - 1·2}{0·2}\right) - \Phi\left(\frac{1·0 - 1·2}{0·2}\right)$$

$$= \Phi(1\cdot5) - \Phi(-1)$$
$$= \Phi(1\cdot5) - [1 - \Phi(1)]$$
$$= 0\cdot93319 - 1 + 0\cdot84134$$
$$\approx 0\cdot7745$$

▶ ADDITIVE PROPERTY

Let X_1, X_2 be independent random variables such that
  X_1 is $N(\mu_1, \sigma_1^2)$ and X_2 is $N(\mu_2, \sigma_2^2)$
Then,
  $X_1 + X_2$ is $N(\mu_1 + \mu_2, \sigma_1^2 + \sigma_2^2)$
  This result generalises as follows. Let X_1, X_2, ... X_n be independent random variables such that X_i is $N(\mu_i, \sigma_i^2)$. Then,

$$\sum_{i=1}^{n} a_i X_i \text{ is } N\left(\sum_{i=1}^{n} a_i \mu_i, \ \sum_{i=1}^{n} a_i^2 \sigma_i^2 \right)$$

where a_1, a_2, ... a_n are constants.
◀ Binomial distribution (Normal approximation) ▶

NULL HYPOTHESIS

◀ Hypothesis ▶

ODD FUNCTION

$f(x)$ is an odd function if, for all x
$$f(x) = -f(x)$$
For example,
$$f(x) = \sin x$$
is an odd function since
$$f(-x) = \sin (-x)$$
$$= -\sin x$$
$$= -f(x)$$
However,
$$f(x) = 1 + \sin x$$
is *not* an odd function since
$$f(-x) = 1 + \sin (-x)$$
$$= 1 - \sin (x)$$
$$\neq -f(x)$$

PAASCHE INDEX

◀ Index numbers ▶

PARABOLA

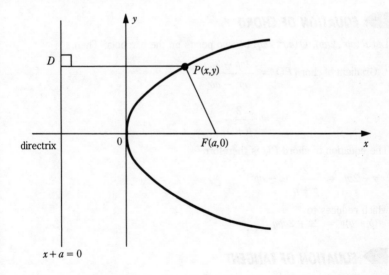

Fig. P.1

A parabola is the locus of a point which moves in such a way that its distance from a fixed point (the focus) is equal to its distance from a fixed line (the directrix). The standard equation of the parabola can be derived by taking the coordinates of the focus as $(a, 0)$ and the equation of the directrix as $x + a = 0$ (Fig. P.1).

If $P(x, y)$ is any point on the parabola, then
$$PF = \sqrt{(x-a)^2 + y^2}$$
If D denotes the foot of the perpendicular from P to the directrix, then
$$PD = x + a$$
Since $PF = PD$, it follows that
$$\sqrt{(x-a)^2 + y^2} = x + a$$
or, squaring
$$(x-a)^2 + y^2 = (x+a)^2$$
$$x^2 - 2ax + a^2 + y^2 = x^2 + 2ax + a^2$$
which reduces to
$$y^2 = 4ax$$
which is the standard equation of the parabola.

▶ PARAMETRIC FORM

The point $P(ap^2, 2ap)$ lies on the parabola, since
$$(2ap)^2 = 4a(ap^2)$$
for all p.

▶ EQUATION OF CHORD

Let $P(ap^2, 2ap)$, $Q(aq^2, 2aq)$ be two points on the parabola. Then,

$$\text{Gradient of chord } PQ = \frac{2ap - 2aq}{ap^2 - aq^2}$$

$$= \frac{2}{p + q}$$

The equation of chord PQ is therefore

$$y - 2ap = \frac{2}{p + q}(x - ap^2)$$

which reduces to
$$(p + q)y = 2x + 2apq$$

▶ EQUATION OF TANGENT

The equation of the tangent at $P(ap^2, 2ap)$ can be found by letting $Q \to P$, which is to say putting $q = p$ in the above equation. This gives
$$py = x + ap^2$$
The equation of the tangent at P can be found using calculus in the following way
$$x = ap^2; \qquad y = 2ap$$
$$\frac{dx}{dp} = 2ap; \qquad \frac{dy}{dp} = 2a$$

Thus, the gradient of the tangent at P is given by

$$\frac{dy}{dx} = \frac{dy}{dp} \Big/ \frac{dx}{dp}$$

$$= 2a/2ap$$

$$= \frac{1}{p}$$

The equation of the tangent at P is therefore

$$y - 2ap = \frac{1}{p}(x - ap^2)$$

that is, $py = x + ap^2$

▶ *EQUATION OF NORMAL*

The gradient of the normal at $P(ap^2,\ 2ap)$ is given by

$$-1 \Big/ \frac{dy}{dx} = -p$$

The equation of the normal at P is therefore

$$y - 2ap = -p(x - ap^2)$$

or

$$y + px = ap(p^2 + 2)$$

PARALLEL AXES THEOREM

◀ Moment of inertia ▶

PARALLEL FORCES

The concept of **moments** is used to determine the line of action of the **resultant** of two or more parallel **forces**. When two forces act in the same direction, the magnitude of the resultant is equal to the sum of the magnitudes of the forces.

Fig. P.2 shows two parallel forces, of magnitudes P and Q, acting through points A and B, where AB is perpendicular to the lines of action of the forces. The **resultant** of these forces has magnitude R, where $R = P + Q$, and is parallel to the lines of action of the forces and acts through the point C in AB such that

$$\complement C \Rightarrow Q.CB - P.AC = 0 \tag{1}$$

(where $\complement C$ is shorthand for 'moments about C')

$$\Rightarrow \frac{AC}{CB} = \frac{Q}{P}$$

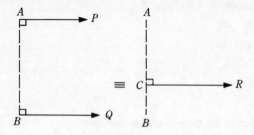

Fig. P.2

and $AC = \left(\dfrac{Q}{P + Q} \right) AB$ and $CB = \left(\dfrac{P}{P + Q} \right) AB$

Note that in (1), we have used a very important result which is worth stating generally – *the sum of the moments of any system of forces about a point on the line of action of the resultant of the system is zero.*

When the two forces of magnitudes P and Q, where $P > Q$, act in parallel lines in opposite directions, their resultant is of magnitude $P - Q$ and the line of action of this resultant is parallel to the line of action of the force of magnitude P (see Fig. P.3).

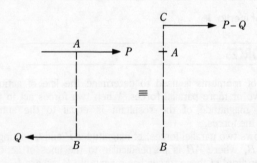

Fig. P.3

When two unlike parallel forces are *equal in magnitude*, their effect is one of *turning only* and this combination of the two forces is called a **couple**. A couple is irreducible and cannot be replaced by any system which is simpler.

PARALLELOGRAM

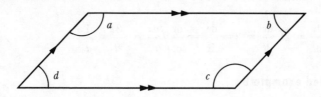

Fig. P.4

A parallelogram (Fig. P.4) has four sides, and the opposite sides are of equal length. The opposite sides are also parallel. In a paralellogram any two angles *next to each other* will always add up to 180°.
For example, $a + b = b + c = c + d = d + a = 180°$.
Also, the angles *opposite each other* will be equal. For example, $a = c$, $b = d$.

The *area* of a parallelogram is found by multiplying the base length by the perpendicular height. In order to find the area of parallelograms you often need to use trigonometry.
◀ Plane shape, Trigonometric equation, Trigonometric function,
Trigonometric identity ▶

PARAMETER

◀ Parametric equations ▶

PARAMETRIC EQUATIONS

It is often more convenient to express a relation between two variables, x and y say, by introducing a third independent variable, t, say. For example, the equation $y^2 = 4x$ can be replaced by the equations $x = t^2$, $y = 2t$, since whatever the value of t, the equations $x = t^2$, $y = 2t$ satisfy the relationship $y^2 = 4x$. The equations $x = t^2$, $y = 2t$ are referred to as parametric equations, the independent variable t as the parameter.

▶ DERIVATIVES OF PARAMETRIC FUNCTIONS

The derivatives of functions given parametrically are obtained by use of the chain rule, thus:
$$\frac{dy}{dx} = \frac{dy}{dt} \cdot \frac{dt}{dx} = \frac{dy}{dt} \bigg/ \frac{dx}{dx}$$

Worked example A

Find $\dfrac{dy}{dx}$ when $x = t^2$, $y = 2t$

$$\Rightarrow \frac{dx}{dt} = 2t, \frac{dy}{dt} = 2 \Rightarrow \frac{dy}{dx} = \frac{dy}{dt} \bigg/ \frac{dx}{dt} = \frac{2}{2t} = \frac{1}{t}$$

Worked example B

Given that $x = 3 \cos \theta - \cos 3\theta$, $y = 3 \sin \theta - \sin 3\theta$, show that $\dfrac{dy}{dx} = \tan 2\theta$

$$\frac{dx}{d\theta} = -3 \sin \theta + 3 \sin 3\theta, \quad \frac{dy}{d\theta} = 3 \cos \theta - 3 \cos 3\theta$$

$$\frac{dy}{d\theta} = \frac{dy}{d\theta} \bigg/ \frac{dx}{d\theta} = \frac{3(\cos \theta - \cos 3\theta)}{3(\sin 3\theta - \sin \theta)} = \frac{2 \sin 2\theta \sin \theta}{2 \cos 2\theta \sin \theta} = \tan 2\theta$$

Second and higher derivatives of functions given parametrically can be obtained once the first derivative has been found. Care must be taken, however, to ensure that the chain rule is applied correctly.

Worked example C

Given that $x = 3 \cos \theta - \cos 3\theta$, $y = 3 \sin \theta - \sin 3\theta$ show that

$$\frac{d^2y}{dx^2} = \frac{1}{3 \cos^3 2\theta \sin \theta}$$

Using the result of worked example B we found

$$\frac{dx}{d\theta} = 3(\sin 3\theta - \sin \theta) \text{ and } \frac{dy}{dx} = \tan 2\theta$$

Hence $\dfrac{d}{dx}\left(\dfrac{dy}{dx}\right) = \dfrac{d}{dx}(\tan 2\theta) \Rightarrow \dfrac{d^2y}{dx^2} = \dfrac{d\theta}{dx} \cdot \dfrac{d}{d\theta}\left(\tan 2\theta\right)$

$$\Rightarrow \frac{d^2y}{dx^2} = \frac{1}{3(\sin 3\theta - \sin \theta)} \cdot 2 \sec^2 2\theta = \frac{1}{6 \cos 2\theta \sin \theta} \cdot \frac{2}{\cos^2 2\theta}$$

$$= \frac{1}{3 \cos^3 2\theta \sin \theta}$$

Warning: do not fall into the trap that many students fall into. Namely '$\dfrac{d^2y}{dx^2} = \dfrac{d^2y}{d\theta^2}\bigg/\dfrac{d^2x}{d\theta^2}$'. This is *not* a correct application of the chain rule.

◀ Curve sketching, Derivative ▶

PARTIAL FRACTIONS

Let $P(x)$, $Q(x)$ be **polynomials** such that the degree of $P(x)$ is less than the degree of $Q(x)$. Then the method of partial fractions enables the ratio $P(x)/Q(x)$ to be expressed in a form more suitable for differentiation and integration. If the degree of $P(x)$ is not less than the degree of $Q(x)$, then long division must precede the method of partial fractions. The method involves factorising the denominator, preferably into linear terms.

Then, *linear factors* such as $(x + a)$ lead to terms like $\dfrac{A}{x + a}$

Repeated factors such as $(x + a)^2$ lead to terms like $\dfrac{A}{x + a} + \dfrac{B}{(x + a)^2}$

Quadratic factors such as $(x^2 + ax + b)$ lead to terms like $\dfrac{Ax + B}{x^2 + ax + b}$

The method involves expressing $P(x)/Q(x)$ as a sum of appropriate terms including unknown constants such as A, B above. These are then found using algebraic methods.

Worked example A

Express $\dfrac{x}{x^2 - 3x + 2}$

in partial fractions.

We note first that the degree of the numerator is less than the degree of the denominator. We can therefore find partial fractions immediately. We also note that
$$x^2 - 3x + 2 = (x - 1)(x - 2)$$

We therefore put

$$\frac{x}{x^2 - 3x + 2} \equiv \frac{A}{x - 1} + \frac{B}{x - 2} = \frac{A(x - 2) + B(x - 1)}{x^2 - 3x + 2}$$

Equating numerators, it follows that
$$x \equiv A(x - 2) + B(x - 1)$$

There are now two standard methods to proceed:

    i) select appropriate values of x to remove one of the unknown constants;
    ii) equate coefficients of like terms on both sides of the equation.

Using method i), we put $x = 1$. This gives
$$A = -1$$
Putting $x = 2$,
$$B = 2$$

Using method ii), we obtain
$$x \equiv (A + B)x - (2A + B)$$
Equating coefficients of like terms,
$$A + B = 1$$
$$2A + B = 0$$
Solving these equations,
$$A = -1 \text{ and } B = 2$$
We therefore conclude that

$$\frac{x}{x^2 - 3x + 2} \equiv \frac{-1}{x - 1} + \frac{2}{x - 2}$$

It is clear from this example that method i) is quicker than method ii) and should be used where possible. In more complex cases, however, it may be necessary to use both methods to solve the problem. Worked examples B and C illustrate this point.

Worked example B

Express $\dfrac{x + 2}{(x - 1)(x^2 + x + 1)}$

in partial fractions.

We let

$$\frac{x + 2}{(x - 1)(x^2 + x + 1)} \equiv \frac{A}{x - 1} + \frac{Bx + C}{x^2 + x + 1}$$

$$= \frac{A(x^2 + x + 1) + (Bx + C)(x - 1)}{(x - 1)(x^2 + x + 1)}$$

Thus,
$$x + 2 \equiv A(x^2 + x + 1) + (Bx + C)(x - 1)$$
Putting $x = 1$,
$$3 = 3A \text{ and } A = 1$$
The constants B, C can be found by equating coefficients. Consider, putting $A = 1$,
$$A(x^2 + x + 1) + (Bx + C)(x - 1) = x^2 + x + 1 + Bx^2 - Bx + Cx - C$$
$$= (1 + B)x^2 + (1 - B + C)x + 1 - C$$
so that
$$x + 2 \equiv (1 + B)x^2 + (1 - B + C)x + 1 - C$$
Equating coefficients of x^2 and the constant terms,
$$1 + B = 0 \text{ whence } B = -1$$
and
$$2 = 1 - C \text{ whence } C = -1$$
Thus,

$$\frac{x + 2}{(x - 1)(x^2 + x + 1)} \equiv \frac{1}{x - 1} - \frac{(x + 1)}{x^2 + x + 1}$$

Worked example C

Simplify $\dfrac{x^4 + x^3 - 3x^2 - x + 6}{x^3 - x^2 - x + 1}$

We note that a) the denominator can be factorised as follows:
$$x^3 - x^2 - x + 1 = x^2(x - 1) - (x - 1)$$
$$(x^2 - 1)(x - 1)$$
$$(x - 1)^2(x + 1)$$

b) the degree of the numerator exceeds the degree of the denominator, so that we must first carry out a long division. Consider

$$
\begin{array}{r}
x + 2 \\
x^3 - x^2 - x + 1 \overline{)x^4 + x^3 - 3x^2 - x + 6} \\
x^4 - x^3 - x^2 + x \\
\hline
2x^3 - 2x^2 - 2x + 6 \\
2x^3 - 2x^2 - 2x + 2 \\
\hline
4
\end{array}
$$

Thus,

$$\frac{x^4 + x^3 - 3x^2 - x + 3}{x^3 - x^2 - x + 1} \equiv x + 2 + \frac{4}{(x - 1)^2(x + 1)}$$

We now put

$$\frac{4}{(x - 1)^2(x + 1)} \equiv \frac{A}{x - 1} + \frac{B}{(x - 1)^2} + \frac{C}{x + 1}$$

$$= \frac{A(x - 1)(x + 1) + B(x + 1) + C(x - 1)^2}{(x - 1)^2(x + 1)}$$

whence
$$4 \equiv A(x - 1)(x + 1) + B(x + 1) + C(x - 1)^2$$

Putting $x = 1$,
$$4 = 2B \text{ whence } B = 2.$$

The constants A, C can be found by equating coefficients. Consider, putting $B = 2$,
$$A(x - 1)(x + 1) + 2(x + 1) + C(x - 1)^2$$
$$= A(x^2 - 1) + 2x + 2 + C(x^2 - 2x + 1)$$
$$= (A + C)x^2 + (2 - 2C)x + 2 - A + C$$

so that
$$4 \equiv (A + C)x^2 + (2 - 2C)x + 2 - A + C$$

Equating coefficients of x,
$$0 = 2 - 2C \text{ whence } C = 1$$

Equating coefficients of x^2,
$$A + C = 0 \text{ whence } A = -C = -1$$

Thus,

$$\frac{x^4 + x^3 - 3x^2 - x + 4}{x^3 - x^2 - x + 1} \equiv x + 2 - \frac{1}{x-1} + \frac{2}{(x-1)^2} + \frac{1}{x+1}$$

PARTS (INTEGRATION BY)

The **product rule** for differentiation states that if u, v are **functions** of x, then

$$\frac{\mathrm{d}}{\mathrm{d}x}(uv) = u\frac{\mathrm{d}v}{\mathrm{d}x} + v\frac{\mathrm{d}u}{\mathrm{d}x}$$

Integrating this equation,

$$uv = \int u\frac{\mathrm{d}v}{\mathrm{d}x}\mathrm{d}x + \int v\frac{\mathrm{d}u}{\mathrm{d}x}\mathrm{d}x$$

or

$$\int u\frac{\mathrm{d}v}{\mathrm{d}x}\mathrm{d}x = uv - \int v\frac{\mathrm{d}u}{\mathrm{d}x}\mathrm{d}x \tag{1}$$

An alternative form is $\displaystyle\int u\,\mathrm{d}v = uv - \int v\,\mathrm{d}u$ \hfill (2)

Equations (1) and (2) give the formula for integration by parts. The following examples show how this result can be used.

Worked example A

Integrate $\int \log_e x \, \mathrm{d}x$

We put $u = \log_e x$ and $v = x$.
Thus,

$$\int \log_e x \, \mathrm{d}x = x \log_e x - \int x \frac{\mathrm{d}}{\mathrm{d}x}(\log_e x)\mathrm{d}x$$

$$= x \log_e x - \int x . \frac{1}{x}\mathrm{d}x$$

$$= x \log_e x - \int \mathrm{d}x$$

$$= x \log_e x - x$$

Worked example B

Integrate $\int x \cos x \, \mathrm{d}x$

We put $u = x$ and $\dfrac{dv}{dx} = \cos x$ or $v = \sin x$

Thus,

$$\int x \cos x \, dx = x \sin x - \int \sin x \, dx$$
$$= x \sin x + \cos x$$

PASCAL'S TRIANGLE

Pascal's triangle is a particular triangular array of numbers, as follows:

										Row sum
1st row				1			=	1		= 2^0
2nd row			1		1		=	2		= 2^1
3rd row		1		2		1		=	4	= 2^2
4th row	1		3		3		1	=	8	= 2^3
5th row	1	4		6		4	1	=	16	= 2^4

Try to write down a) the 6th row and row sum, b) the 11th row sum.

You should be able to see how the pattern builds itself down to give the 6th row as $1 + 5 + 10 + 10 + 5 + 1$, with a row sum of $32 = 2^5$.

Look at the number of the row and the row sum, and you should see that the row sum of the nth row is 2^{n-1}. Hence the row sum of the 11th row will be 2^{11-1} which is 2^{10}. Now, 2^{10} is $2^5 \times 2^5$ which will be 32×32 which is 1024, that is, the row sum will be $1024 = 2^{10}$.

Also, looking diagonally down the columns you will see the triangle numbers as well as some polyhedron numbers.

PENDULUM (SIMPLE)

A simple pendulum is a length of string, fixed at one end (O) having a mass (m) attached to the other end. Suppose the pendulum is pulled to one side and released. Consider the situation when the string makes an angle θ with the vertical – see Fig. P.5.

Resolving perpendicular to the string, in the direction of increasing θ,

Acceleration of mass $= l\ddot{\theta}$

Component of force $= -mg \sin \theta$

where l denotes the length of the pendulum.

Thus, using **Newton's third law**,

$$-mg \sin \theta = ml\ddot{\theta}$$

or $\quad \ddot{\theta} = -\dfrac{g \sin \theta}{l} \approx -\dfrac{g\theta}{l}$

if θ is small.

This is the **simple harmonic motion** equation with (in the usual notation),

$$w^2 = \frac{g}{l}$$

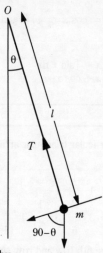

Fig. P.5

The period T is therefore given by

$$T = \frac{2\pi}{w} = 2\pi\sqrt{\frac{l}{g}}$$

PERMUTATION

A permutation of r objects from n is a selection of r of the objects in which the order of selection is taken into account. The number of permutations of r objects from n is denoted by ^nP_r and

$$^nP_r = n(n-1)\ldots(n-r+1) = \frac{n!}{(n-r)!}$$

where $n!$ (n factorial) is defined by

$$n! = n(n-1)\ldots 2.1$$

For example, the number of permutations of 3 letters from the 5 letters A, B, C, D, E is given by

$$^5P_3 = 5 \times 4 \times 3 = 60$$

The ten **combinations** of the 3 letters are

ABC, ABD, ABE, ACD, ACE, ADE, BCD, BCE, BDE, CDE

Each combination corresponds to 6 permutations – for instance, ABC corresponds to

ABC, ACB, BAC, BCA, CAB, CBA

Worked example

How many four-digit numbers can be made from the set 1, 2, 3, 4, 5 when

  i) no integer is used more than once
  ii) an integer can be used any number of times?

i) $^5P_4 = \dfrac{5!}{(5-4)!} = 5! = 120$

ii) $5^4 = 625$,

because any of the 5 numbers can now fill each place

◀ Combination ▶

PERPENDICULAR AXES THEOREM

◀ Moment of inertia ▶

PI (π)

Pi is the ratio found when you divide the **circumference** of a circle by its **diameter**. Its presence has been known for a long time. However, its accuracy has troubled many mathematicians throughout history in that it is an **irrational number** and as such we cannot state it exactly.

Your calculator holds the value of pi to as accurate a level as you will need, and you are advised always to use the *calculator value* of pi whenever you need to use pi.

Examination questions will accept the use of **rounded-off** values of pi, such as 3·14 or 3·142. When using any value of pi, do remember to round off to a suitable degree of accuracy.

Pi is particularly used in the following formulae:

Circumference of circle $= \pi \times$ diameter of the circle
Area of circle $= \pi \times$ square of the radius of the circle

◀ Circle ▶

PIE CHART

A pie chart is a circular picture which is divided into the ratio of the frequencies of the different events occuring. Fig. P.6 is a pie chart, so called since it has the appearance of a pie. This pie chart illustrates the transport used by pupils of High Storres School one day. The actual information is difficult to read accurately, but it does show us that the vast majority of pupils at the school come by bus.

You are quite likely to be asked in an examination question to extract information from a pie chart.

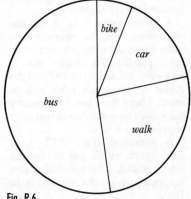

Fig. P.6

PLANE SHAPE

A plane shape is one that is two-dimensional; that is, it will have width and height, but no depth.

An *isosceles triangle* (Fig. P.7), has two of its sides the same length and two angles the same. It will have a line of symmetry bisecting the angle included between the two equal sides.

An *equilateral triangle* (Fig. P.8) has all its three sides the same length and all its angles are 60°. Each angle bisector will bisect the opposite side and be a line of symmetry. It has rotational symmetry of order three.

A *right-angled triangle* (Fig. P.9) contains a right-angle.

A *square* (Fig. P.10) has all four sides equal in length and each angle is 90°. It has four lines of symmetry, namely the two line bisectors and the two angle bisectors. It also has rotational symmetry of order four.

A *kite* (Fig. P.11) is recognisable as a kite shape. It has four sides as shown; the top two sides are the same length and the bottom two sides are the same length. There is one line of symmetry, namely the line that bisects both angles included between the equal sides.

A *parallelogram* (Fig. P.12) has four sides, and the opposite two sides are equal in length as well as being parallel. The angles *next to each other* will add up to 180° and the angles *opposite each other will be equal.* There is no line of symmetry but it does have rotational symmetry of order two.

A *trapezium* (Fig. P.13) is a quadrilateral with a pair of opposite sides parallel. The pairs of angles between each parallel side add up to 180°.

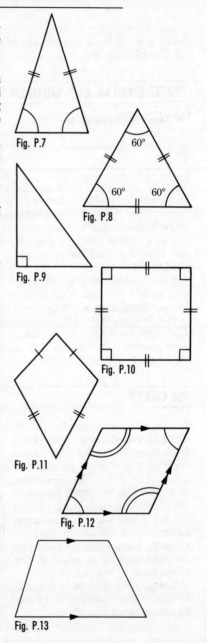

Fig. P.7

Fig. P.8

Fig. P.9

Fig. P.10

Fig. P.11

Fig. P.12

Fig. P.13

A *rhombus* (Fig. P.14) is a parallelogram that has all its sides the same length. Its diagonals are perpendicular, and bisect each other. There are two lines of symmetry, namely the angle bisectors. It has rotational symmetry of order two.

◄ Symmetry ►

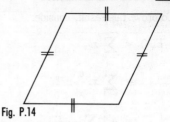

Fig. P.14

POISSON APPROXIMATION

◄ Binomial distribution ►

POISSON DISTRIBUTION

The random variable X has the Poisson distribution if its probability function is

$$p_x = P(X = x) = \frac{\mu^x}{x!} e^{-\mu} \qquad (x = 0, 1, 2, \dots)$$

where μ is a positive constant. A common notation for this distribution is $P_0(\mu)$.

This distribution arises in practice either as an approximation to the binomial distribution or in its own right; for instance, the number of emissions from a radioactive source in a fixed time satisfies a Poisson distribution.

It can be shown by division that

$$\frac{p_{x+1}}{p_x} = \frac{\mu}{(x+1)}$$

or $\quad p_{x+1} = \frac{\mu}{(x+1)} p_x$

This result can be used for the calculation of successive Poisson probabilities.

Many statistical tables include a table of Poisson probabilities. The quantity usually tabulated is

$$F(x, \mu) = \sum_{y=0}^{x} \frac{\mu^y}{y!} e^{-\mu} = P(X \leq x \,|\, X \text{ is } P_0(\mu))$$

Single probabilities can be found using the result
$$P(X = x \,|\, X \text{ is } P_0(\mu)) = F(x, \mu) - F(x - 1, \mu)$$

▶ MEAN AND VARIANCE OF POISSON DISTRIBUTION

The standard results are
$$E(X) = \mu \text{ and } Var(X) = \mu$$

To prove this result, consider

$$E(X) = \sum_{x=0}^{\infty} x p_x$$

$$= \sum_{x=1}^{\infty} x . \frac{\mu^x}{x!} e^{-\mu}$$

$$= e^{-\mu} \sum_{x=1}^{\infty} \frac{\mu^x}{(x-1)!}$$

$$= \mu e^{-\mu} \sum_{y=0}^{\infty} \frac{\mu^y}{y!} \qquad \text{(putting } y = x - 1\text{)}$$

$$= \mu e^{-\mu} e^{\mu}$$

$$= \mu$$

Furthermore, consider

$$E[X(X-1)] = \sum_{x=0}^{\infty} x(x-1) p_x$$

$$= \sum_{x=2}^{\infty} x(x-1) . \frac{\mu^x}{x!} e^{-\mu}$$

$$= e^{-\mu} \sum_{x=2}^{\infty} \frac{\mu^x}{(x-2)!}$$

$$= \mu^2 e^{-\mu} \sum_{y=0}^{\infty} \frac{\mu^y}{y!} \qquad \text{(putting } y = x - 2\text{)}$$

$$= \mu^2 e^{-\mu} e^{\mu}$$

$$= \mu^2$$

Thus

$$E(X^2) = E[X(X-1)] + E(X)$$
$$= \mu^2 + \mu$$

Thus

$$\text{Var}(X) = E(X^2) - [E(X)]^2$$
$$= \mu^2 + \mu - \mu^2$$
$$= \mu$$

◀ Binomial distribution ▶

POLAR COMPONENTS (OF VELOCITY AND ACCELERATION)

We first consider the vector

$$\mathbf{a} = \cos \theta \mathbf{i} + \sin \theta \mathbf{j}$$

and we suppose that θ increases at a uniform rate. Thus, $\mathbf{a}$ is a rotating unit vector (see Fig. P.15).

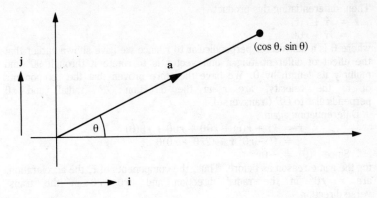

Fig. P.15

Then, differentiating,
$$\dot{\mathbf{a}} = -\dot{\theta} \sin \theta \mathbf{i} + \dot{\theta} \cos \theta \mathbf{j}$$
$$= \dot{\theta}(-\sin \theta \mathbf{i} + \cos \theta \mathbf{j})$$
$$= \dot{\theta}\mathbf{b}$$
where $\mathbf{b} = -\sin \theta \mathbf{i} + \cos \theta \mathbf{j}$

We note that
$$\mathbf{a} \cdot \dot{\mathbf{a}} = \dot{\theta}(\cos \theta \mathbf{i} + \sin \theta \mathbf{j}) \cdot (-\sin \theta \mathbf{i} + \cos \theta \mathbf{j})$$
$$= 0$$

Thus, the derivative $\dot{\mathbf{a}}$ of the unit vector $\mathbf{a}$ is perpendicular to $\mathbf{a}$ and has $\dot{\theta}$ times the magnitude.

We are now in a position to consider the general problem in which P has polar coordinates (r, θ) – see Fig. P.16. Consider the position vector $\mathbf{r}$ of P in the

$$\mathbf{r} = r\hat{\mathbf{r}}$$

where $\hat{\mathbf{r}}$ is a unit vector in the direction OP

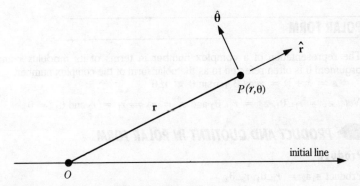

Fig. P.16

Then, differentiating this product,

$$\dot{\mathbf{r}} = \dot{r}\hat{\mathbf{r}} + r(\dot{\hat{\mathbf{r}}})$$
$$= \dot{r}\hat{\mathbf{r}} + r\dot{\theta}\hat{\boldsymbol{\theta}}$$

where $\hat{\boldsymbol{\theta}}$ is a unit vector perpendicular to $\hat{\mathbf{r}}$ since we have shown earlier that the effect of differentiating a unit vector is to rotate it through 90° and multiply its length by $\dot{\theta}$. We have therefore proved that the components of $\dot{\mathbf{r}}$, the velocity, are $\dot{r}$ in the direction OP (radial) and $r\dot{\theta}$ perpendicular to OP (transverse).

Differentiating again,

$$\ddot{\mathbf{r}} = \ddot{r}\hat{\mathbf{r}} + \dot{r}(\dot{\hat{\mathbf{r}}}) + \dot{r}\dot{\theta}\hat{\boldsymbol{\theta}} + r\ddot{\theta}\hat{\boldsymbol{\theta}} + r\dot{\theta}(\dot{\hat{\boldsymbol{\theta}}})$$
$$= (\ddot{r} - r\dot{\theta}^2)\hat{\mathbf{r}} + (2\dot{r}\dot{\theta} + r\ddot{\theta})\hat{\boldsymbol{\theta}}$$

Since $(\dot{\hat{\boldsymbol{\theta}}}) = -\dot{\theta}\hat{\mathbf{r}}$

for the same reason as before. Thus, the components of $\ddot{\mathbf{r}}$, the acceleration, are $\ddot{r} - r\dot{\theta}^2$ in the radial direction and $2\dot{r}\dot{\theta} + r\ddot{\theta}$ in the transverse direction.

Note the following special results where r is constant, that is, when P moves in a circle centre O.

	radial	transverse
$\dot{\mathbf{r}}$	0	$r\dot{\theta}$
$\ddot{\mathbf{r}}$	$-r\dot{\theta}^2$	$r\ddot{\theta}$

The radial component of $\ddot{\mathbf{r}}$, which is $-r\dot{\theta}^2$, is directed towards the centre and is called the *centripetal acceleration*.

POLAR COORDINATES

◀ Coordinates ▶

POLAR EQUATIONS

◀ Curve sketching ▶

POLAR FORM

The representation of a **complex number** in terms of its **modulus** r and **argument** θ is often referred to as the polar form of the complex number.

$$\Rightarrow z = x + iy = r\cos\theta + ir\sin\theta \equiv r\angle\theta$$

Note: $z_1 = r_1\angle\theta_1$, $z_2 = r_2\angle\theta_2$ and $z_1 = z_2 \iff r_1 = r_2$ and $\theta_1 = \theta_2$.

▶ PRODUCT AND QUOTIENT IN POLAR FORM

Product

Product $z_1 z_2 = r_1\angle\theta_1 . r_2\angle\theta_2$
$$= r_1(\cos\theta_1 + i\sin\theta_1) . r_2(\cos\theta_2 + i\sin\theta_2)$$

$$= r_1 r_2 [(\cos \theta_1 \cos \theta_2 - \sin \theta_1 \sin \theta_2) + i(\sin \theta_1 \cos \theta_2 + \cos \theta_1 \sin \theta_2)]$$

$$= r_1 r_2 [\cos (\theta_1 + \theta_2) + i\sin (\theta_1 + \theta_2)] \equiv (r_1 r_2) \angle (\theta_1 + \theta_2).$$

that is, we multiply the moduli and add the arguments.

Worked example

$z_1 \equiv 2\angle 135°$, $z_2 \equiv 3\angle 63°$

$z_1 z_2 \equiv (2 \times 3)\angle(135° + 63°) = 6\angle 198° \equiv 6\angle(-162°)$; $-162°$ being the principal value of the argument

Quotient

$$\text{Quotient } \frac{z_1}{z_2} = \frac{r_1 \angle \theta_1}{r_2 \angle \theta_2} = \frac{r_1}{r_2} \frac{(\cos \theta_1 + i\sin \theta_1)}{(\cos \theta_2 + i\sin \theta_2)} \cdot \frac{(\cos \theta_2 - i\sin \theta_2)}{(\cos \theta_2 - i\sin \theta_2)}$$

$$= \frac{r_1}{r_2} \frac{(\cos \theta_1 \cos \theta_2 + \sin \theta_1 \sin \theta_2) + i(\sin \theta_1 \cos \theta_2 - \cos \theta_1 \sin \theta_2)}{(\cos^2 \theta_2 + \sin^2 \theta_2)}$$

$$= \frac{r_1}{r_2} \left[\frac{\cos (\theta_1 - \theta_2) + i\sin (\theta_1 - \theta_2)}{1} \right] \equiv \frac{r_1}{r_2} \angle (\theta_1 - \theta_2)$$

that is, we divide the moduli and subtract the arguments

Worked example

$z_1 = 3\angle 124°$, $z_2 = 4\angle(-16°)$

$$\frac{z_1}{z_2} = \frac{3\angle 124°}{4\angle(-16°)} = 0 \cdot 75 \angle [(124° - (-16°)] = 0 \cdot 75 \angle 140°$$

◀ Argument, Complex number, Modulus ▶

POLYGON

A polygon is a **plane** figure with many straight sides. Common names of polygons are:

triangle	3 sides
quadrilateral	4 sides
pentagon	5 sides
hexagon	6 sides
septagon	7 sides
octagon	8 sides
nonagon	9 sides
decagon	10 sides

Polygons have two main types of angle, *interior angles* and *exterior angles*. A polygon will have as many exterior angles as interior angles, which will be the same as the number of sides of the polygon. All the exterior angles of any polygon will add up to 360°; all the interior angles of a polygon add up to $180 \times (N - 2)°$

REGULAR POLYGONS

A *regular* polygon is one which has all its sides the same length and all its angles are the same. The *exterior angle* of a regular N-sided polygon is found by dividing 360° by N. The *interior angle* of a regular N-sided polygon can be found by either subtracting the exterior angle from 180°, or by using the

formula $\dfrac{180 \, (N - 2)°}{N}$.

Symmetry: an N-sided regular polygon will have N lines of symmetry and rotational symmetry of order N.
◀ Plane shape ▶

POLYGON OF FORCES

Any number of forces acting at a point are in equilibrium if and only if they can be represented by the sides of a polygon taken in order.
◀ Triangle (polygon) of forces ▶

POLYHEDRON/POLYHEDRA

A polyhedron is a solid figure bounded by plane polygonal faces. There are various types of polyhedra. For example, the *regular tetrahedron* has four equilateral triangular faces.

POLYNOMIAL

A polynomial is an algebraic expression consisting of a number of terms, each of which is integral and rational.
$2x + 3y + 5z, \; x^2y - 2y^2x + 3x^2 + 4y - 2$
A frequently occurring polynomial is one involving a single variable, that is

$$a_0 + a_1x + a_2x^2 + \ldots + a_nx^n = \sum_{r=0}^{n} a_rx^r \text{ where } a_0, a_1, a_2, \ldots a_n \text{ are}$$

constants. It is said to be a polynomial of degree n, where n is the highest power of x. You must be able to add, subtract, multiply and divide polynomials. Use the same rules as in arithmetic, but leave spaces for missing terms.

Worked example A

Add $1 + 2x + x^3$ to $2 - 3x + x^2 - 5x^4$

$$
\begin{array}{l}
1 + 2x + \quad\; x^3 \\
\underline{2 - 3x + x^2 \qquad - 5x^4} \\
3 - \; x + x^2 + x^3 - 5x^4
\end{array}
$$

Worked example B

Subtract $3x^2 - 2xy + 5y^3$ from $-x^2 + 2xy + 3y^3$

$$
\begin{array}{l}
-x^2 + 2xy + 3y^3 \\
\underline{3x^2 - 2xy + 5y^3} \\
-4x^2 + 4xy - 2y^3
\end{array}
$$

Worked example C

Multiply $2 - 3x + x^3$ by $x + 3x^2 - x^3$

$$
\begin{array}{ll}
& 2 - 3x + \quad x^3 \\
& \underline{x + 3x^2 - \quad x^3} \\
(\times \quad x\;) & 2x - 3x^2 \qquad\qquad + x^4 \\
(\times \;\; 3x^2) & \quad\;\; 6x^2 - \;9x^3 \qquad\quad + 3x^5 \\
(\times \;\; -x^3) & \qquad\qquad - 2x^3 + 3x^4 \qquad\qquad - x^6 \\
& \overline{2x + 3x^2 - 11x^3 + 4x^4 + 3x^5 - x^6}
\end{array}
$$

Worked example D

Divide $3 + x^2 - 2x^3 + x^5$ by $1 - 2x + x^2$

Write the polynomials in descending powers of x and arrange your work as follows:

$$
\begin{array}{r}
x^3 + 2x^2 + \;x\; + 1 \\
x^2 - 2x + 1 \;\overline{\smash{\big)}\; x^5 \qquad - 2x^3 + x^2 \qquad\quad + 3} \\
\underline{x^5 - 2x^4 + \;x^3} \\
2x^4 - 3x^3 + \;x^2 \\
\underline{2x^4 - 4x^3 + 2x^2} \\
x^3 - \;x^2 \\
\underline{x^3 - 2x^2 + \;x} \\
x^2 - \;x + 3 \\
\underline{x^2 - 2x + 1} \\
x + 2
\end{array}
$$

$\Rightarrow$ Answer $x^3 + 2x^2 + x + 1 + \dfrac{x + 2}{x^2 - 2x + 1}$

POTENTIAL ENERGY

Potential **energy** is the energy that an object has because of its position or its condition. If you lift an object upwards, you do **work** against gravity and that same quantity of energy can be recovered by allowing the object to return to its original level. The additional energy that the object contained at the higher position is called **gravitationl potential energy**.

The potential energy of a particle of mass m, height h, above the reference level, is equal to mgh.

◀ **Energy, Gravitational potential energy** ▶

POWER

The power is the rate at which a **force** does **work**. It is measured in joules per second or watts.

If the force is moving in its own direction, then

power = force × speed

More generally, if a force **F** is moving its point of application with velocity **v** then

Power = **F** . **v**

Worked example

An engine is required to pump water from a reservoir to a position which is 80 m vertically higher than the level of water in the reservoir. Given that a mass of 300 kg of water is raised each second and discharged with speed $20 \, \text{ms}^{-1}$, find the power, in kW, required by the engine to achieve this. Take $g = 10 \, \text{ms}^{-2}$.

Work required per second to raise water = $300 \times 10 \times 80 \text{J} = 240\,000 \text{J}$

Work required per second to produce speed of discharge = $\frac{1}{2} \times 300 \times 20^2 \text{J}$
$$= 60\,000 \text{J}$$

Total work per second required = $300\,000 \text{J}$

Power required by engine = 300kW

NB. The water has to be raised and given a speed of discharge, that is, the work required is determined by finding the increases in the kinetic and potential energies of the water being raised each second. In practice, the amount of work required by the engine of the pump would have to be appreciably greater than 300kW, and often, the efficiency, that is the fraction of the total work which is effective, is given as a percentage. If, for example, we were told that the efficiency is 60 per cent, the total amount of work required by the engine of the pump would be $300 \times 100/60 \text{kW} = 500 \text{kW}$.

◀ **Force, Work** ▶

POWER (DEGREE)

When a product is formed by multiplying together letters of the same kind, the number of the letters forming the product is said to be the power (or degree) of that letter: $x.x.x = x^3 \Rightarrow$ third power, or degree 3; $7y^6 \Rightarrow$ sixth power, or degree 6.

PRINCIPAL VALUE

◀ Argument ▶

PRISM

A prism is a three-dimensional shape with a regular cross-section through its height or its length. All the shapes in Fig. P.17 are prisms, since they are shapes you could 'slice' up in such a way that each cross-section would be identical.

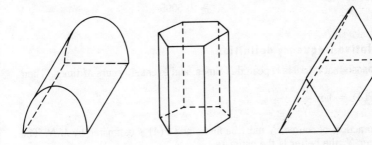

Fig. P.17

The volume of any prism is found by multiplying the area of the regular cross-section by its length (or height if it is stood on its regular cross-section).

PROBABILITY

Probability is a measure of the likelihood of an event taking place. It takes values between 0 and 1, and
  Impossible → Probability 0
  Certain → Probability 1

 DEFINITIONS OF PROBABILITY

The following definitions of probability are used in various cases.

A priori definition

Suppose a trial has n equally likely (equilikely) outcomes, m of which result in event A occurring. Then, the probability of A is defined as

$$P(A) = \frac{m}{n}$$

Worked example

A random selection of 5 cards is made from a pack of 52 cards. What is the probability that all 5 chosen cards are spades?

Total number of selections $= {}^{52}C_5$
Number of selections containing 5 spades $= {}^{13}C_5$
Thus,

Probability of 5 spades being chosen $= \dfrac{{}^{13}C_5}{{}^{52}C_5}$

$$\approx 0 \cdot 0005$$

Relative frequency definition

Suppose that a trial is repeated N times, and event A occurs M times. Then

$$P(A) = \lim_{N \to \infty} \frac{M}{N}$$

In practice, of course, N must be finite, and $P(A)$ is estimated by M/N. The larger N, the better is the estimate.

Subjective definition

In cases where neither of the two previous definitions can be used, a subjective measure of probability is often used. For example, a surgeon might tell a patient that he has a $0 \cdot 6$ chance (often stated as '60/40' chance) of surviving a certain operation.

 COMBINATIONS OF EVENTS

Given events A and B,

  i) The event $A \cup B$ (read A union B or A or B) is defined as the event which occurs when either A occurs or B occurs or both A and B occur.
 ii) the event $A \cap B$ (read A intersection B or A and B) is defined as the event which occurs when both A and B occur.

This can be illustrated on a Venn diagram, as in Fig. P.18. $A \cap B$ is denoted by

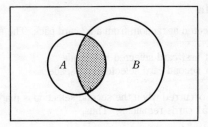

Fig. P.18

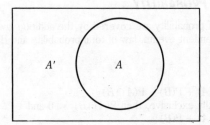

Fig. P.19

the shaded area. $A \cup B$ is denoted by the figure of eight including both A and B. Furthermore, the complement A' (also written $\bar{A}$) is the event which occurs when A does not occur and vice versa. Diagrammatically, this is as shown in Fig. P.19.

The *null* or impossible event ϕ is the event which contains no outcomes and so cannot occur. Two events A, B are *mutually exclusive* or disjoint if $A \cap B = \phi$, that is, they have no outcomes in common and cannot therefore occur simultaneously.

Two events A, B are *exhaustive* if $A \cup B = S$, where S denotes the sample space, that is, between them they contain all possible outcomes. More generally, the events A_1, A_2, ... A_n are *mutually exclusive* if no pair of events has outcomes in common, and *exhaustive* if their union is the whole sample space.

We can note finally that any event and its complement are mutually exclusive and exhaustive.

▶ CONDITIONAL PROBABILITY

The probability that A occurs given that B occurs is called the conditional probability of A given B, written $P(A|B)$. To illustrate this concept, consider the following example.

Worked example

Two cards are selected at random from a 52 card pack. The events A, B are defined as follows.

$A \equiv$ event that first card selected is a spade
$B \equiv$ event that second card selected is a spade
Calculate $P(B|A)$.

Here, since A has occurred when the second selection is made, there are 12 spades left in the 51 cards remaining. Thus,

$$P(B|A) = \frac{12}{51} = \frac{4}{17}$$

 RULES OF PROBABILITY

The main rules of probability are covered by the addition law, multiplication law, rule of independent events, law of total probability and Bayes' theorem.

Addition law

$$P(A \cup B) = P(A) + P(B) - P(A \cap B)$$
If A, B are mutually exclusive, then $P(A \cap B) = 0$ and
$$P(A \cup B) = P(A) + P(B)$$
This rule generalises so that if A_1, A_2, ... A_n are mutually exclusive, then
$$P(A_1 \cup A_2 \cup \ldots \cup A_n) = P(A_1) + P(A_2) + \ldots P(A_n)$$
As a special case, since an event A and its complement A' are mutually exclusive,
$$P(A \cup A') = P(A) + P(A')$$
that is, $P(A) + P(A') = P(S) = 1$

Multiplication law

$$P(A \cap B = P(A) P(B|A)$$
An alternative form obtained by interchanging A and B is
$$P(A \cap B) = P(B) P(A|B)$$

Independent events

If $P(A|B) = P(A)$, it follows from the above equations that $P(B|A) = P(B)$. In this case the occurrence of A is unaffected by the occurrence of B and vice versa, and A, B are called independent.

For independent events, the multiplication rule simplifies to
$$P(A \cap B) = P(A) P(B)$$

Law of total probability

Let A_1, $A_2 \ldots A_n$ be n mutually exclusive and exhaustive events – that is one and only one must occur. Let B be any other event.

Then,

$$P(B) = P(B|A_1) P(A_1) + P(B|A_2) P(A_2) + \ldots + P(B|A_n) P(A_n)$$

$$= \sum_{i=1}^{n} P(B|A_i) P(A_i)$$

Bayes' theorem

Consider

$$P(A_j \cap B) = P(A_j|B) P(B)$$

so that

$$P(A_j|B) = \frac{P(A_j \cap B)}{P(B)}$$

$$= \frac{P(B|A_j) P(A_j)}{\sum_{i=1}^{n} P(B|A_i) P(A_i)}$$

This is Bayes' theorem.

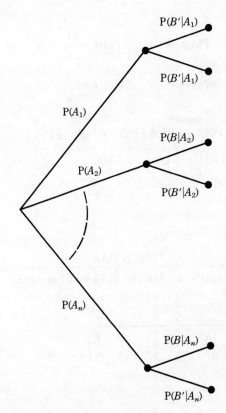

Fig. P.20

The rules of probability can be illustrated by means of a **tree diagram**, as shown in Fig. P.20.

Worked example

Three urns A_1, A_2, A_3 each contain a mixture of red and blue balls. Urn A_1 contains 1 red and 4 blue balls. Urn A_2 contains 2 red and 3 blue balls and Urn A_3 contains 3 red and 2 blue balls. An urn is selected at random and a ball is drawn at random from it.

i) Calculate the probability that the selected ball is blue.
ii) Given that the selected ball is blue, calculate the probability that A_1 was the selected urn.

Here, we take (without confusion in notation),
A_1 = event that Urn A_1 is selected
A_2 = event that Urn A_2 is selected
A_3 = event that Urn A_3 is selected
B = event that a blue ball is chosen.

We are given that

$$P(A_1) = \frac{1}{3}; \qquad P(A_2) = \frac{1}{3}; \qquad P(A_3) = \frac{1}{3}$$

$$P(B|A_1) = \frac{4}{5}; \quad P(B|A_2) = \frac{3}{5}; \quad P(B|A_3) = \frac{2}{5}$$

Using the law of total probability
$$P(B) = P(B|A_1)\,P(A_1) + P(B|A_2)\,P(A_2) + P(B|A_3)\,P(A_3)$$
$$= \left(\frac{4}{5} \times \frac{1}{3}\right) + \left(\frac{3}{5} \times \frac{1}{3}\right) + \left(\frac{2}{5} \times \frac{1}{3}\right)$$
$$= \frac{3}{5}$$

Using Bayes' theorem,

$$P(A_1|B) = \frac{P(B|A_1)\,P(A_1)}{P(B|A_1)\,P(A_1) + P(B|A_2)\,P(A_2) + P(B|A_3)\,P(A_3)}$$

$$= \frac{\dfrac{4}{5} \times \dfrac{1}{3}}{\left(\dfrac{4}{5} \times \dfrac{1}{3}\right) + \left(\dfrac{3}{5} \times \dfrac{1}{3}\right) + \left(\dfrac{2}{5} \times \dfrac{1}{5}\right)}$$

$$= \frac{4}{9}$$

The **tree diagram** for these calculations is shown in Fig. P.21.

$P(B)$ is obtained by adding the probabilities corresponding to routes including B. $P(A \mid B)$ is obtained by dividing the probability corresponding to the route containing A_1 by the sum of all probabilities above.

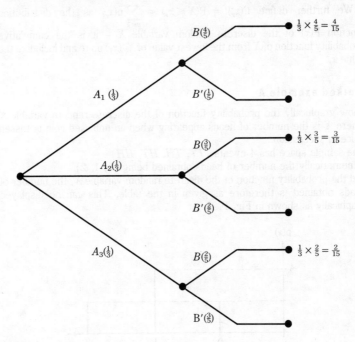

$$B(\tfrac{4}{5}) \qquad \tfrac{1}{3} \times \tfrac{4}{5} = \tfrac{4}{15}$$

$$A_1 (\tfrac{1}{3}) \qquad B'(\tfrac{1}{5})$$

$$B(\tfrac{3}{5}) \qquad \tfrac{1}{3} \times \tfrac{3}{5} = \tfrac{3}{15}$$

$$A_2(\tfrac{1}{3})$$

$$B'(\tfrac{2}{5})$$

$$A_3(\tfrac{1}{3}) \qquad B(\tfrac{2}{5}) \qquad \tfrac{1}{3} \times \tfrac{2}{5} = \tfrac{2}{15}$$

$$B'(\tfrac{3}{5})$$

Fig. P.21

PROBABILITY FUNCTION

▶ DISCRETE RANDOM VARIABLE

Many, but not all, of the events in problems of probability result in a sample space S that is a set of numerical values. For instance, the throwing of a die results in a sample space of 1, 2, 3, 4, 5 and 6. The drawing of a ball from a bag containing black, white and red balls, however, does not. It would, though, be possible by assigning numbers, say 1 to black, 2 to white and 3 to red, to make the outcome numerical.

This is particularly useful in probability. By assigning a real number x_r to each event E_r in the sample S we then have a function X defined at all points of the sample space. (That is, X takes the value x_r when event E_r occurs.) The function X is called a **random variable**. When the number of possible values of X is finite, we define X to be a *discrete random variable*.

Consider the discrete random variable X which takes values $x_1, x_2, \ldots, x_n$ when events $E_1, E_2, \ldots, E_n$ occur respectively. Then, if the probability that $X = x_r$, which is to say $P(X = x_r) = p(x_r)$, we define $p(x)$ where $P(X = x) \equiv p(x)$ as the probability function of the discrete random variable X.

We further define $F(x_r) = P(X \leqslant x_r) = \displaystyle\sum_{r=1}^{r} p(x_r)$ as the distribution function $F(x)$ of the discrete random variable X – it is the cumulative probability function of X from the lowest value of X, (x_1) up to and including the value x_r.

Worked example A

Show graphically the probability function of the discrete random variable X where X is the number of heads appearing when an unbiased coin is tossed twice in succession.

The sample space has 4 events $\{TT, TH, HT, HH\}$
$\Rightarrow$ numerically the number of heads obtained being $\{0, 1, 2\}$
and the probability function of the discrete random variable X, the number of heads obtained is therefore as given in the table. This can be displayed graphically as shown in Fig. P.22.

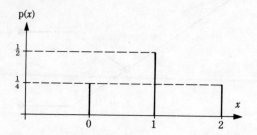

Fig. P.22

x	0	1	2
$P(X = x)$	$\dfrac{1}{4}$	$\dfrac{1}{2}$	$\dfrac{1}{4}$

NB. the sum of the length of the bars in the graph represents the sum of the probabilities of all the possible outcomes $= 1$, (certainty), i.e. $\displaystyle\sum_{r=1}^{3} p(x_r) = 1$

Worked example B

The probability function of a discrete random variable X is given by

$$p(x) = \frac{K}{3^x} \quad (x = 1, 2, 3 \ldots)$$

Find a) the value of K b) $P(X \leq 4)$

a) $\displaystyle\sum_{x=1}^{\infty} p(x) = 1 \Rightarrow 1 = \sum_{x=1}^{\infty} \frac{K}{3^x} = K\left(\frac{1}{3} + \frac{1}{3^2} + \frac{1}{3^3} + \ldots\right),$

an infinite geometrical progression.

Hence $\displaystyle\sum_{x=1}^{\infty} \frac{K}{3^x} = \frac{K \cdot \frac{1}{3}}{1 - \frac{1}{3}} = 1 = \frac{K}{2} \Rightarrow K = 2$

b) $P(X \leq 4) = 2 \cdot \left(\frac{1}{3} + \frac{1}{3^2} + \frac{1}{3^3} + \frac{1}{3^4}\right) = 2 \cdot \frac{(27 + 9 + 3 + 1)}{81} = \frac{80}{81}$

Mean and variance of a discrete probability function

For a discrete random variable X the mean, μ, sometimes called the *expected value* or the expectation of X, is defined as follows:

$\mu = E(X) = \displaystyle\sum_{r=1}^{n} x_r p(x_r)$ i.e. summed over all possible values of X

The variance, σ^2, of X is defined as follows:

$\sigma^2 = Var(X) = \displaystyle\sum_{r=1}^{n} (x_r - \mu)^2 \, p(x_r)$ which can be shown to be

$= \displaystyle\sum_{r=1}^{n} x_r^2 p(x_r) - \mu^2$

The *standard deviation* of the probability is the square root of the variance, that is, σ.

Worked example C

A discrete random variable X takes values x only from the set N, where $N = \{0, 1, 2, 3\}$. The probability that X takes the value x is given by
$P(X = x) = k(x + 1)$
where k is a constant.

a) Determine the value of k
b) Find the mean and the variance of X

From the data given, we can make up a table:

x	0	1	2	3
$P(X = x)$	k	$2k$	$3k$	$4k$

a) Since $\sum P(X = x) = 1$, we have

$k + 2k + 3k + 4k = 1 \Rightarrow k = \dfrac{1}{10}$

b) Mean $= \mu = \displaystyle\sum_{i=0}^{4} x_i\, p(x_i)$

$$= 0 + 2k + 6k + 12k = 20k$$

But $k = \dfrac{1}{10}$ and therefore $\mu = 2$

$$\text{Var}(X) = \sigma^2 = \sum_{i=1}^{4} x_i^2\, p(x_i) - \mu^2$$

$$= 0 + 2k + 12k + 36k - 2^2$$

$$= 50k - 4 = 5 - 4 = 1$$

Worked example D

Consider another discrete random variable Y, where $Y = 3X + 2$ and X is the random variable with mean 2 and variance 1, as given in worked example C. As X takes values 0, 1, 2, 3, Y takes values 2, 5, 8, 11 respectively and the probability distribution for Y in tabular form is

Y	2	5	8	11
P(Y)	0·1	0·2	0·3	0·4

The mean of Y, $\mu_Y = 0\cdot2 + 1\cdot0 + 2\cdot4 + 4\cdot4 = 8$
The variance of Y, $\sigma_Y^2 = 4(0\cdot1) + 25(0\cdot2) + 64(0\cdot3) + 121(0\cdot4) - 8^2$
$$= 73 - 64 = 9$$
In this example we note that $\mu_Y = 3(\mu_X) + 2$ and $\sigma_Y^2 = 3^2\sigma_X^2$

Generally, if $Y = aX + b$, where a and b are constants, it is true that

 i) Mean of $Y = a$(Mean of X) $+ b$
 ii) Var $(Y) = a^2\,\text{Var}(X)$

Result i) is also often written as $E(Y) = aE(X) + b$
Note also that the standard deviation of $Y = a \times$ (the standard deviation of X)

▶ CONTINUOUS RANDOM VARIABLE

For a continuous probability distribution, the random variable may take any value between specified limits or just any real value. The number of possible values that could be taken by the random variable is infinite, and we cannot speak of the probability that the variable will take some specific value. Instead we consider ways of finding the probability that the value of the random variable will be in a particular interval. For instance, if we are measuring the lengths of leaves to the nearest mm and we wish to find the probability that a given leaf will measure 8 mm, we are really asking 'What is the probability of the leaf measuring between 7·5 mm and 8·5 mm?' since length is a continuous variable and we are measuring to the nearest mm.

The probability density function (pdf) of a continuous variable X is defined as the function f that satisfies the conditions

i) $f(x) \geq 0$ for all $x \in S$, the sample space,

ii) $\int_s f(x)dx = 1$

where $\int_s$ means integration over the sample space

iii) $P(a \leq X \leq b) = \int_a^b f(x)dx$ for any $a < b$ in S,

and hence $P(a \leq X \leq b)$ is represented by the area of the region under the graph of the pdf $f(x)$, between limits a and b. When we are given a problem in which X takes values only in a finite interval, we assume that the pdf is zero everywhere else. We can then write

$$\int_{-\infty}^{+\infty} f(x)dx = 1 \text{ (the certain event)}$$

You should note that if we let a approach b, then, in the limit

$$\int_a^b f(x)dx$$

becomes zero. This means that, where we can speak of the probability that the value of a discrete random variable is exactly b, there is no equivalent to this for a continuous variable.

The mean μ, often called the expected value or the expectation of X, is defined to be

$$E(X) = \mu = \int_{-\infty}^{+\infty} x f(x)dx$$

The variance σ^2 of X is defined to be

$$\begin{aligned}
\text{Var}(X) &= \int_{-\infty}^{+\infty} (x - \mu)^2 f(x)dx \\
&= \int_{-\infty}^{+\infty} x^2 f(x)dx - 2\mu \int_{-\infty}^{+\infty} x f(x)dx + \mu^2 \int_{-\infty}^{+\infty} f(x)dx \\
&= \int_{-\infty}^{+\infty} x^2 f(x)dx - \mu^2, \text{ from the results above}
\end{aligned}$$

(Compare this last result with the analogous formula for discrete probability functions.)

Continuous random variable questions

Worked example E

A continuous random variable X takes all real values x in the interval $0 \leq x \leq 3$. The probability density function f of X is given by

$$f(x) = \frac{1}{9}(3 - 4x + 2x^2) \text{ for } 0 \leq x \leq 3$$

$$f(x) = 0, \text{ otherwise}$$

Sketch the graph of f and calculate the mean and the variance of X. Find the probability that X lies in the interval $0 \leq x \leq 1$.

The graph of f is shown in Fig. P.23 as the curve $(0 \leq x \leq 3)$, the x-axis to the right of $(3, 0)$ and the whole negative x-axis to the left of O

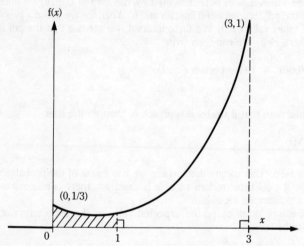

Fig. P.23

$$\text{Mean of } X = \int_0^3 \frac{x}{9}(3 - 4x + 2x^2)dx$$

$$= \left[\frac{x^2}{6} - \frac{4x^3}{27} + \frac{x^4}{18} \right]_0^3$$

$$= (3/2 - 4 + 9/2) = 2$$

$$\text{Variance of } X = \int_0^3 \frac{1}{9}(x - 2)^2(3 - 4x + 2x^2)dx$$

$$= \int_0^3 \frac{1}{9}(12 - 28x + 27x^2 - 12x^3 + 2x^4)dx$$

$$= \frac{1}{9}\left[12x - 14x^2 + 9x^3 - 3x^4 + 2x^5/5 \right]_0^3$$

$$= \frac{1}{9}(36 - 126 + 243 - 243 + 486/5)$$

$$= 0 \cdot 8$$

$$P(0 \leqslant x < 1) = \int_0^1 \frac{1}{9}(3 - 4x + 2x^2)dx$$
  (this is the area of the shaded region shown)

$$= \left[\frac{1}{9}(3x - 2x^2 + 2x^3/3) \right]_0^1$$

$$= \frac{1}{9}(3 - 2 + 2/3) = \frac{5}{27} \approx 0 \cdot 185$$

NB. The graph of f is sketched as for an algebraic function, but remember that no part of the curve for a probability density function can lie below the x-axis. The calculation for σ^2 can be much shortened by using the result

$$\sigma^2 = \int x^2 f(x)dx - \mu^2$$

$$= \int_0^3 \frac{1}{9}x^2(3 - 4x + 2x^2)dx - 2^2$$

$$= \left[\frac{1}{9}x^3 - \frac{1}{4}x^4 + \frac{2}{45}x^5 \right]_0^3 = \left(3 - 9 + \frac{54}{5} \right) - 4 = 0 \cdot 8$$

Worked example F

A random variable X has probability density function f given by
$f(x) = Kx^a$, $0 \leqslant x \leqslant 1$
$f(x) = 0$, otherwise,
where K and a are constants.

Calculate, giving your answers in terms of a

a) K
b) the expected value of X

Since f is a probability density function

$$\int_0^1 Kx^a dx = 1$$

$$\Rightarrow \left[\frac{K}{a+1}x^{a+1} \right]_0^1 = 1$$

$$\frac{K}{a+1} = 1 \Rightarrow K = a+1$$

b) $\mathrm{E}(X) = \displaystyle\int_0^1 x(Kx^a)\mathrm{d}x = (a+1)\int_0^1 x^{a+1}\mathrm{d}x$

$$= (a+1)\left[\frac{x^{a+2}}{a+2}\right]_0^1 = \frac{a+1}{a+2}$$

PRODUCT MOMENT

◀ Correlation coefficient (product moment) ▶

PRODUCT RULE (FOR DIFFERENTIATION)

This rule states that if u, v are functions of x, then

$$\frac{\mathrm{d}}{\mathrm{d}x}(uv) = u\frac{\mathrm{d}v}{\mathrm{d}x} + v\frac{\mathrm{d}u}{\mathrm{d}x}$$

◀ Derivative, Differentiation ▶

PROJECTILE MOTION

Suppose that a particle is projected at ground level with velocity v at an angle θ to the horizontal (Fig. P.24). Then the horizontal and vertical distances (x and y respectively) travelled after time t are given by

$$x = v\cos\theta \cdot t = vt\cos\theta \tag{1}$$

and $\quad y = v\sin\theta \cdot t - \dfrac{1}{2}gt^2 = vt\sin\theta - \dfrac{1}{2}gt^2 \tag{2}$

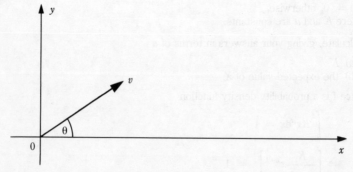

Fig. P.24

Now

$$\frac{\mathrm{d}y}{\mathrm{d}t} = v \sin \theta - gt$$

and

$$\frac{\mathrm{d}^2y}{\mathrm{d}t^2} = -g < 0$$

Now y is maximised when

$$\frac{\mathrm{d}y}{\mathrm{d}t} = v \sin \theta - gt = 0$$

that is, $\quad t = \dfrac{v \sin \theta}{g}$

$\left(\text{This is a maximum since } \dfrac{\mathrm{d}^2y}{\mathrm{d}t^2} < 0.\right)$

With this value of t,

$$y_{\max} = v \cdot \frac{v \sin \theta}{g} \cdot \sin \theta - \frac{1}{2}g \cdot \frac{v^2 \sin^2 \theta}{g^2}$$

$$= \frac{v^2 \sin^2 \theta}{2g}$$

This gives the maximum height attained by the particle.

Furthermore, $y = 0$ when

$$t\left(v \sin \theta - \frac{1}{2}gt\right) = 0$$

$$t = 0$$

$$\text{or} \quad t = \frac{2v \sin \theta}{g}$$

$t = 0$ corresponds to the time of projection; $t = 2v \sin \theta/g$ corresponds to the time at which the particle returns to ground level. At this time,

$$x_{\max} = v \cdot \frac{2v \sin \theta}{g} \cdot \cos \theta$$

$$= \frac{v^2 \sin 2\theta}{g}$$

This gives the range R of the particle. Clearly, the range is maximised when $\sin 2\theta = 1$, that is, $\theta = 45°$.

Thus,

$$R_{max} = \frac{v^2}{g}$$

It follows from (1) above that

$$t = \frac{x}{v \cos \theta}$$

Substituting in (2),

$$y = v \cdot \frac{x}{v \cos \theta} \cdot \sin \theta - \frac{g}{2} \cdot \frac{x^2}{v^2 \cos^2 \theta}$$

$$= x \tan \theta - \frac{g x^2 \sec^2 \theta}{2 v^2}$$

This gives the equation of the path of the particle, which is seen to be a parabola.

PYRAMID

◄ Solid shape ►

QUADRANT

◀ Angle ▶

QUADRATIC

A quadratic in x is an expression of the form
$$f(x) = ax^2 + bx + c \qquad \text{where } a \neq 0$$
Completing the square,

$$f(x) = a\left(x^2 + \frac{b}{a}x + \frac{c}{a}\right)$$

$$= a\left[\left(x + \frac{b}{2a}\right)^2 + \left(\frac{c}{a} - \frac{b^2}{4a^2}\right)\right]$$

$$= a\left[\left(x + \frac{b}{2a}\right)^2 - \left(\frac{b^2 - 4ac}{4a^2}\right)\right]$$

This shows that, if $a > 0$, $f(x)$ is *minimised* where $x = -b/2a$; if $a < 0$, $f(x)$ is *maximised* where $x = -b/2a$. The curves in Fig. Q.1 illustrate this point.

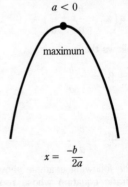

Fig. Q.1

QUADRATIC EQUATION

A quadratic equation is an equation of the form
$$ax^2 + bx + c = 0 \qquad \text{where } a \neq 0$$
Completing the square, the equation is equivalent to

$$a\left[\left(x + \frac{b}{2a}\right)^2 - \left(\frac{b^2 - 4ac}{4a^2}\right)\right] = 0$$

that is, $\left(x + \dfrac{b}{2a}\right)^2 = \dfrac{b^2 - 4ac}{4a^2}$

or, taking square roots,

$$x + \frac{b}{2a} = \pm\sqrt{\frac{b^2 - 4ac}{4a^2}}$$

$$\text{or} \quad x = \frac{-b \pm \sqrt{b^2 - 4ac}}{2a}$$

The type of root depends upon the discriminant $\Delta = b^2 - 4ac$. If $\Delta > 0$, the roots are real and distinct. If $\Delta = 0$, the roots are real and coincident. If $\Delta < 0$, the roots are complex.

▶ SUM AND PRODUCTS OF ROOTS

Let α, β denote the roots of the quadratic equation. Then, the equation can be rewritten in the form
$$(x - \alpha)(x - \beta) = 0$$
$$\text{or} \quad x^2 - (\alpha + \beta)x + \alpha\beta = 0$$

Comparing this with the equation
$$ax^2 + bx + c = 0$$

$$\text{or} \quad a\left(x^2 + \frac{b}{a}x + \frac{c}{a}\right) = 0$$

It follows that

$$\alpha + \beta = -\frac{b}{a}$$

and

$$\alpha\beta = \frac{c}{a}$$

The following example shows how this result can be used to obtain the quadratic equation whose roots are symmetric functions of the roots of another quadratic equation.

Worked example

The roots of the quadratic equataion
$$x^2 + 3x + 4 = 0$$
are denoted by α, β. Find the quadratic equation whose roots are $\alpha + 1/\beta$, $\beta + 1/\alpha$.

Using the above result,
$$\alpha + \beta = -3; \quad \alpha\beta = 4$$
put

$$\gamma = \alpha + \frac{1}{\beta} \quad \text{and } \delta = \beta + \frac{1}{\alpha}$$

Consider

$$\gamma + \delta = \alpha + \beta + \frac{1}{\alpha} + \frac{1}{\beta}$$

$$= \alpha + \beta + \frac{\alpha + \beta}{\alpha\beta}$$

$$= -3 - \frac{3}{4}$$

$$= -\frac{15}{4}$$

$$\gamma\delta = \left(\alpha + \frac{1}{\beta}\right)\left(\beta + \frac{1}{\alpha}\right)$$

$$= \alpha\beta + \frac{1}{\alpha\beta} + 2$$

$$= 4 + \frac{1}{4} + 2$$

$$= \frac{25}{4}$$

The equation whose roots are γ, δ is therefore
$$x^2 + \frac{15}{4}x + \frac{25}{4} = 0$$

or $\quad 4x^2 + 15x + 25 = 0.$

RADIAN

A radian is defined as a fraction $\dfrac{1}{2\pi}$ of a whole revolution; alternatively 2π radians correspond to a whole revolution. A comparison between radians and degrees is given in the table.

radians	degrees
2π	360
π	180
$\pi/2$	90
1	57·30

RANDOM SAMPLE

To take a random sample in effect means that every member of the whole population has an equal chance of being selected in the sample. This simple idea is often very difficult to achieve in practice, and you must always bear this in mind when collecting data for your own project work. It is normal to consider samples containing a fairly large number of members. These samples then have similar properties to the whole population, and it is possible to avoid taking the special precautions that would be necessary for a small sample from a large (or infinite) population.

RANDOM VARIABLE

A random variable is a variable whose value on any particular occasion is determined by a **probability distribution**; its value cannot be predicted exactly.

A random variable is called *discrete* or *continuous* according to whether the set of values it can take is discrete or continuous. Random variables are denoted by capital letters, such as X, and the values they can take by the corresponding lower-case letters, say x.

DISCRETE RANDOM VARIABLES

Here, the set of probabilities corresponding to possible values is given by the probability (mass) function $p_x = P(X = x)$. This can be expressed algebraically or by means of a table, as shown in the following example.

Worked example

Three coins are tossed simultaneously. What is the probability distribution of the number X of heads obtained?

Here, the sample space is
{HHH, HHT, HTH, HTT, THH, THT, TTH, TTT}
We see by enumeration that the probability distribution of X is as follows.

x	$p_x = P(X = x)$
0	$\dfrac{1}{8}$
1	$\dfrac{3}{8}$
2	$\dfrac{3}{8}$
3	$\dfrac{1}{8}$

We can also, however, consider this as a binomial distribution so that
$$p_x = {}^3C_x(\tfrac{1}{2})^3 \qquad (x = 0, 1, 2, 3)$$

 GENERAL PROPERTIES OF PROBABILITY FUNCTIONS

Given any probability function p_x
$$p_x \geqslant 0 \qquad \text{for all } x$$

$$\sum_x p_x = 1$$

where the summation is over all possible values of x.

 CONTINUOUS RANDOM VARIABLES

For a continuous random variable X,
$$P(X = x) = 0 \qquad \text{for all } x$$
so that the probability function cannot be used in this case. The probability

distribution can now be characterised by the **probability density function** $f(x)$, such that

$$P(a < X < b) = \int_a^b f(x)\mathrm{d}x$$

All probability density functions $f(x)$ have the following properties,

$$f(x) \geqslant 0 \qquad \text{for all } x$$

and $\int_{-\infty}^{\infty} f(x)\mathrm{d}x = 1$

Worked example

A random variable X has probability density function f given by

$$f(x) = Kx^a, \quad 0 \leqslant x \leqslant 1$$
$$f(x) = 0, \text{ otherwise, where } K \text{ and } a \text{ are constants.}$$

Calculate, giving your answers in terms of a: i) K; ii) the expected value of X.

i) Since f is a probability density function

$$\int_0^1 Kx^a\mathrm{d}x = 1$$

$$\Rightarrow \left[\frac{K}{a+1}x^{a+1} \right]_0^1 = 1$$

$$\frac{K}{a+1} = 1 \Rightarrow K = a+1$$

ii) $E(X) = \int_0^1 x(Kx^a)\mathrm{d}x = (a+1)\int_0^1 x^{a+1}\mathrm{d}x$

$$= (a+1)\left[\frac{x^{a+2}}{a+2} \right]_0^1 = \frac{a+1}{a+2}$$

RANGE

◀ Domain, Function ▶

RATIONAL ALGEBRAIC FRACTION

The division of a polynomial $f(x)$ of degree n, by a polynomial $g(x)$ of degree m, gives a rational algebraic fraction.

If $n < m$, the fraction is a *proper* fraction, for instance $\dfrac{x^2 + 1}{3x^3 - 2x + 4}$

If $n \geqslant m$, the fraction is an *improper* fraction, for instance $\dfrac{x^3}{x^2 - 2x - 1}$

When the denominator of a proper fraction factorises it is possible to express the fraction as the sum or difference of other proper fractions. This is known as the resolution of the fraction into its **partial fractions**.
◀ Partial fractions ▶

RATIONAL TERM

A term in which the indices of the letters are rational.

$6xy^2, \dfrac{x}{y^2}, \dfrac{7}{x}$

RATIO THEOREM (FOR VECTORS)

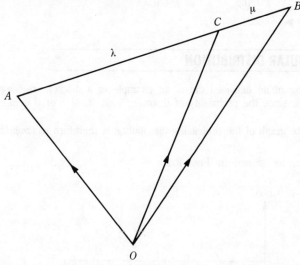

Fig. R.1

Let the points A, B have position vectors **a**, **b** with respect to an origin O (Fig. R.1). Let the point C divide the line segment AB in the ratio $\lambda : \mu$.

Then the ratio theorem states that the position vector of **C** is given by

$$\mathbf{C} = \frac{\mu\mathbf{a} + \lambda\mathbf{b}}{\lambda + \mu}$$

A simpler expression can be obtained by ensuring that $\lambda + \mu = 1$. In this case,

$$\mathbf{C} = \mu\mathbf{a} + (1 - \mu)\mathbf{b}$$

To prove this result, consider

$$\overrightarrow{OB} = \overrightarrow{OA} + \overrightarrow{AB}$$

so that $\overrightarrow{AB} = \overrightarrow{OB} - \overrightarrow{OA} = \mathbf{b} - \mathbf{a}$

It follows that

$$\overrightarrow{AC} = \frac{\lambda}{(\lambda + \mu)} \overrightarrow{AB} = \frac{\lambda}{(\lambda + \mu)}(\mathbf{b} - \mathbf{a})$$

Thus,

$$\begin{aligned}
\mathbf{C} &= \overrightarrow{OC} \\
&= \overrightarrow{OA} + \overrightarrow{AC} \\
&= \mathbf{a} + \frac{\lambda}{(\lambda + \mu)}(\mathbf{b} - \mathbf{a}) \\
&= \frac{(\lambda + \mu)\mathbf{a} + \lambda(\mathbf{b} - \mathbf{a})}{\lambda + \mu} = \frac{\mu\mathbf{a} + \lambda\mathbf{b}}{\lambda + \mu}
\end{aligned}$$

◀ Vector ▶

RECTANGULAR DISTRIBUTION

The tossing of an unbiased die is an example of a discrete rectangular distribution, since the probability of throwing 1, 2, 3, 4, 5 or 6 is in each case $\frac{1}{6}$. The graph of the probability distribution is therefore *rectangular* in appearance, as shown in Fig. R.2.

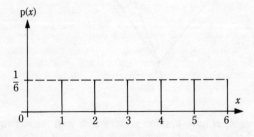

Fig. R.2

The mean of the distribution is

$$\mu = E(X) = \frac{1}{6}(1 + 2 + 3 + 4 + 5 + 6)$$

$$\Rightarrow E(X) = \frac{21}{6} = 3\cdot5$$

The variance is $\sigma^2 = \text{Var}(X) = \frac{1}{6}(1^2 + 2^2 + 3^2 + 4^2 + 5^2 + 6^2) - 3\cdot5^2$

$$= \frac{35}{12}$$

Generally if $p(x_r) = \frac{1}{n}$ (a constant) for $r = 1, 2 \ldots n$

then $\mu = E(X) = \frac{n+1}{2}$

and $\sigma^2 = \text{Var}(X) = \frac{n^2 - 1}{12}$

RECTANGULAR HYPERBOLA

◀ Hyperbola ▶

REFLECTION

A mathematical reflection is the mirror image of a shape drawn on the opposite side of a mirror line, such that each line drawn from one point to its reflection is perpendicular to the mirror line.

REGRESSION (LEAST SQUARES)

Let x, y be two variables related by a linear equation of the form

$$y = \alpha + \beta x$$

where α, β are constants. Suppose that x can be measured accurately, but that measurements of y are subject to a random measurement error. It is customary to assume that these errors are independent and normally distributed with zero **mean** and **variance** σ^2. Thus, if y is measured for the x values x_1, x_2, ... x_n, the true value y_i corresponding to x_i is $\alpha + \beta x_i$. The measured value, however, is given by

$$Y_i = y_i + \epsilon_i = \alpha + \beta x_i + \epsilon_i$$

where ϵ_i is N(0, σ^2).

The plots of the points (x_1, Y_1), (x_2, Y_2), ... (x_n, Y_n) is called a scatter diagram – see Fig. R.3. Now the relationship between x and Y is linear plus a random error, so that the points should lie approximately on a straight line. The least squares principle can be used to estimate this line as follows.

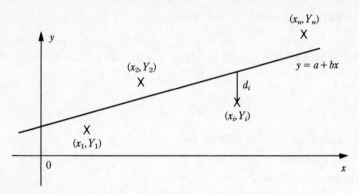

Fig. R.3

Consider the line $y = a + bx$, and let
$$d_i = a + bx_i - Y_i$$
Then d_i is shown on the graph in Fig. R.3; it represents the difference between the value of y predicted by the line for $x = x_i$ and the measured value Y_i. Define
$$S = \sum_{i=1}^{n} d_i^2$$
$$= \sum_{i=1}^{n} (a + bx_i - Y_i)^2$$

The least squares principle chooses a, b to minimise S.

The simplest way to achieve this minimisation is to use *partial differentiation*, although this is outside the A-level Mathematics curriculum. The derivation is given below, although only the results are of importance. For most examining boards, these are given in an information booklet.

Consider the partial **derivatives**.
$$\frac{\delta S}{\delta a} = \sum_{i=1}^{n} 2(a + bx_i - Y_i)$$
and $$\frac{\delta S}{\delta b} = \sum_{i=1}^{n} 2x_i(a + bx_i - Y_i)$$

For a minimum, these derivatives are zero, that is
$$\sum_{i=1}^{n} (a + bx_i - Y_i) = na + b\sum_{i=1}^{n} x_i - \sum_{i=1}^{n} Y_i = 0 \qquad (1)$$

and $\displaystyle\sum_{i=1}^{n} x_i(a + bx_i - Y_i) = a\sum_{i=1}^{n} x_i + b\sum_{i=1}^{n} x_i^2 - \sum_{i=1}^{n} x_i Y_i = 0$ (2)

Equations (1) and (2) are called the *normal equations*. It follows from (1), dividing by n, that

$$\bar{Y} = a + b\bar{x} \tag{3}$$

where

$$\bar{x} = \frac{\displaystyle\sum_{i=1}^{n} x_i}{n} \quad \text{and} \quad \bar{Y} = \frac{\displaystyle\sum_{i=1}^{n} Y_i}{n}$$

This shows that the *least squares line* passes through the point $(\bar{x}, \bar{Y})$.

Multiplying (1) by $\displaystyle\sum_{i=1}^{n} x_i$, (2) by n and subtracting, we obtain

$$b\left[\left(\sum_{i=1}^{n} x_i\right)^2 - n\sum_{i=1}^{n} x_i^2\right] - \left[\sum_{i=1}^{n} x_i \sum_{i=1}^{n} Y_i - n\sum_{i=1}^{n} x_i Y_i\right] = 0$$

Whence

$$b = \frac{\displaystyle\sum_{i=1}^{n} x_i Y_i - n\bar{x}\bar{Y}}{\displaystyle\sum_{i=1}^{n} x_i^2 - n\bar{x}^2}$$

$$= \frac{S_{xy}}{S_{xx}}$$

where

$$S_{xy} = \sum_{i=1}^{n} x_i Y_i - n\bar{x}\bar{Y} = \sum_{i=1}^{n} (x_i - \bar{x})(Y_i - \bar{Y})$$

and $\displaystyle S_{xx} = \sum_{i=1}^{n} x_i^2 - n\bar{x}^2 = \sum_{i=1}^{n} (x_i - \bar{x})^2$

We can now find a from (3) above, so that $a = \bar{Y} - b\bar{x}$. The least squares line, called the *regression line* of y on x, is therefore $y = a + bx$. An equivalent form of the equation, since it is passes through $(\bar{x}, \bar{Y})$ is $y - \bar{Y} = b(x - \bar{x})$. We can regard the line $y = a + bx$ as an estimator for the true relationship $y = \alpha + \beta x$. In addition, a and b are estimators for α and β. It can be shown that

$$E(a) = \alpha \quad \text{and} \quad E(b) = \beta$$

so that both estimators are unbiased.

Furthermore,

$$\text{Var}(a) = \sigma^2\left(\frac{\bar{x}^2}{S_{xx}} + \frac{1}{n}\right)$$

and $\displaystyle \text{Var}(b) = \frac{\sigma^2}{S_{xx}}$

Finally, under the assumption that the errors are normally distributed, it follows that a, b are normally distributed so that

$$a \text{ is N}\left(\alpha, \sigma^2\left(\frac{\bar{x}^2}{S_{xx}} + \frac{1}{n}\right)\right)$$

and

$$b \text{ is N}\left(\beta, \frac{\sigma^2}{S_{xx}}\right)$$

This enables the following 95 per cent confidence limits for α, β to be calculated.

$$\alpha: \quad a \pm 1\cdot96\,\sigma\sqrt{\frac{\bar{x}^2}{S_{xx}} + \frac{1}{n}}$$

$$\beta: \quad b \pm 1\cdot96\,\frac{\sigma}{\sqrt{S_{xx}}}$$

The true value of y when $x = x_i$ is $\alpha + \beta x_i$. This can be estimated by $\hat{y} = a + bx_i$. It can be shown that $E(\hat{y}) = \alpha + \beta x_i$ so that $\hat{y}$ is unbiased. Furthermore,

$$\text{Var}(\hat{y}) = \sigma^2\left[\frac{(x_i - \bar{x})^2}{S_{xx}} + \frac{1}{n}\right]$$

and $\hat{y}$ is $\text{N}\left(\alpha + \beta x_i, \sigma^2\left[\frac{(x_i - \bar{x})^2}{S_{xx}} + \frac{1}{n}\right]\right)$

This enables the following 95 per cent confidence limits to be calculated for $\alpha + \beta x_i$:

$$a + bx_i \pm 1\cdot96\,\sigma\sqrt{\frac{(x_i - \bar{x})^2}{S_{xx}} + \frac{1}{n}}$$

Worked example

Find the equation of the least squares line for the following data in the form $y = a + bx$.

x	1	2	3	4	5	6
Y	2·6	3·7	4·4	5·1	6·3	6·7

Calculate confidence intervals for α, β and the value of y when $x = 2$. Assume that the standard deviation (σ) of the measurement errors for y is $0\cdot1$. We find, using a calculator, that

$$\sum_{i=1}^{6} x_i = 21; \quad \sum_{i=1}^{6} x_i^2 = 91; \quad \sum_{i=1}^{6} Y_i = 28\cdot8; \quad \sum_{i=1}^{6} x_i Y_i = 115\cdot3$$

It follows that

$$S_{xy} = \sum_{i=1}^{6} x_i Y_i - 6\bar{x}\bar{Y}$$

$$= 115 \cdot 3 - 6 \times \frac{21}{6} \times \frac{28 \cdot 8}{6}$$

$$= 14 \cdot 5$$

$$S_{xx} = \sum_{i=1}^{6} x_i^2 - 6\bar{x}^2$$

$$= 91 - 6 \times \left(\frac{21}{6}\right)^2$$

$$= 17 \cdot 5$$

Thus,

$$b = \frac{S_{xy}}{S_{xx}} = \frac{14 \cdot 5}{17 \cdot 5} \approx 0 \cdot 83$$

$$a = \bar{Y} - b\bar{x}$$

$$= \frac{28 \cdot 8}{6} - \frac{14 \cdot 5}{17 \cdot 5} \times \frac{21}{6}$$

$$= 1 \cdot 9$$

The estimated line is therefore $y = 1 \cdot 9 + 0 \cdot 83x$.

The 95 per cent confidence limits for α are

$$1 \cdot 9 \pm 1 \cdot 96 \times 0 \cdot 1 \sqrt{\frac{3 \cdot 5^2}{17 \cdot 5} + \frac{1}{6}}$$

leading to the 95 per cent confidence interval $[1 \cdot 72, 2 \cdot 08]$.

The 95 per cent confidence limits for β are

$$\frac{14 \cdot 5}{17 \cdot 5} \pm \frac{1 \cdot 96 \times 0 \cdot 1}{\sqrt{17 \cdot 5}}$$

leading to the 95 per cent confidence interval $[0 \cdot 78, 0 \cdot 88]$.

The 95 per cent confidence limits for y when $x = 2$ are

$$1 \cdot 9 + 2 \times \frac{14 \cdot 5}{17 \cdot 5} \pm 1 \cdot 96 \times 0 \cdot 1 \sqrt{\frac{(2 - 3 \cdot 5)^2}{17 \cdot 5} + \frac{1}{6}}$$

leading to the confidence interval $[3 \cdot 45, 3 \cdot 64]$.

REMAINDER THEOREM

This theorem states that if the polynomial $f(x)$ is divided by $x - a$, then the remainder is equal to $f(a)$.

This is easily seen by letting

$$\frac{f(x)}{x - a} = g(x) + \frac{R}{x - a}$$

where R denotes the remainder.

It follows, multiplying throughout by $x - a$, that

$$f(x) = (x - a)g(x) + R$$

whence putting $x = a$,

$$R = f(a)$$

RESISTIVE FORCE

◀ Force, Work ▶

RESULTANT OF A SET OF FORCES

The resultant of a system of forces F_1, F_2, ... F_n is the algebraic sum of these forces, that is

$$R = F_1 + F_2 + \ldots + F_n$$

The simplest way to find R in a given situation is to resolve all forces in two perpendicular directions, add the two sets of components, and then combine the two resulting components using the **vector** *addition law*.

Worked example

Fig. R.4 shows a rectangle $ABCD$, and $B\hat{D}C = 30°$. Forces of 2N, 5N and 3N act along DA, DB and CD respectively. Find the resultant force.

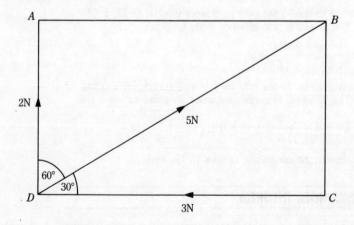

Fig. R.4

We resolve all forces in the directions DC and DA.

Component along DC = $0 + 5 \cos 30° - 3$

$\approx 1 \cdot 33$

Component along DA = $2 + 5 \cos 60°$

$= 4 \cdot 50$

This can be represented as shown in Fig. R.5.

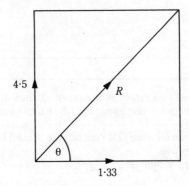

Fig. R.5

Then,

$$R^2 = 4 \cdot 5^2 + 1 \cdot 33^2$$

whence $R = \sqrt{4 \cdot 5^2 + 1 \cdot 33^2}$

$= 4 \cdot 69 \text{N}$

In this case, the three forces are concurrent and the resultant also passes through this point of concurrence, that is, D.

To find the direction of the resultant, let θ denote the angle between R and CD. Then

$$\tan \theta = \frac{4 \cdot 5}{1 \cdot 33}$$

so that $\theta = \tan^{-1} \left(\dfrac{4 \cdot 5}{1 \cdot 33} \right) \approx 74°$

◀ Equilibrium, Triangle (polygon) of forces ▶

RHOMBUS

◀ Plane shape ▶

RIGID BODIES

◀ Centre of mass, Equilibrium ▶

SAMPLE SPACE

The sample space of an experiment is the set of all possible outcomes. For example, if 2 coins are tossed simultaneously, the sample space is
    {HH, HT, TH, TT}
where the first letter denotes the first coin and the second letter the second coin (H = head, T = tail).
◀ Probability density function ▶

SAMPLE VARIANCE

◀ Variance ▶

SCALAR (AND VECTOR)

A quantity which has magnitude and no direction is referred to as a scalar quantity. It is specified by a real number when appropriate units have been chosen: length in metres, temperature in degrees centigrade, for instance.

You should remember that a non-zero **vector** is a combination of i) a positive real number, (that is, the magnitude or length of the vector) and ii) a direction in space. A vector is often represented by a segment of a straight line, the length of the line segment indicating the magnitude of the vector, and the direction of the line (indicated by an arrow), the direction of the vector. Consequently, such vectors are often denoted by $\overrightarrow{PQ}$, where P and Q are the end points of the segment and the arrow indicates the direction. An alternative notation is to denote the vector by a single bold letter, say **F**.

The magnitude of the vector is usually denoted by $|\overrightarrow{PQ}|$ or PQ and $|\mathbf{F}|$ or F.
◀ Vector ▶

SCALAR PRODUCT (DOT PRODUCT)

The scalar product of the two vectors **a**, **b** written **a.b**, is a scalar defined by
    $\mathbf{a}.\mathbf{b} = ab \cos \theta$

where a, b denote the magnitudes of $\mathbf{a}$, $\mathbf{b}$ and θ denotes the angle between $\mathbf{a}$ and $\mathbf{b}$.

It follows that $\mathbf{a} \cdot \mathbf{b} = 0$ if $\theta = 90°$, that is, if $\mathbf{a}$, $\mathbf{b}$ are perpendicular. If $\mathbf{a}$, $\mathbf{b}$ are expressed in component form

$$\mathbf{a} = a_x\mathbf{i} + a_y\mathbf{j} + a_z\mathbf{k}$$
and $$\mathbf{b} = b_x\mathbf{i} + b_y\mathbf{j} + b_z\mathbf{k}$$

where $\mathbf{i}$, $\mathbf{j}$, $\mathbf{k}$ is a set of mutually perpendicular unit vectors, then

$$\begin{aligned}
\mathbf{a} \cdot \mathbf{b} &= (a_x\mathbf{i} + a_y\mathbf{j} + a_z\mathbf{k}) \cdot (b_x\mathbf{i} + b_y\mathbf{j} + b_z\mathbf{k}) \\
&= a_x b_x \mathbf{i} \cdot \mathbf{i} + a_x b_y \mathbf{i} \cdot \mathbf{j} + a_x b_z \mathbf{i} \cdot \mathbf{k} \\
&\quad + a_y b_x \mathbf{j} \cdot \mathbf{i} + a_y b_y \mathbf{j} \cdot \mathbf{j} + a_y b_z \mathbf{j} \cdot \mathbf{k} \\
&\quad + a_z b_x \mathbf{k} \cdot \mathbf{i} + a_z b_y \mathbf{k} \cdot \mathbf{j} + a_z b_z \mathbf{k} \cdot \mathbf{k} \\
&= a_x b_x + a_y b_y + a_z b_z
\end{aligned}$$

since $\mathbf{i} \cdot \mathbf{i} = \mathbf{j} \cdot \mathbf{j} = \mathbf{k} \cdot \mathbf{k} = 1$ and $\mathbf{i} \cdot \mathbf{j} = \mathbf{j} \cdot \mathbf{i} = \mathbf{j} \cdot \mathbf{k} = \mathbf{k} \cdot \mathbf{j} = \mathbf{k} \cdot \mathbf{i} = \mathbf{i} \cdot \mathbf{k} = 0$.

This formula leads to a method for calculating the angle θ between the vectors $\mathbf{a}$, $\mathbf{b}$. Since

$$\mathbf{a} \cdot \mathbf{b} = ab \cos \theta$$

it follows that

$$\cos \theta = \frac{\mathbf{a} \cdot \mathbf{b}}{ab}$$

$$= \frac{a_x b_x + a_y b_y + a_z b_z}{\sqrt{a_x^2 + a_y^2 + a_z^2}\sqrt{b_x^2 + b_y^2 + b_z^2}}$$

The condition for $\mathbf{a}$, $\mathbf{b}$ to be perpendicular is that

$$a_x b_x + a_y b_y + a_z b_z = 0$$

◀ Vector ▶

SECTOR

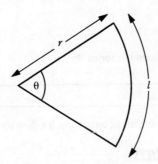

Fig. S.1

A sector of a **circle** is a region bounded by two radii and part of the circumference, as, for instance, in Fig. S.1.

If the angle between the two radii is θ and the length of the radius is r, then

  i) arc length $l = r\theta$
  ii) Area of sector $A = \frac{1}{2}r^2\theta$

SEGMENT

A **segment** of a **circle** is the region enclosed between a chord and part of the circumference, as, for example, in Fig. S.2. A chord generates two segments; the larger is called the *major segment* and the smaller the *minor segment*.

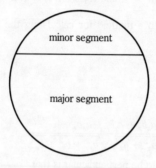

Fig. S.2

SEQUENCE

A sequence is a set of terms in order with a definite rule for calculating each term, such as
  1, 4, 9, 16, 25...
Here, the rth term is given by
  $T_r = r^2$
◀ Arithmetic series, Geometric series ▶

SERIES

A series is the sum of a number of terms which follow some set pattern.

▶ *STANDARD RESULTS*

Standard results are as follows.

$$\sum_{r=1}^{n} r = \frac{n(n + 1)}{2}$$

$$\sum_{r=1}^{n} r^2 = \frac{n(n+1)(2n+1)}{6}$$

$$\sum_{r=1}^{n} r^3 = \frac{n^2(n+1)^2}{4}$$

These standard results can be used to sum more complicated series, as shown in the following example.

Worked example

Sum the series
$$1.2.3 + 2.3.5 + 3.4.7 + \ldots + n(n+1)(2n+1)$$

Here, the rth term T_r is given by
$$T_r = r(r+1)(2r+1)$$
Thus, we require

$$\begin{aligned}
S_n &= \sum_{r=1}^{n} T_r \\
&= \sum_{r=1}^{n} r(r+1)(2r+1) \\
&= \sum_{r=1}^{n} r(2r^2 + 3r + 1) \\
&= \sum_{r=1}^{n} (2r^3 + 3r^2 + r) \\
&= 2\sum_{r=1}^{n} r^3 + 3\sum_{r=1}^{n} r^2 + \sum_{r=1}^{n} r \\
&= \frac{2n^2(n+1)^2}{4} + \frac{3n(n+1)(2n+1)}{6} + \frac{n(n+1)}{2} \\
&= \frac{n(n+1)}{2}(n^2 + n + 2n + 1 + 1) \\
&= \frac{n(n+1)^2(n+2)}{2}
\end{aligned}$$

◀ Arithmetic series, Geometric series ▶

SHEAR

A shear is a transformation that pushes a shape over in a way such that the further a point is from the *invariant line*, the further it will move.

For example, suppose we wish to shear the triangle ABC in Fig. S.3 with a shear factor 3, where the x-axis is the invariant line. The diagram shows you what we have done.

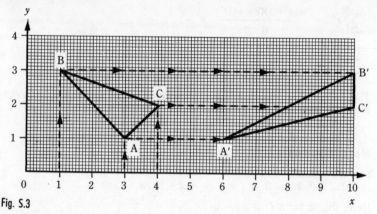

Fig. S.3

Each point, and in particular each *vertex*, must move parallel to the x-axis in a positive sense by the simple expression:

distance from invariant line × shear factor

Hence A is to move $1 \times 3 = 3$ units
       B is to move $3 \times 3 = 9$ units
       C is to move $2 \times 3 = 6$ units
This moves the shape to A'B'C' as seen in the diagram.

SHELL METHOD

◀ Volume of revolution ▶

SHM

◀ Simple harmonic motion ▶

SIGNIFICANCE LEVEL

The significance level of a **hypothesis** test is the probability of making a *Type 1* error, that is, of accepting H_1 when H_0 is true.

SIMPLE HARMONIC MOTION (SHM)

A point P is said to execute simple harmonic motion if its displacement x from an origin O satisfies the **differential equation**

$$\text{Acceleration} = \frac{d^2x}{dt^2} = -\omega^2 x$$

where ω is a positive constant.

The differential equation can be written in the form

$$\frac{d^2x}{dt^2} + \omega^2 x = 0$$

This is a second-order differential equation with constant coefficients. The general solution is

$$x = Ae^{\alpha t} + Be^{\beta t}$$

where A, B are arbitrary constants and α, β are the roots of the auxiliary equation $m^2 + \omega^2 = 0$. The roots are α, $\beta = \pm i\omega$. The general solution is therefore

$$x = Ae^{i\omega t} + Be^{-i\omega t}$$
$$= A(\cos \omega t + i \sin \omega t) + B(\cos \omega t - i \sin \omega t)$$
$$= C \cos \omega t + D \sin \omega t$$

where C, D are arbitrary constants.

We now assume that $x = 0$ when $t = 0$, that is, that the particle is passing through the origin at time $t = 0$. Substituting,

$$0 = C.$$

so that

$$x = D \sin \omega t$$

Further assume that the maximum value of x is a, so that $D = a$. Thus,

$$x = a \sin \omega t$$

We note that if t is increased by an amount $\dfrac{2\pi}{\omega}$, x is unchanged. Thus, the period T is given by

$$T = \frac{2\pi}{\omega}$$

The velocity v at time t is given by

$$v = \frac{dx}{dt} = \omega a \cos \omega t$$

Since

$$\sin \omega t = \frac{x}{a}$$

and

$$\cos \omega t = \frac{x}{a}$$

it follows that

$$\left(\frac{x}{a}\right)^2 + \left(\frac{v}{\omega a}\right)^2 = 1$$

which reduces to

$$v^2 = \omega^2(a^2 - x^2)$$

SIMPSON'S RULE

Simpson's rule is a formula which gives an approximation to a definite integral. The basic result is that, for small $b - a$,

$$\int_a^b f(x)\mathrm{d}x \approx \frac{(b - a)}{6}\left[f(a) + 4f\left(\frac{a + b}{2}\right) + f(b)\right]$$

An alternative form is

$$\int_{x_0}^{x_2} y\,\mathrm{d}x \approx \frac{h}{3}(y_0 + 4y_1 + y_2)$$

where $h = \frac{1}{2}(b - a)$ and y_0, y_1, y_2 are the values of y corresponding to x_0, x_1, x_2 where $x_1 = \frac{1}{2}(x_0 + x_2)$.

The derivation of Simpson's rule is outside most A-level syllabuses, but it is interesting to note that the formula is derived by fitting a quadratic curve through the points P_0, P_1 and P_2 and using the area under the quadratic as an approximation to the area under the curve.

Fig. S.4 shows that the approximation is based on three ordinates and two strips; h is sometimes called the *interval*.

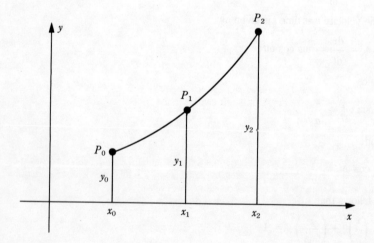

Fig. S.4

Worked example A

Use Simpson's rule to find an approximate value of

$$\int_0^1 \frac{dx}{1+x}$$

NB. This integral can be evaluated exactly as $\ln 2 \approx 0.6931$. We are considering this simple example so that we can compare the approximation with the true value. In practice, of course, we would use an approximate method such as Simpson's rule only if the exact value cannot be determined using standard methods of integration.

Here $x_0 = 0$, $x_1 = \dfrac{1}{2}$ and $x_2 = 1$.

Thus

$$y_0 = \frac{1}{1+0} = 1$$

$$y_1 = \frac{1}{1+\dfrac{1}{2}} = \frac{2}{3}$$

and

$$y_2 = \frac{1}{1+1} = \frac{1}{2}$$

Finally, $h = \dfrac{1}{2}(1-0) = \dfrac{1}{2}$ so that Simpson's rule gives

$$\int_0^1 \frac{dx}{1+x} \approx \frac{1}{6}\left(1 + \left(4 \times \frac{2}{3}\right) + \frac{1}{2}\right) = 0.6944$$

The error is seen to be 0.0013 or approximately 0.2 per cent.

A more accurate approximation can be found by noting that

$$\int_{x_0}^{x_2} y\,dx = \int_{x_0}^{x_1} y\,dx + \int_{x_1}^{x_2} y\,dx$$

and then applying the basic Simpson's rule to each of the integrals on the right-hand side. This can be extended by expressing the integral on the left-hand side as the sum of m integrals on equal intervals.

This leads to the following extended form of Simpson's rule:

$$\int_{x_0}^{x_n} y\,dx \approx \frac{h}{3}(y_0 + 4y_1 + 2y_2 + 4y_3 + \ldots + 2y_{n-2} + 4y_{n-1} + y_n)$$

where $h = \dfrac{x_n - x_0}{n}$, $x_r = x_0 + rh$ $(r = 0, 1, 2, \ldots n)$

and y_r is the value of y corresponding to $x = x_r$. This approximation is based on $(n + 1)$ ordinates and therefore n strips, and is valid for *even* values of n.

NB. The right-hand side can be remembered as 'first and last plus twice the evens plus four times the odds'.

Worked example B

Use Simpson's rule with 6 strips (and therefore 7 ordinates) to calculate an approximation to

$$\int_0^1 \frac{dx}{1 + x}$$

Here $x_0 = 0$, $x_6 = 1$, $h = \dfrac{1}{6}$ and $x_r = \dfrac{r}{6}$

Thus,

$$y_0 = \frac{1}{1 + 0} = 1$$

$$y_1 = \frac{1}{1 + \dfrac{1}{6}} = \frac{6}{7}$$

$$y_2 = \frac{1}{1 + \dfrac{1}{3}} = \frac{3}{4}$$

$$y_3 = \frac{1}{1 + \dfrac{1}{2}} = \frac{2}{3}$$

$$y_4 = \frac{1}{1 + \dfrac{2}{3}} = \frac{3}{5}$$

$$y_5 = \frac{1}{1 + \dfrac{5}{6}} = \frac{6}{11}$$

and

$$y_6 = \frac{1}{1 + 1} = \frac{1}{2}$$

Thus,

$$\int_0^1 \frac{dx}{1+x} \approx \frac{1}{18}\left[1 + \left(4 \times \frac{6}{7}\right) + \left(2 \times \frac{3}{4}\right) + \left(4 \times \frac{2}{3}\right) + \left(2 \times \frac{3}{5}\right) \right.$$
$$\left. + \left(4 \times \frac{6}{11}\right) + \frac{1}{2}\right]$$

$$= 0\cdot6931698$$

The true value (to seven decimal places) is $0\cdot6931472$, and the error has dropped to approximately $0\cdot003$ per cent.

These results illustrate the point that Simpson's rule can be used to evaluate an integral to any desired accuracy, if we take a large enough number of ordinates, and therefore a small enough interval (that is, h).

SIMULTANEOUS LINEAR EQUATIONS

Consider the equations

$$a_{11}x_1 + a_{12}x_2 + \ldots + a_{1n}x_n = b_1$$
$$a_{21}x_1 + a_{22}x_2 + \ldots + a_{2n}x_n = b_2$$
$$a_{n1}x_1 + a_{n2}x_2 + \ldots + a_{nn}x_n = b_n$$

or

$$\mathbf{AX} = \mathbf{B}$$

where

$$\mathbf{A} = \begin{bmatrix} a_{11} & a_{12} & & a_{1n} \\ a_{21} & a_{22} & & a_{2n} \\ & & & \\ a_{n1} & a_{n2} & & a_{nn} \end{bmatrix}; \quad \mathbf{X} = \begin{bmatrix} x_1 \\ x_2 \\ \\ x_n \end{bmatrix}; \quad \mathbf{B} = \begin{bmatrix} b_1 \\ b_2 \\ \\ b_n \end{bmatrix}$$

If $\mathbf{A}$ is non-singular, then these n simultaneous equations in n unknowns have a unique solution. There are two standard methods for finding this unique solution.

▶ *METHOD 1*

Since

$$\mathbf{AX} = \mathbf{B}$$

It follows, pre-multiplying by $\mathbf{A}^{-1}$, that

$$\mathbf{A}^{-1}\mathbf{AX} = \mathbf{A}^{-1}\mathbf{B}$$

or

$$\mathbf{X} = \mathbf{A}^{-1}\mathbf{B}$$

The problem of solving the equations is therefore equivalent to inverting the coefficient matrix $\mathbf{A}$.

▶ *METHOD 2*

The idea here is to reduce the equations to echelon form, that is, to a set of equations in which the first equation contains x_1, x_2, ... x_n, the second equation contains x_2, x_3, ... x_n, the third equation contains x_3, x_4, ... x_n, and the last equation contains only x_n. This is done by adding and subtracting equations systematically. The equations can then be solved sequentially.

We can illustrate by means of an example, taking $n = 3$.

Worked example for standard methods

Solve the equations

$$x + 2y + 4z = 1$$
$$2x + 3y + 6z = 3$$
$$3x + 5y + 8z = 2$$

or, in matrix form

$$\begin{bmatrix} 1 & 2 & 4 \\ 2 & 3 & 6 \\ 3 & 5 & 8 \end{bmatrix} \begin{bmatrix} x \\ y \\ z \end{bmatrix} = \begin{bmatrix} 1 \\ 3 \\ 2 \end{bmatrix}$$

Method 1

$$\begin{bmatrix} x \\ y \\ z \end{bmatrix} = \begin{bmatrix} 1 & 2 & 4 \\ 2 & 3 & 6 \\ 3 & 5 & 8 \end{bmatrix}^{-1} \begin{bmatrix} 1 \\ 3 \\ 2 \end{bmatrix}$$

$$= \begin{bmatrix} -3 & 2 & 0 \\ 1 & -2 & 1 \\ \frac{1}{2} & \frac{1}{2} & -\frac{1}{2} \end{bmatrix} \begin{bmatrix} 1 \\ 3 \\ 2 \end{bmatrix}$$

(See the entry on **matrix / matrices** for this inversion.)

$$= \begin{bmatrix} 3 \\ -3 \\ 1 \end{bmatrix}$$

that is, $x = 3$, $y = -3$, $z = 1$.

Method 2

$$x + 2y + 4z = 1$$
$$2x + 3y + 6z = 3$$
$$3x + 5y + 8z = 2$$

Replace second equation by second equation minus $2 \times$ first equation

$$x + 2y + 4z = 1$$
$$-y - 2z = 1$$
$$3x + 5y + 8z = 2$$

Replace third equation by third equation minus $3 \times$ first equation

$$x + 2y + 4z = 1$$
$$-y - 2z = 1$$
$$-y - 4z = -1$$

Replace third equation by third equation minus second equation

$$x + 2y + 4z = 1$$
$$-y - 2z = 1$$
$$-2z = -2$$

These equations can now be solved starting from the bottom and working upwards.

From the third equation, $z = 1$. Substituting into the second equation,
$$-y = 1 + 2z = 3$$
so that $y = -3$
Substituting into the 1st equation
$$x = 1 - 2y - 4z$$
$$= 1 + 6 - 4 = 3$$

This case is equivalent geometrically to three planes meeting in a single point.

▶ AMBIGUOUS CASES

If **A** is singular, then the equations do not have a unique solution. In fact, they may have no solution at all; if they do have solutions, the equations are called *consistent*. We can consider only the case $n = 3$, and proceed by the following example.

Worked example for ambiguous case A

Solve the equations
$$x + 2y + 4z = 1$$
$$2x + 3y + 6z = 3$$
$$3x + 5y + 10z = 2$$
or in matrix form
$$\begin{bmatrix} 1 & 2 & 4 \\ 2 & 3 & 6 \\ 3 & 5 & 10 \end{bmatrix} \begin{bmatrix} x \\ y \\ z \end{bmatrix} = \begin{bmatrix} 1 \\ 3 \\ 2 \end{bmatrix}$$

If we try to solve these equations using Method 1, we find that we cannot invert the coefficient matrix since it is singular (its determinant is zero). The formula

$$\mathbf{A}^{-1} = \frac{\text{adj } \mathbf{A}}{|\mathbf{A}|}$$

therefore cannot be used.

Let us try Method 2.
$$x + 2y + 4z = 1$$
$$2x + 3y + 6z = 3$$
$$3x + 5y + 10z = 2$$
Replace second equation by second equation minus 2 × first equation
$$x + 2y + 4z = 1$$
$$-y - 2z = 1$$
$$3x + 5y + 10z = 2$$
Replace third equation by third equation minus 3 × first equation
$$x + 2y + 4z = 1$$
$$-y - 2z = 1$$
$$-y - 2z = -1$$
There is now an immediate difficulty, since $-y - 2z$ cannot equal both 1 and -1. The equations are inconsistent and have no solutions. This leads to another, modified example.

Worked example for ambiguous case B

$$x + 2y + 4z = 1$$
$$2x + 3y + 6z = 3$$
$$3x + 5y + 10z = 4$$

Proceeding as before, we reach the equations

$$x + 2y + 4z = 1$$
$$-y - 2z = 1$$
$$-y - 2z = 1$$

The second and third equations are now consistent. We have, effectively, two equations for three unknowns. There is no unique solution, and we proceed as follows.

Let $z = \zeta$. Then, from the second or third equation,

$$-y = 1 + 2z$$

or $y = -1 - 2\zeta$

Substituting in the first equation,

$$x = 1 - 2y - 4z$$
$$= 1 - 2(-1 - 2\zeta) - 4\zeta$$
$$= 3$$

The general solution is therefore

$$x = 3, \; y = -1 - 2\zeta, \; z = \zeta \text{ for any } \zeta$$

As we vary ζ, the general solution generates a straight line. The case is equivalent geometrically to three planes intersecting in a line (a sheaf).

Yet another possibility can arise, as can be seen from the following example.

Worked example for ambiguous case C

$$x + 2y + 4z = 1$$
$$2x + 4y + 8z = 3$$
$$3x + 6y + 12z = 2$$

It is clear that, dividing the second equation by 2 and the third equation by 3,

$$x + 2y + 4z = 1$$
$$x + 2y + 4z = 3/2$$
$$x + 2y + 4z = 2/3$$

Now $x + 2y + 4z$ cannot equal 1, 3/2 and 2/3 simultaneously. The equations are inconsistent. This leads us to consider a further example.

Worked example for ambiguous case D

$$x + 2y + 4z = 1$$
$$2x + 4y + 8z = 2$$
$$3x + 6y + 12z = 3$$

Proceeding as before, the equations reduce to

$$x + 2y + 4z = 1$$
$$x + 2y + 4z = 1$$
$$x + 2y + 4z = 1$$

The three equations are identical and, of course, consistent. We have effectively one equation for three unknowns. There is no unique solution and we proceed as follows.

Let $y = \eta$, $z = \zeta$. Then, substituting
$$x = 1 - 2y - 4z$$
$$= 1 - 2\eta - 4\zeta$$
The general solution is
$$x = 1 - 2\eta - 4\zeta, \ y = \eta, \ z = \zeta$$
As we vary η, ζ, the general solution generates the plane
$$x + 2y + 4z = 1$$
◀ Matrix/matrices ▶

SINE RULE

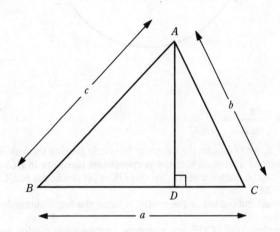

Fig. S.5

The sine rule for a triangle states that

$$\frac{a}{\sin A} = \frac{b}{\sin B} = \frac{c}{\sin C}$$

To prove this result, drop a perpendicular from A to BC. Referring to the diagram in Fig. S.5,
$$AD = c \sin B = b \sin C$$
whence

$$\frac{b}{\sin B} = \frac{c}{\sin C}$$

By **symmetry**, both ratios are also equal to $a/\sin A$.

A more general result is that if R denotes the radius of the circle passing through A, B, C (the circumscribing circle), then

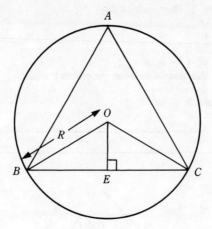

Fig. S.6

$$\frac{a}{\sin A} = \frac{b}{\sin B} = \frac{c}{\sin C} = 2R$$

In Fig. S.6, let O denote the centre of the circle passing through A, B, C; O is the point of intersection of the perpendicular bisectors of BC, CA and AB. Let E be the midpoint of BC, so that OE is perpendicular to BC. Now

$$B\hat{O}C = 2A$$

since the angle subtended at the centre is twice the angle subtended at the circumference.

The triangles BOE, COE are *congruent* (corresponding sides are equal) so that $B\hat{O}E = C\hat{O}E$. Thus,

$$B\hat{O}E = A$$

Now,

$$\sin B\hat{O}E = \frac{BE}{BO}$$

or

$$\sin A = \frac{\frac{1}{2}a}{R}$$

or

$$2R = \frac{a}{\sin A}$$

Using the previous result, $2R$ is also equal to $\dfrac{b}{\sin B}$ and $\dfrac{c}{\sin C}$

Worked example A

A and B are two points on one bank of a straight river such that AB is 649 m.

C is on the other bank and angles CAB, CBA are respectively $48°31'$ and $75°25'$. Find the width of the river (see Fig. S.7).

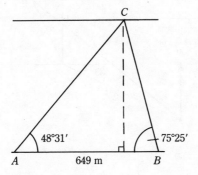

Fig. S.7

$\angle ACB = 180° - (48°31' + 75°25') = 180° - 123°56' = 56°4'$

Sine rule $\Rightarrow \dfrac{AC}{\sin 75°25'} = \dfrac{649}{\sin 56°4'} \Rightarrow AC = 757{\cdot}0\,\text{m}$

Width of river $= AC \sin 48°31' = 757 \sin 48°31' = 567{\cdot}1\,\text{m} \approx 567\,\text{m}$

Worked example B

Use the sine rule to show that for any plane triangle ABC

$$\tan\frac{A}{2}\tan\frac{B-C}{2} = \frac{b-c}{b+c}$$

Three ships at sea are such that the bearings of ships B and C from A are $36°$ and $247°$ respectively. Given that B is $120\,\text{km}$ from A and C is $234\,\text{km}$ from A calculate the bearing and distance of ship B from ship C (Fig. S.8).

$$\frac{b-c}{b+c} = \frac{\sin B - \sin C}{\sin B + \sin C} = \frac{2\cos\left(\dfrac{B+C}{2}\right)\sin\left(\dfrac{B-C}{2}\right)}{2\sin\left(\dfrac{B+C}{2}\right)\cos\left(\dfrac{B-C}{2}\right)}$$

$$= \cot\left(\frac{B+C}{2}\right)\tan\left(\frac{B-C}{2}\right) = \cot\left(\frac{\pi}{2} - \frac{A}{2}\right)\tan\left(\frac{B-C}{2}\right)$$

$$= \tan\frac{A}{2}\tan\frac{(B-C)}{2}$$

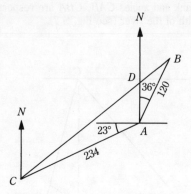

Fig. S.8

In solving problems such as this, the first step is to draw an accurate diagram of the situation, marking all known angles and distances.

$b = 234$, $c = 120$, $\angle BAC = 149°$

$$\Rightarrow \tan\left(\frac{149°}{2}\right) \tan\left(\frac{B-C}{2}\right) = \frac{234 - 120}{234 + 120} = \frac{114}{354}$$

$$\Rightarrow \tan\left(\frac{B-C}{2}\right) = 0.0893 \Rightarrow \frac{B-C}{2} = 5.1°$$

$\Rightarrow \angle B - \angle C = 10.2°$
But $\angle B + \angle C = 180° - 149° = 31° \Rightarrow \angle B = 20.6°$, $\angle C = 12.95°$
Hence $\angle CDA = 36° + 20.6° = 56.6°$
That is, bearing of ship B from ship C is $56.6°$

From $\triangle ABC \Rightarrow \dfrac{BC}{\sin 149°} = \dfrac{234}{\sin 20.6°} \Rightarrow BC = 342.5$

$\Rightarrow$ Distance of ship B from ship C is approximately 342.5 km.

SKEW LINES

Two non-parallel straight lines in three dimensions are called skew if they do not intersect. The method for finding whether or not two such lines are skew is to attempt to find their point of intersection. If no point of intersection can be found, then the lines are skew. The following example illustrates the method.

Worked example

Investigate whether or not the following lines are skew.

i) $\dfrac{x}{2} = \dfrac{y-2}{3} = \dfrac{z+1}{4}$ $(= \lambda)$

ii) $\dfrac{x-2}{3} = y+1 = \dfrac{z-1}{2}$ $(= \mu)$

Line i) can be written in the form
$x = 2\lambda$
$y = 3\lambda + 2$
$z = 4\lambda - 1$

Line ii) can be written in the form
$x = 3\mu + 2$
$y = \mu - 1$
$z = 2\mu + 1$

At a point of intersection, therefore,
$$2\lambda = 3\mu + 2$$
$$3\lambda + 2 = \mu - 1$$
and $4\lambda - 1 = 2\mu + 1$
which reduce to
$$2\lambda - 3\mu = 2 \tag{1}$$
$$3\lambda - \mu = -3 \tag{2}$$
$$4\lambda - 2\mu = 2 \tag{3}$$

If values of λ, μ can be found to satisfy these three equations, then the lines intersect; if not, then the lines are skew. We proceed by solving (1) and (2). Subtracting 3 times (2) from (1) gives
$$-7\lambda = 7$$
or $\lambda = -1$
Substituting in (2),
$$\mu = 3(-1) + 3 = 0$$
Thus $\lambda = -1$ and $\mu = 0$ satisfy equations (1) and (2). We see by inspection that these values do not satisfy equation (3) so that values of λ, μ to satisfy all three equations cannot be found. The lines are therefore skew.

SOLID SHAPE

Solid shapes are three-dimensional figures.

A *cube* (Fig. S.9) has all its sides the same length; each face is a square; volume = length³.

A *cuboid* (Fig. S.10) has each opposite edge the same length; each face is a rectangle; volume = length × breadth × height.

In a *sphere* (Fig. S.11) the distance from the centre of the sphere to its outer edge is *constant* and is called

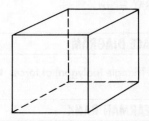

Fig. S.9

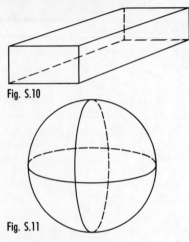

Fig. S.10

Fig. S.11

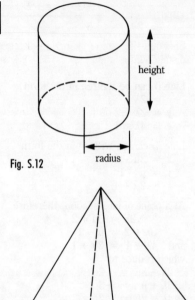

Fig. S.12

its *radius* (r); volume = $\frac{4}{3} \times \pi \times r^3$; surface area = $4 \times \pi \times r^2$.

A *cylinder* (Fig. S.12) is a prism whose regular cross-section is a circle; volume = $\pi \times$ radius$^2 \times$ height, curved surface area = $2 \times \pi \times$ radius $\times$ height; total surface area = $2 \times \pi \times$ radius $\times$ height *plus* $2 \times \pi \times$ radius^2.

In a *pyramid* (Fig. S.13) the base can be any shape; from each point on the perimeter of the base there is a straight line that goes up to the same point at the top (the *vertex*); volume = $\frac{1}{3} \times$ base area $\times$ height.

A *cone* (Fig. S.14) is a pyramid with a circular base; where a *cone* of height h has a base radius r and a slant height of l, then: volume = $\frac{1}{3} \times \pi \times r^2 \times h$; curved surface area (CSA) = $\pi r l$.

Fig. S.13

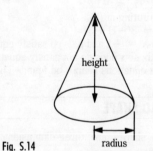

Fig. S.14

SPACE DIAGRAM

◄ Triangle (polygon) of forces ►

SPEARMAN RANK

◄ Correlation coefficient (Spearman rank) ►

SPEED

Speed is the rate of change of distance. It can be found by the *gradient* of a distance/time graph.

▶ AVERAGE SPEED

Average speed is found by the total distance travelled divided by the total travelling time. The units of speed can vary with the data used to calculate it.

For example, James cycled 28 mile in 2 hours, or $\frac{28}{2} = 14$ miles per hour. John ran 10,000 metres in 14 minutes, or $\frac{10,000}{14} = 714$ metres per minute.

◀ Kinematics, Velocity ▶

SPHERE

◀ Solid shape ▶

SQUARE

◀ Plane shape ▶

SQUARE MATRIX

◀ Matrix/matrices ▶

STANDARD DEVIATION

The standard deviation is the positive square root of the **variance**.
◀ Variance ▶

STANDARD ERROR

◀ Estimator ▶

STATICS

Statics is that branch of Applied Mathematics which deals with the **equilibrium** of bodies. Most problems are solved by considering horizontal and vertical equilibrium and by taking **moments**.

Worked example

The foot of a uniform ladder of length 2m and weight W(N) rests on rough horizontal ground, and the top of the ladder rests against a smooth vertical wall. The ladder is inclined at an angle α to the horizontal, and the ground is rough enough to prevent slipping. Find, in terms of W and α,

  i) the frictional force;
 ii) the magnitude of the total force exerted by the ground on the ladder;
iii) the minimum possible value of μ, the coefficient of friction between the ladder and the ground.

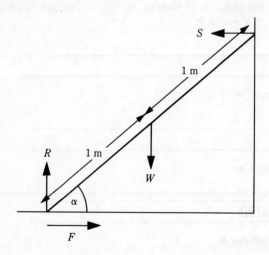

Fig. S.15

In Fig. S.15, let F, R, S (N) denote respectively the frictional force, the normal reaction on the foot of the ladder and the normal reaction on the top of the ladder.

  i) Since the ladder is in equilibrium,
$$F = S$$
and $R = W$
Taking moments about the foot of the ladder,
$$W \cos \alpha = S.2 \sin \alpha$$
whence
$$F = S = \tfrac{1}{2}W \cot \alpha$$

 ii) Magnitude of force exerted by ground on ladder
$$= \sqrt{R^2 + F^2}$$
$$= \sqrt{W^2 + \tfrac{1}{4}W^2 \cot^2 \alpha}$$
$$= W\sqrt{1 + \tfrac{1}{4} \cot^2 \alpha}$$

iii) Since

$$\frac{F}{R} \leq \mu$$

it follows that

$$\mu \geq \frac{\frac{1}{2}W \cot \alpha}{W}$$

$$= \tfrac{1}{2} \cot \alpha$$

Thus

$$\mu_{\min} = \tfrac{1}{2} \cot \alpha$$

STATISTIC

Given a **random sample** $X_1, X_2, \ldots X_n$ from some distribution, a statistic is defined as a function of $X_1, X_2, \ldots X_n$ that does not also depend upon unknown parameters.

For example, if the sample is taken from the $N(\mu, \sigma^2)$ where μ is unknown,

$$\sum_{i=1}^{n} X_i^2 \text{ is a statistic}$$

whereas $\displaystyle\sum_{i=1}^{n} (X_i - \mu)^2$ is *not* a statistic.

This latter function would be a statistic if the value of μ were known.

STATISTICAL HYPOTHESIS

◀ Hypothesis ▶

STRAIGHT LINE (COORDINATE GEOMETRY)

◀ Line ▶

STRETCH

A stretch is a geometrical transformation which enlarges a shape in different directions with different 'stretch factors'. A *one-way* stretch is in one direction only; a *two-way* stretch is in two directions at once.

STUDENT'S *t*-DISTRIBUTION

The continuous **random variable** T has the student's *t*-distribution with n

degrees of freedom if its **probability density function** is given by

$$f(t) = k\left(1 + \frac{t^2}{n}\right)^{-\left(\frac{n+1}{2}\right)} \qquad \text{(all } t\text{)}$$

where k is a 'normalising constant' ensuring that the total area under the curve is equal to unity.

The graph of $f(t)$ is shown in Fig. S.16. The importance of this distribution is that if $X_1, X_2, \ldots X_n$ is a random sample from the normal distribution $N(\mu, \sigma^2)$, then

$$\frac{\bar{X} - \mu}{S/\sqrt{n}}$$

has the Student's t-distribution with $(n - 1)$ degrees of freedom,

where $\bar{X} = \dfrac{\sum\limits_{i=1}^{n} X_i}{n}$

and $S^2 = \dfrac{\sum\limits_{i=1}^{n} (X_i - \bar{x})^2}{n - 1}$

The consequence of this result is that 95 per cent **confidence** limits for μ are given by

$$\bar{x} \pm t_{.975}(n - 1) . \frac{S}{\sqrt{n}}$$

where $t_p(n)$ is the $100p$th percentile of the student's t-distribution with n degrees of freedom.

This shows that the consequence of replacing σ by its estimated value S is that the normal percentile (1·96) has to be replaced by the corresponding Student's t percentile.

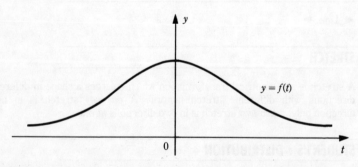

$y = f(t)$

Fig. S.16

SUBSTITUTION (INTEGRATION BY)

The basic result here is that, if $x = \phi(y)$,

$$\int f(x)\mathrm{d}x = \int f[\phi(y)] \frac{\mathrm{d}x}{\mathrm{d}y} \mathrm{d}y$$

The idea is to choose a function ϕ which transforms the integral into a standard form. In the case of a *definite integral*, the limits also have to be transformed as follows:

$$\int_a^b f(x)\mathrm{d}x = \int_{\phi^{-1}(a)}^{\phi^{-1}(b)} f[\phi(y)] \frac{\mathrm{d}x}{\mathrm{d}y} \mathrm{d}y$$

Worked example A

Evaluate

$$\int_0^1 \frac{x}{\sqrt{x+1}} \mathrm{d}x$$

using the substitution $x = y - 1$.

Here

$$\frac{\mathrm{d}x}{\mathrm{d}y} = 1$$

and when $x = 0$, $y = 1$ (that is, $\phi^{-1}(0) = 1$)
when $x = 1$, $y = 2$ (that is, $\phi^{-1}(1) = 2$)
Thus,

$$\int_0^1 \frac{x}{\sqrt{x+1}} \mathrm{d}x = \int_1^2 \frac{y-1}{\sqrt{y}} \mathrm{d}y$$

$$= \int_1^2 (y^{\frac{1}{2}} - y^{-\frac{1}{2}}) \mathrm{d}y$$

$$= \left[\frac{2}{3}y^{\frac{3}{2}} - 2y^{\frac{1}{2}} \right]_1^2$$

$$= \frac{2}{3}.2\sqrt{2} - 2\sqrt{2} - \frac{2}{3} + 2$$

$$= \frac{4 - 2\sqrt{2}}{3}$$

In some cases, it is easier to introduce the new variable y in the form $y = \phi(x)$ (rather than $x = \phi(y)$). The same method is used, as illustrated in worked example B.

Worked example B

Evaluate

$$\int_0^1 \frac{x}{x^2 + 1} \, dx$$

using the substitution $y = x^2 + 1$

Here

$$\frac{dy}{dx} = 2x$$

or $x \, dx = \dfrac{dy}{2}$

When $x = 0, y = 1$.
When $x = 1, y = 2$.
Thus,

$$\int_0^1 \frac{x}{x^2 + 1} \, dx = \int_1^2 \frac{1}{y} \cdot \frac{dy}{2}$$

$$= \frac{1}{2} \left[\log_e y \right]_1^2$$

$$= \frac{1}{2} \log_e 2$$

▶ *EVALUATING THE TRANSFORMED INTEGRAL*

The art of integration by substitution is to choose a new variable in such a way that the transformed integral can be evaluated. Some points to watch are given here.

Integrals of the form

$$\int \frac{f'(x)}{[f(x)]^n} \, dx$$

can be integrated by putting $y = f(x)$ – for instance, see worked example B.

For integrands containing $a^2 - x^2$,
try $x = a \sin \theta$

For integrands containing $a^2 + x^2$,
try $x = a \tan \theta$
or $x = a \sinh \theta$

For integrands containing $x^2 - a^2$,
try $x = a \sec \theta$
or $x = a \cosh \theta$

◀ Integration ▶

SYMMETRY

Symmetry is found in two- and three-dimensional shapes. There are two particular types of two-dimensional symmetry, *line* and *rotational* symmetry.

▶ LINE SYMMETRY

If you can fold a shape over so that one half fits exactly on top of the other half, then the line over which you have folded is called a *line of symmetry*. The examples in Figure S.17 illustrate this. The dotted lines are lines of symmetry.

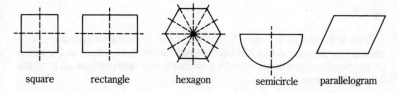

square   rectangle   hexagon   semicircle   parallelogram

Fig. S.17

▶ ROTATIONAL SYMMETRY

This is sometimes called *point symmetry*. A shape has rotational symmetry according to how many different positions it can be turned round to, so as to look exactly the same.

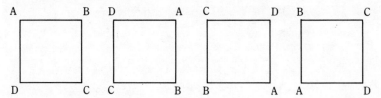

Fig. S.18

For example, a square has rotational symmetry of *order 4*, since if you turn it round its centre there are four different positions that it can take that all look the same, as shown in Figure S.18.

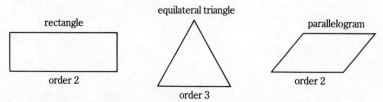

rectangle

order 2

equilateral triangle

order 3

parallelogram

order 2

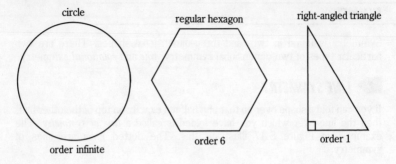

circle

regular hexagon

right-angled triangle

order infinite

order 6

order 1

Fig. S.19

Look at the shapes in Figure S.19; their orders of rotational symmetry have been given. Any shape that has what we call 'no symmetry', such as the letter Q, has rotational symmetry of *order 1*, since there is only *one* position in which it looks the same.

TANGENT

A tangent to a curve is a straight line which touches the curve, that is, it cuts the curve in two coincident points. At the point of contact, the gradients of the tangent and curve are equal. The two main methods for calculating equations of tangents are shown in the two worked examples.

Worked example showing first method

Find the equation of the tangent to the parabola $y^2 = 4x$ at the point $(4, 4)$.

Since $y^2 = 4x$, it follows, differentiating with respect to x, that

$$2y \frac{dy}{dx} = 4$$

so that $\quad \dfrac{dy}{dx} = \dfrac{4}{2y} = \dfrac{1}{2} \quad$ where $y = 4$

The gradient of the tangent is therefore equal to $\dfrac{1}{2}$, and since the tangent passes through the point $(4, 4)$, its equation is

$$(y - 4) = \frac{1}{2}(x - 4)$$

that is, $\quad y = \dfrac{1}{2}x + 2$

Worked example showing second method

Find the equations of the two tangents from the origin to the circle having equation

$$x^2 + y^2 + 6x + 2y + 2 = 0$$

The line of gradient m passing through the origin has equation $y = mx$. This meets the circle where

$$x^2 + (mx)^2 + 6x + 2mx + 2 = 0$$

or $(1 + m^2)x^2 + (6 + 2m)x + 2 = 0$

The line will be a tangent if the two roots are coincident, that is, if

$$(6 + 2m)^2 = 4 \times 2(1 + m^2)$$
$$36 + 24m + 4m^2 = 8 + 8m^2$$

which reduces to

$$m^2 - 6m - 7 = 0$$

or $(m + 1)(m - 7) = 0$

which gives $m = -1$ or 7

The equations of the two tangents are therefore $y = -x$ and $y = 7x$.

TAYLOR SERIES

The Taylor series is a power **series** for a function $f(x)$ containing **powers** of $(x - a)$. The result is

$$f(x) = f(a) + (x - a)f'(a) + \frac{(x - a)^2}{2!}f''(a) + \ldots + \frac{(x - a)^r}{r!}f^{(r)}(a) + \ldots$$

or alternatively,

$$f(x) = \sum_{r=0}^{\infty} \frac{(x - a)^r f^r(a)}{r!}$$

To prove this result, let

$$f(x) = b_0 + b_1(x - a) + b_2(x - a)^2$$
$$+ b_3(x - a)^3 + b_4(x - a)^4 + \ldots + b_r(x - a)^r + \ldots$$

By successive differentiation,

$$f'(x) = b_1 + 2b_2(x - a) + 3b_3(x - a)^2$$
$$+ 4b_4(x - a)^3 + \ldots + rb_r(x - a)^{r-1} + \ldots$$
$$f''(x) = 2b_2 + 6b_3(x - a) + 12b_4(x - a)^2 + \ldots + r(r - 1)b_r(x - a)^{r-2} + \ldots$$

and in general

$$f^{(r)}(x) = r!b_r + \text{terms involving powers of } (x - a)$$

Putting $x = a$,

$$b_0 = f(a)$$
$$b_1 = f'(a)$$
$$b_2 = \frac{f''(a)}{2}$$

and in general

$$b_r = \frac{f^{(r)}(a)}{r!}$$

The question of *convergence* is outside the A-level curriculum. Suffice it here to say that some series are convergent for all x, some only for restricted values of x (often $|x - a| < 1$).

The **McLaurin series** can be derived as a special case by putting $a = 0$. This gives

$$f(x) = f(0) + xf'(0) + \frac{x^2}{2!}f''(0) + \ldots + \frac{x^r}{r!}f^{(r)}(0) + \ldots$$

or $f(x) = \sum_{r=0}^{\infty} \frac{x^r f^{(r)}(0)}{r!}$

◀ McLaurin series ▶

TENSION

A stretching or pulling force.
◀ Force, Triangle (polygon) of forces ▶

THREE-DIMENSIONAL PROBLEM

◀ Trigonometric equation ▶

TRANSFORMATION

A transformation (Fig. T.1) is a term often used to refer to how plane shapes change their position and/or shape. Transformations often include: enlargements; rotations; stretches; reflections; shears; and translations.

▶ TRANSFORMATION MATRIX

A transformation matrix is a 2 by 2 matrix that represents a particular transformation. This will multiply a matrix containing the *position vectors* of the *vertices* of a shape to give the vertices of the *transformed* shape.

▶ IDENTITY TRANSFORMATION

The identity transformation is the transformation that leaves a shape where it originally was; for example a *rotation* of 0° or 360°, or even an *enlargement* of scale factor 1.

▶ INVERSE TRANSFORMATION

The inverse transformation (T') of a transformation T is the transformation that will move a shape back to its original position after first being moved by T. For example, the inverse of any *reflection* is the same reflection (a *self-inverse*), and the inverse of any *rotation* of angle A will be a rotation of $-A$ around the same point.
◀ Linear transformation, Matrix/matrices ▶

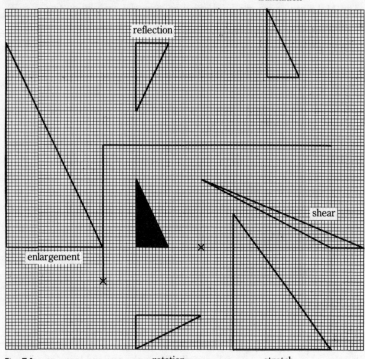

translation

reflection

shear

enlargement

Fig. T.1   rotation   stretch

TRANSFORMATION (OF RANDOM VARIABLE)

Let X be a continuous **random variable** with **probability density function** $f(x)$ and let Y be an increasing function of X. Then the probability density function of Y is given by

$$g(y) = f(x) \frac{dx}{dy}$$

where, on the right-hand side, x is expressed as a function of y. To prove this result, let $F(x)$, $G(y)$ denote the distribution functions of X, Y respectively. Consider

$$\begin{aligned}
G(y) &= P(Y \leqslant y)\\
&= P(Y(X) \leqslant y(x))\\
&= P(X \leqslant x)\\
&= F(x)
\end{aligned}$$

Differentiating with respect to y,

$$g(y) = f(x) \frac{dx}{dy} \quad \text{as required}$$

A similar result can be obtained if Y is a decreasing function of X. Here,

$$
\begin{aligned}
G(y) &= \mathrm{P}(Y \leq y) \\
&= \mathrm{P}(Y(X) \leq y(x)) \\
&= \mathrm{P}(X \geq x) \\
&= 1 - F(x)
\end{aligned}
$$

whence by differentiation with respect to y

$$
g(y) = -f(x)\frac{\mathrm{d}x}{\mathrm{d}y}
$$

Both results for $g(y)$ can be summed up by

$$
g(y) = f(x)\left|\frac{\mathrm{d}x}{\mathrm{d}y}\right|
$$

where Y is an increasing or decreasing function of X.

When using this result, it is necessary to check that Y is increasing or decreasing. If not, this result is invalid, and a different method based on distribution functions from first principles must be used.

Worked example

The random variable X has probability density function

$$
\begin{aligned}
f(x) &= 2x \quad \text{if } 0 \leq x \leq 1 \\
&= 0 \quad \text{otherwise}
\end{aligned}
$$

Find the probability density of

$$
Y = \sqrt{X}
$$

We note first that Y is an increasing function of X, so that we can use the above result.

Here,

$$
X = Y^2
$$

or $\quad x = y^2$

so that

$$
\frac{\mathrm{d}x}{\mathrm{d}y} = 2y
$$

The probability density of Y is therefore

$$
\begin{aligned}
g(y) &= 2 \cdot y^2 \cdot 2y \\
&= 4y^3
\end{aligned}
$$

The range of the distribution is $[0, 1]$ since as x increases from 0 to 1, so does y.

TRANSLATION

A translation is a movement along the plane *without* any rotating, reflecting or enlarging. It is described by a movement horizontally and a movement vertically which we put together as a **vector**.

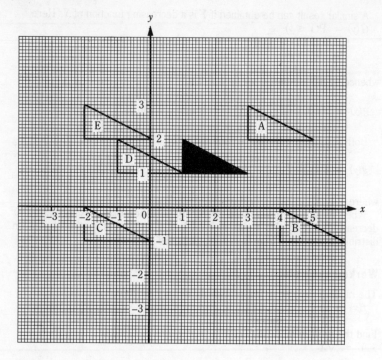

Fig. T.2

For example, the heavily shaded triangle in Figure T.2 has been *translated* to position A by moving 2 to the right and 1 up (notice how every point on and in the triangle moves in exactly the same way). We write this movement as a vector $\begin{pmatrix} 2 \\ 1 \end{pmatrix}$

In a similar way we write the following translations:

To B, 3 to the right and 2 down... $\begin{pmatrix} 3 \\ -2 \end{pmatrix}$

To C, 3 to the left and 2 down... $\begin{pmatrix} -3 \\ -2 \end{pmatrix}$

To D, 2 to the left, nothing up... $\begin{pmatrix} -2 \\ 0 \end{pmatrix}$

To E, 3 to the left and 1 up... $\begin{pmatrix} -3 \\ 1 \end{pmatrix}$

Notice how we use the *negative* to indicate movement *to the left* and to indicate movement *down*.

TRANSPOSE (OF A MATRIX)

The transpose $\mathbf{A}'$ of the **matrix** $\mathbf{A}$ is defined as the matrix whose ith row is the ith column of $\mathbf{A}$ (or whose jth column is the jth row of $\mathbf{A}$).

For example, if

$$\mathbf{A} = \begin{bmatrix} 1 & 2 & 3 & 4 \\ 5 & 6 & 7 & 8 \\ 9 & 10 & 11 & 12 \end{bmatrix}$$

then

$$\mathbf{A} = \begin{bmatrix} 1 & 5 & 9 \\ 2 & 6 & 10 \\ 3 & 7 & 11 \\ 4 & 8 & 12 \end{bmatrix}$$

◀ Matrix/matrices ▶

TRAPEZIUM

◀ Plane shape ▶

TRAPEZIUM RULE

The trapezium rule is a formula which gives an approximation to a definite integral. The basic result is that, for small $b - a$,

$$\int_a^b f(x)\mathrm{d}x \approx \frac{(b - a)}{2}[f(a) + f(b)]$$

An alternative form is

$$\int_{x_0}^{x_1} y\mathrm{d}x \approx \frac{h}{2}(y_0 + y_1)$$

where $h = b - a$ and y_0, y_1 are the values of y corresponding to x_0, x_1.

The trapezium rule is derived by using the area of the trapezium $P_0P_1F_1F_0$ as an approximation to the area under the curve (Fig. T.3).

Worked example A

Use the trapezium rule to find an approximate value of

$$\int_0^1 \frac{\mathrm{d}x}{1 + x}$$

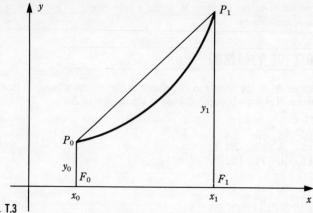

Fig. T.3

NB. This integral can be evaluated exactly as ln2 = 0·6931. We are considering this simple example so that we can compare the approximation with the true value. In practice, of course, we would use an approximate method such as the trapezium rule *only if the exact value cannot be determined* using standard methods of integration.

Here $x_0 = 0$, $x_1 = 1$ so that

$$y_0 = \frac{1}{1 + 0} = 1$$

and

$$y_1 = \frac{1}{1 + 1} = \frac{1}{2}$$

Finally, $h = 1 - 0 = 1$ so that the trapezium rule gives

$$\int_0^1 \frac{dx}{1 + x} \approx \frac{1}{2}\left(1 + \frac{1}{2}\right) = 0·75$$

The error is seen to be 0·0569, or approximately 8 per cent. A more accurate approximation can be found by expressing the integral as the sum of m integrals on equal intervals. This leads to the following extended form of the trapezium rule:

$$\int_{x_0}^{x_n} y\,dx \approx \frac{h}{2}(y_0 + 2y_1 + 2y_2 + \ldots + 2y_{n-1} + y_n)$$

where $\quad h = \dfrac{x_n - x_0}{n}$, $x_r = x_0 + rh\,(r = 0, 1, 2, \ldots n)$

and y_r is the value of y corresponding to $x = x_r$. This approximation is based on $(n + 1)$ ordinates and therefore n strips.

Worked example B

Use the trapezium rule with 6 strips (and therefore 7 ordinates) to calculate an approximation to

$$\int_0^1 \frac{dx}{1+x}$$

Here,

$$x_0 = 0, x_6 = 1, h = \frac{1}{6} \text{ and } x_r = \frac{r}{6}$$

Thus,

$$y_0 = \frac{1}{1+0} = 1$$

$$y_1 = \frac{1}{1+\dfrac{1}{6}} = \frac{6}{7}$$

$$y_2 = \frac{1}{1+\dfrac{1}{3}} = \frac{3}{4}$$

$$y_3 = \frac{1}{1+\dfrac{1}{2}} = \frac{2}{3}$$

$$y_4 = \frac{1}{1+\dfrac{2}{3}} = \frac{3}{5}$$

$$y_5 = \frac{1}{1+\dfrac{5}{6}} = \frac{6}{11}$$

and

$$y_6 = \frac{1}{1+1} = \frac{1}{2}$$

Thus, $\displaystyle\int_0^1 \frac{dx}{1+x} \approx \frac{1}{12}\left[1 + \left(2 \times \frac{6}{7}\right) + \left(2 \times \frac{3}{4}\right) + \left(2 \times \frac{2}{3}\right) + \left(2 \times \frac{3}{5}\right)\right.$

$$\left. + \left(2 \times \frac{6}{11}\right) + \frac{1}{2}\right]$$

$$= 0\cdot6949$$

The error is seen to be 0·0018, or approximately 0·25 per cent.

The trapezium rule can be used to evaluate an integral to any desired accuracy by taking a large enough interval (that is, h). However, the trapezium rule has little practical application since **Simpson's rule** is more accurate and involves no more computation.

◀ Simpson's rule ▶

TREE DIAGRAM

The tree diagram can be a very useful notation in the solution of certain probability questions. The example below provides illustration.

Worked example

A bag contains 5 red balls (R), 7 black balls (B) and 4 white balls (W). Two balls are drawn from the bag, one after the other, and without replacement. Find the probability of drawing: a) 2 balls of the same colour; b) 1 red and 1 black ball.

The different ways in which the balls can be drawn from the bag are represented by the branches of a tree, each branch showing the probability of drawing the ball (R, B or W) indicated at the end of the branch. See Fig. T.4.

◀ Probability ▶

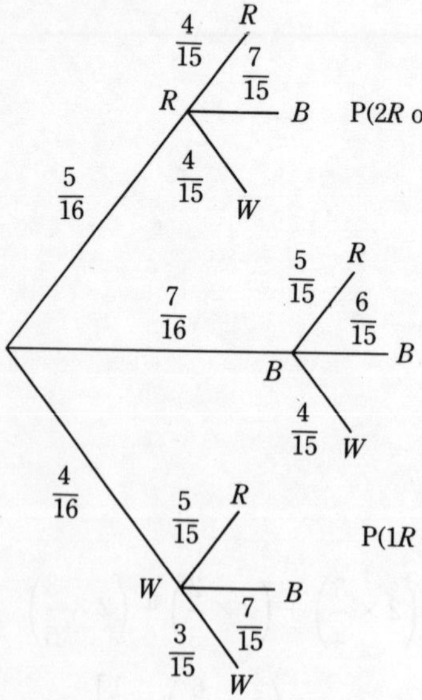

$$P(2R \text{ or } 2B \text{ or } 2W) = \frac{5}{16} \cdot \frac{4}{15} + \frac{7}{16} \cdot \frac{6}{15} + \frac{4}{16} \cdot \frac{3}{15}$$

$$= \frac{20 + 42 + 12}{16.15} = \frac{37}{120}$$

$$P(1R + 1B \text{ or } 1B + 1R) = \frac{5}{16} \cdot \frac{7}{15} + \frac{7}{16} \cdot \frac{5}{15}$$

$$= \frac{70}{16.15} = \frac{7}{24}$$

Fig. T.4

TRIANGLE

A **plane shape** with three straight sides.
◀ Area, Cosine rule, Inverse trigonometric equation, Sine rule,
Trigonometric equation, Trigonometric function, Trigonometric identity ▶

TRIANGLE (POLYGON) OF FORCES

Three **forces** acting at a point are in **equilibrium** if and only if they can be
represented by the sides of a triangle taken in order.

▶ RESOLUTION OF A FORCE

A force P acting at an angle α to the horizontal is equivalent to forces $P \cos \alpha$
horizontally and $P \sin \alpha$ vertically, as shown in Fig. T.5.

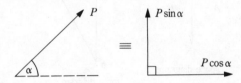

Fig. T.5

▶ POLYGON OF FORCES

We can generalise the above results to more than three forces. Any number of
forces acting at a point are in equilibrium if and only if they can be represented
by the sides of a polygon taken in order.

The **resultant** of a system of co-planar forces can be formed by the following
methods.

    i) Drawing a force polygon in which the *resultant force* is represented by
    the line required to complete the polygon, but remembering that the
    resultant will act in the opposite sense to all the other forces.

    ii) Using the sum of the components of all the forces in two directions,
    usually perpendicular, say ΣF_x and ΣF_y, then the resultant has
    magnitude

$$\sqrt{[(\Sigma F_x)^2 + (\Sigma F_y)^2]}$$

and the direction is at

$$\arctan \left[\frac{\Sigma F_y}{\Sigma F_x} \right] \text{ with the } x\text{-direction}$$

Worked example

A particle P, of mass $0 \cdot 4$ kg, is in equilibrium, suspended by two light inextensible strings which are inclined at $30°$ and $45°$ to the horizontal. Find, giving your answer to $0 \cdot 1$ N, the **tension** in each string
There are several methods of solving this problem; we consider three solutions to show some of these.

First solution A graphical solution using the triangle of forces.
Taking $g = 10 \text{ms}^{-2}$, the weight of P is 4N
The **space diagram** (Fig. T.6) shows the forces acting on P.

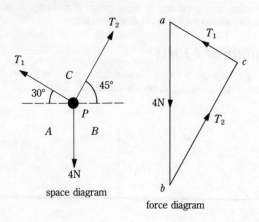

space diagram

force diagram

Fig. T.6

The regions into which the plane is partitioned by the lines of action of the weight of P, T_1 and T_2 are labelled A, B and C in the space diagram. Then, since the directions of T_1 and T_2 are known, we can draw to scale the force diagram abc, where ab represents the weight of P, T_1 and T_2 represent the tensions in the strings.
We obtain by measuring $T_1 = 2 \cdot 9$N, $T_2 = 3 \cdot 6$N

Second solution A *sketch* of the force diagram is sufficient when a solution is given by calculation using the **sine rule**.

$$\frac{T_1}{\sin 45°} = \frac{T_2}{\sin 60°} = \frac{4}{\sin 75°}$$

$$T_1 = \frac{4 \sin 45°}{\sin 75°} \approx 2 \cdot 9 \text{N}$$

$$T_2 = \frac{4 \sin 60°}{\sin 75°} \approx 3 \cdot 6 \text{N}$$

Third solution Since the forces are in equilibrium, many students solve this type of problem by 'balancing' the resolved parts of forces in two directions (often horizontal and vertical) and solving the resulting equations.

Horizontally $\leftrightarrow$ $T_1 \cos 30° = T_2 \cos 45°$ (1)

Vertically $\updownarrow$ $T_1 \sin 30° + T_2 \sin 45° = 4$ (2)

Solving (1) and (2) simultaneously then gives

   $T_1 \approx 2 \cdot 9 \text{N}$ and $T_2 \approx 3 \cdot 6 \text{N}$ as before

◀ Bow's notation ▶

TRIGONOMETRICAL RATIOS

The trigonometrical ratios associated with the angles 30°, 45° and 60° are used very frequently in problems involving trigonometry. Their exact values can be easily obtained using either an equilateral triangle (of side two units) or an isosceles right-angled triangle (Fig. T.7).

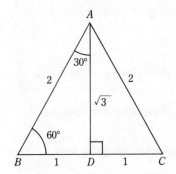 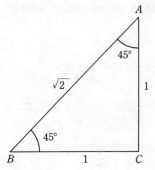

Fig. T.7   Fig. T.8

$AD^2 = 2^2 - 1^2 = 3,$ $AD = \sqrt{3}$

$\sin 60° = \dfrac{\sqrt{3}}{2}$ $\cos 60° = \dfrac{1}{2}$ $\tan 60° = \sqrt{3}$

$\sin 30° = \dfrac{1}{2}$ $\cos 30° = \dfrac{\sqrt{3}}{2}$ $\tan 30° = \dfrac{1}{\sqrt{3}}$

In Fig. T.8, $AB^2 = 1^2 + 1^2 = 2$ $AB = \sqrt{2}$

$\sin 45° = \dfrac{1}{\sqrt{2}} \text{ or } \dfrac{\sqrt{2}}{2}$ $\cos 45° = \dfrac{1}{\sqrt{2}} \text{ or } \dfrac{\sqrt{2}}{2}$ $\tan 45° = 1$

◀ Inverse trigonometric equation, Trigonometric equation, Trigonometric function, Trigonometric identity ▶

TRIGONOMETRIC EQUATION

It will be seen that as the **trigonometric functions** are periodic, there are many solutions to an equation of the form $\sin x = \dfrac{1}{2}$; that is, there are many angles whose sine is $\dfrac{1}{2}$. Reference to the graphs in Figs. T.13–T.17 shows that the general solution of such equations can be summarised in the following formulae.

$\sin x = a \Rightarrow x = n\pi + (-1)^n\alpha,$ where $n\epsilon\mathbb{Z}$ and $\sin \alpha = a$
$\cos x = a \Rightarrow x = 2n\pi \pm \alpha,$ where $n\epsilon\mathbb{Z}$ and $\cos \alpha = a$
$\tan x = a \Rightarrow n\pi + \alpha,$ where $n\epsilon\mathbb{Z}$ and $\tan \alpha = a$

Worked example A

Find the general solution of the equations a) $\sin \theta = \dfrac{1}{2}$; b) $\cos \theta = -\dfrac{1}{2}$; c) $\tan 3\theta = 1$

a) $\sin \theta = \dfrac{1}{2} \Rightarrow \theta = \dfrac{\pi}{6} \Rightarrow$ general solution is $\theta = n\pi + (-1)^n \dfrac{\pi}{6}$

b) $\cos \theta = -\dfrac{1}{2} \Rightarrow \theta = \dfrac{2\pi}{3} \Rightarrow$ general solution is $\theta = 2n\pi \pm \dfrac{2\pi}{3}$

c) $\tan 3\theta = 1 \Rightarrow 3\theta = \dfrac{\pi}{4} \Rightarrow$ general solution is $3\theta = n\pi + \dfrac{\pi}{4}$

or $\theta = \dfrac{n\pi}{3} + \dfrac{\pi}{12}$

NB. It would be wrong to say $3\theta = \dfrac{\pi}{4} \Rightarrow \theta = \dfrac{\pi}{12}$

$\Rightarrow$ general solution is $\theta = n\pi + \dfrac{\pi}{12}$

You must always leave the division by the 3 until the general value has been taken. Do not make this common mistake.

Worked example B

Solve the equation $4 \cos^2 3\theta - \cos 3\theta - 3 = 0$ for $0° \le \theta \le 180°$

$4 \cos^2 3\theta - \cos 3\theta - 3 = (4 \cos 3\theta + 3)(\cos 3\theta - 1) = 0$

$\Rightarrow \cos 3\theta = -\dfrac{3}{4}$ or $\cos 3\theta = 1$

$\cos 3\theta = -\dfrac{3}{4} \Rightarrow 3\theta = 360°n \pm 138\cdot6° \Rightarrow \theta = 120°n \pm 46\cdot2°$

$\qquad \Rightarrow \theta = 46\cdot2°,\ 166\cdot2°$ (from +ve sign) or $73\cdot8°$ (from $-$ve sign).

$\cos 3\theta = 1 \Rightarrow 3\theta = 360°n \pm 0° \Rightarrow \theta = 120°n$

$\qquad \Rightarrow \theta = 0°,\ 120°$

$\Rightarrow$ Required solution is $\theta = 0°,\ 46\cdot2°,\ 73\cdot8°,\ 120°,\ 166\cdot2°$

Worked example C

Find the general solution of the equation $\cos 2\theta = \sin \theta$

$$\cos 2\theta = \sin \theta = \cos\left(\dfrac{\pi}{2} - \theta\right)$$

$$\Rightarrow 2\theta = 2n\pi \pm \left(\dfrac{\pi}{2} - \theta\right)$$

$$2\theta = 2n\pi + \left(\dfrac{\pi}{2} - \theta\right) \Rightarrow 3\theta = 2n\pi + \dfrac{\pi}{2} \text{ or } \theta = \dfrac{2}{3}n\pi + \dfrac{\pi}{6}$$

$$2\theta = 2n\pi - \left(\dfrac{\pi}{2} - \theta\right) \Rightarrow \theta = 2n\pi - \dfrac{\pi}{2}$$

General solution is $\theta = \dfrac{2}{3}n\pi + \dfrac{\pi}{6}$ or $2n\pi - \dfrac{\pi}{2}$

▶ THREE-DIMENSIONAL PROBLEMS

In solving such problems always try to draw a good *three-dimensional diagram* and mark clearly on it the values of all known angles, particularly the right-angles. Do not try to depend upon a series of two-dimensional diagrams, as this often leads to incorrect figures. Remember the following rules.

    i) A line perpendicular to a plane is perpendicular to every line in that plane.

    ii) Two non-parallel planes meet in a line, normally called the *common line*.

    iii) The angle between two planes is the angle between two lines, one in each plane and both perpendicular to the common line.

    iv) The angle between a line and a plane is the angle between the line and its projection on the plane.

    v) The line of greatest slope in a plane is a line perpendicular to the line of intersection of the plane and a horizontal plane.

Worked example D

A pole AB of length 10m is held in a vertical position with B on horizontal ground by three equal stays AC, AD and AE, fixed so that CDE forms an equilateral triangle of side 12m. Show that

a) the length of each stay is $2\sqrt{37}$m
b) the inclination of each stay to the horizontal is θ where $\tan \theta = (5\sqrt{3})/6$
c) the angle contained between the planes ACD and CDE is ϕ where $\tan \phi = (5\sqrt{3})/3$.

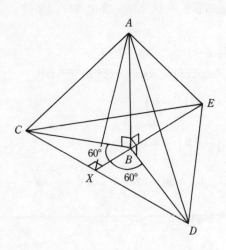

Fig. T.9

Using the diagram in Fig. T.9, let EB produced meet CD at X, then $CX = XD = 6$m

a) From $\triangle CXB$, right-angled at X, $\dfrac{CX}{CB} = \sin 60° = \dfrac{\sqrt{3}}{2}$

$$\Rightarrow CB = \frac{6 \cdot 2}{\sqrt{3}} = 4\sqrt{3}\text{m}$$

From $\triangle ABC$, right-angled at B, $AC^2 = AB^2 + BC^2$
$$\Rightarrow AC^2 = 10^2 + (4\sqrt{3})^2 = 148 \Rightarrow AC = \sqrt{148}\text{m} = 2\sqrt{37}\text{m}$$
$$\Rightarrow \text{each stay is of length } 2\sqrt{37}\text{m}$$

b) From $\triangle ABC$, $\tan \angle ACB = \dfrac{AB}{BC} = \dfrac{10}{4\sqrt{3}} = \dfrac{5\sqrt{3}}{6}$

$\Rightarrow$ inclination of each stay to horizontal is θ
where $\tan \theta = \dfrac{5\sqrt{3}}{6}$.

c) The angle contained between the plances ACD and CDE is $\angle AXB$

From $\triangle CXB$ right-angled at X, $\dfrac{CX}{BX} = \tan 60° = \sqrt{3}$

$$\Rightarrow BX = \frac{6}{\sqrt{3}} = 2\sqrt{3}\,\text{m}$$

From $\triangle AXB$ right-angled at B, $\tan \angle AXB = \dfrac{AB}{BX} = \dfrac{10}{2\sqrt{3}}$

$$\Rightarrow \tan \phi = \frac{5}{\sqrt{3}} = \frac{5\sqrt{3}}{3}$$

Worked example E

Towns A and B are 350 m and 690 m respectively above town C, which is at sea level. Town B is due north of C and A lies to the east of B and C. Given that the elevation of B from C is 10·3°, that of A from C is 6·7° and that of B from A is 4·6°, calculate the bearing of A from C.
Use the diagram in Fig. T.10.

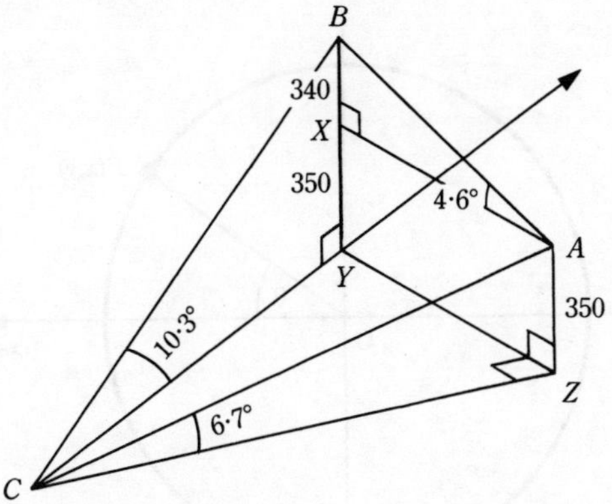

Fig. T.10

From $\triangle ACZ$ right-angled at Z, $CZ = (350 \cot 6\cdot7°)\text{m} = 2979\cdot4\,\text{m}$
From $\triangle ABX$ right-angled at X, $AX = (340 \cot 4\cdot6°)\text{m} = 4225\cdot8\,\text{m} = YZ$
From $\triangle CBY$ right-angled at Y, $CY = (690 \cot 10\cdot3°)\text{m} = 3796\cdot8\,\text{m}$
From $\triangle CYZ$, using the cosine rule

$$\cos \angle YCZ = \frac{CY^2 + CZ^2 - YZ^2}{2CY\cdot CZ} = 0\cdot24023$$

$\Rightarrow \angle YCZ = 76\cdot1°$
$\Rightarrow$ bearing of A from C is 76·1°

◀ Inverse trigonometric equation, Trigonometric function, Trigonometric identity ▶

TRIGONOMETRIC FUNCTION

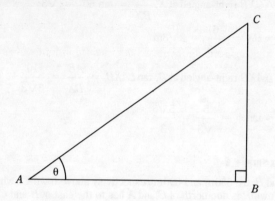

Fig. T.11

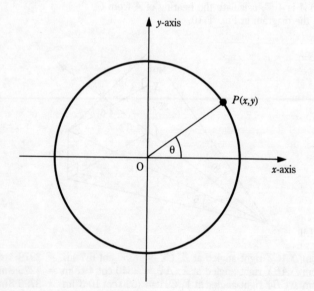

Fig. T.12

The basic functions $\sin \theta$ and $\cos \theta$ are defined for $0° < \theta < 90°$ using a right-angled triangle as shown in Fig. T.11.

$$\sin \theta = \frac{BC}{AC}; \quad \cos \theta = \frac{AB}{AC}$$

In order to extend these definitions to cover all values of θ, we proceed as follows. Take perpendicular axes as shown in Fig. T.12, and let the point

$P(x, y)$ be a general point on the unit circle, that is, the circle centre O and radius unity. Let θ be the angle between the x-axis and OP measured in the direction shown. Then, we define

$$\sin \theta = y \text{ and } \cos \theta = x$$

Note that P is not restricted to the first quadrant, and θ may now take any value.

The other trigonometric functions are now defined in terms of $\sin \theta$ and $\cos \theta$ as follows:

$$\tan \theta = \frac{\sin \theta}{\cos \theta}; \qquad \cot \theta = \frac{\cos \theta}{\sin \theta}$$

$$\sec \theta = \frac{1}{\cos \theta}; \qquad \operatorname{cosec} \theta = \frac{1}{\sin \theta}$$

The signs of $\sin \theta$, $\cos \theta$ and $\tan \theta$ in the four quadrants are as shown. The mnemonic **CAST** may be useful to remember which are positive in the four quadrants.

sin +	sin +
cos −	cos +
tan −	tan +
(**S**in)	(**A**ll)
sin −	sin −
cos −	cos +
tan +	tan −
(**T**an)	(**C**os)

The graphs of the six trigonometric functions in the range $0° \leqslant \theta \leqslant 360°$ (or $0 \leqslant \theta \leqslant 2\pi$) are shown in Figs. T.13–T.17. For values of θ outside this range, the graphs simply repeat themselves.

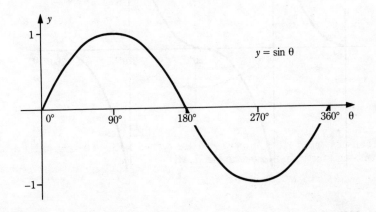

Fig. T.13

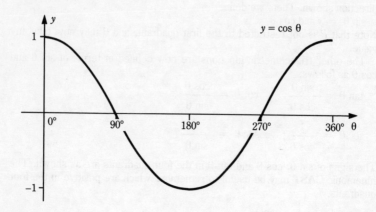

Fig. T.14

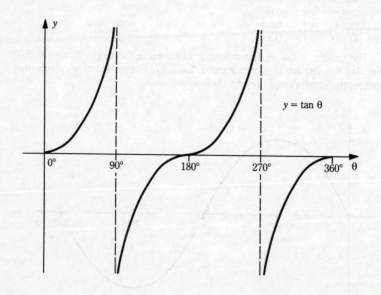

Fig. T.15

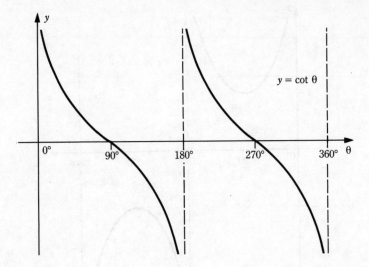

Fig. T.16

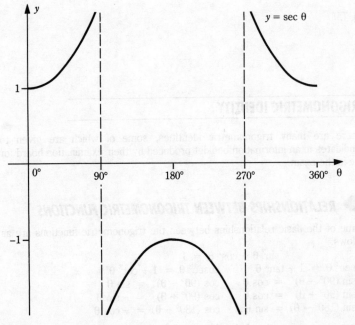

Fig. T.17

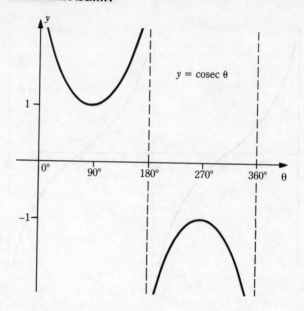

Fig. T.18

TRIGONOMETRIC IDENTITY

There are many trigonometric identities, some of which are given to candidates in an information booklet produced by their examination board for use in the exam.

▶ RELATIONSHIPS BETWEEN TRIGONOMETRIC FUNCTIONS

Some of the basic relationships between the trigonometric functions are as follows.

$$\sin^2 \theta + \cos^2 \theta = 1$$

$$\sec^2 \theta = 1 + \tan^2 \theta \qquad \operatorname{cosec}^2 \theta = 1 + \cot^2 \theta$$
$$\sin (90° - \theta) = \cos \theta \qquad \cos (90° - \theta) = \sin \theta$$
$$\sin (90° + \theta) = \cos \theta \qquad \cos (90° + \theta) = -\sin \theta$$
$$\sin (180° - \theta) = \sin \theta \qquad \cos (180° - \theta) = -\cos \theta$$

There are many such relationships, and there is insufficient space to give a complete list here.

▶ *ADDITION FORMULAE*

The basic results here are

$$\sin (A \pm B) = \sin A \cos B \pm \cos A \sin B$$
$$\cos (A \pm B) = \cos A \cos B \mp \sin A \sin B$$

$$\tan (A \pm B) = \frac{\tan A \pm \tan B}{1 \mp \tan A \tan B}$$

The following *double-angle formulae* can be derived from these results.

$$\sin 2A = 2 \sin A \cos A$$
$$\cos 2A = \cos^2 A - \sin^2 A = 2 \cos^2 A - 1 = 1 - 2 \sin^2 A$$

$$\tan 2A = \frac{2 \tan A}{1 - \tan^2 A}$$

The following results can also be deduced.

$$\sin A \cos B = \tfrac{1}{2}[\sin (A + B) + \sin (A - B)]$$
$$\sin A \sin B = \tfrac{1}{2}[\cos (A - B) - \cos (A + B)]$$
$$\cos A \cos B = \tfrac{1}{2}[\cos (A + B) + \cos (A - B)]$$
$$\sin A + \sin B = 2 \sin \tfrac{1}{2}(A + B) \cos \tfrac{1}{2}(A - B)$$
$$\cos A + \cos B = 2 \cos \tfrac{1}{2}(A + B) \cos \tfrac{1}{2}(A - B)$$
$$\cos A - \cos B = -2 \sin \tfrac{1}{2}(A + B) \sin \tfrac{1}{2}(A - B)$$

The following *half-angle formulae* are useful. If

$$t = \tan \tfrac{1}{2}x$$

then

$$\sin x = \frac{2t}{1 + t^2}$$

$$\cos x = \frac{1 - t^2}{1 + t^2}$$

$$\tan x = \frac{2t}{1 - t^2}$$

Worked example A

Prove that $\cos 3x = 4\cos^3 x - 3\cos x$

Hence solve, for $0 \leqslant x \leqslant 2\pi$, the equation $\cos 3x + 2\cos x = 0$

$$\begin{aligned}
\cos 3x &= \cos (2x + x) = \cos 2x \cos x - \sin 2x \sin x \\
&= (2\cos^2 x - 1) \cos x - (2\sin x \cos x) \sin x \\
&= 2\cos^3 x - \cos x - 2\cos x (1 - \cos^2 x) \\
&= 4\cos^3 x - 3\cos x
\end{aligned}$$

$$\cos 3x + 2\cos x = 0 \Rightarrow 4\cos^3 x - 3\cos x + 2\cos x = 0$$

$$\Rightarrow \cos x (4\cos^2 x - 1) = 0 \Leftrightarrow \cos x = 0 \text{ or } \pm \frac{1}{2}$$

$$\cos x = 0 \Rightarrow x = \frac{\pi}{2} \text{ or } \frac{3\pi}{2}$$

$$\cos x = \frac{1}{2} \Rightarrow x = \frac{\pi}{3} \text{ or } \frac{5\pi}{3}$$

$$\cos x = -\frac{1}{2} \Rightarrow x = \frac{2\pi}{3} \text{ or } \frac{4\pi}{3}$$

$$\Rightarrow x = \frac{\pi}{3}, \frac{\pi}{2}, \frac{2\pi}{3}, \frac{4\pi}{3}, \frac{3\pi}{2} \text{ or } \frac{5\pi}{3}$$

NB. In proving the bookwork realise that $\cos 3x$ is required entirely in terms of $\cos x$. Hence break $3x$ down to $2x + x$ and always be prepared to use the three very important and most frequently used identities

$$\cos 2x = 2\cos^2 x - 1; \quad \sin 2x = 2\sin x \cos x; \quad \cos^2 x + \sin^2 x = 1$$

Worked example B

Express $3\cos \theta - \sin \theta$ in the form $r\sin (\theta + \alpha)$ where $r > 0$ and $0° < \alpha < 360°$

Hence, or otherwise, solve for $0° \leqslant \theta \leqslant 360°$, the equation $3\cos \theta - \sin \theta = 2$
To express $3\cos \theta - \sin \theta$ in the form $r\sin (\theta + \alpha)$ equate the two expressions; thus, $3\cos \theta - \sin \theta = r\sin (\theta + \alpha) = r\sin \theta \cos \alpha + r\cos \theta \sin \alpha$
For the two sides to be equal for all values of θ the coefficient of $\cos \theta$ on the L.H.S. must equal the coefficient of $\cos \theta$ on the R.H.S. Similarly for the coefficients of $\sin \theta$
Equating coefficients of $\cos \theta \Rightarrow 3 = r\sin \alpha$
Equating coefficients of $\sin \theta \Rightarrow -1 = r\cos \alpha$
The two equations in two unknowns, r and α, can now be solved. Squaring and adding them

$$\Rightarrow 3^2 + (-1)^2 = r^2(\sin^2 \alpha + \cos^2 \alpha) = r^2 \Rightarrow r^2 = 10, \, r = \sqrt{10}$$

Dividing $\Rightarrow \dfrac{3}{-1} = \dfrac{r \sin \alpha}{r \cos \alpha} \Leftrightarrow \tan \alpha = -3$

There are two angles between $0°$ and $360°$ with tangent equal to (-3) and it is essential that the correct one is chosen. Since r is positive we know that the cosine is negative and the sine is positive. Hence α must be an angle in the second quadrant $\Rightarrow \alpha = 180° - 71·57° = 108·43°$
$\Rightarrow 3\cos \theta - \sin \theta = \sqrt{10} \sin (\theta + 108·43°)$.

To solve the given equation we now proceed as follows.
$3\cos \theta - \sin \theta = \sqrt{10} \sin (\theta + 108·43°) = 2$

$$\Rightarrow \sin (\theta + 108·43°) = \frac{2}{\sqrt{10}} = 0·6325$$

$\Rightarrow \theta + 108·43° = n \times 180° + (-1)^n \times 39·25°$ (remember you must go immediately to the general value)

$n = 1 \Rightarrow \theta = 180° - 39 \cdot 25° - 108 \cdot 43° = 32 \cdot 32°$
$n = 2 \Rightarrow \theta = 360° + 39 \cdot 25° - 108 \cdot 43° = 290 \cdot 82°$
The required solutions are $\theta = 32 \cdot 3°$ or $290 \cdot 8°$ to one decimal place.

NB. An alternative method of solving an equation such as $3\cos \theta - \sin \theta = 2$ is to use the formula known as the *tan half-angle formula*, that is:

$$\sin 2A = \frac{2t}{1 + t^2}, \cos 2A = \frac{1 - t^2}{1 + t}$$

where $t = \tan A$, A being half of the original angle $2A$

$3\cos \theta - \sin \theta = 2 \Rightarrow \frac{3(1 - t^2)}{1 + t^2} - \frac{2t}{1 + t^2} = 2$

$\Rightarrow 3 - 3t^2 - 2t = 2 + 2t^2 \Leftrightarrow 5t^2 + 2t - 1 = 0$

$\Leftrightarrow t = \frac{-2 \pm \sqrt{(4 + 20)}}{10} = 0 \cdot 2899$ or $-0 \cdot 6899$

$\Rightarrow \frac{\theta}{2} = n \times 180° + 16 \cdot 17°$ or $n \times 180° - 34 \cdot 60°$

$\Rightarrow \theta = n \times 360° + 32 \cdot 34°$ or $n \times 360° - 69 \cdot 20°$

$\Rightarrow \theta = 32 \cdot 3°$ or $290 \cdot 8°$ in the given range, to one decimal place

Worked example C

Find, in radians, the general solution of the equation $\sin x + \sin 3x + \sin 5x = 0$
When solving equations such as this, in which you are asked to consider the sum or difference of two or more sine or cosine terms, always expect to use the formulae for $\sin A \pm \sin B$ or $\cos A \pm \cos B$. Take care when pairing to make sure that you can bring in any remaining terms as factors at a later stage.

$\sin x + \sin 3x + \sin 5x = 0 \Rightarrow (\sin x + \sin 5x) + \sin 3x = 0$
$\Rightarrow 2\sin 3x \cos 2x + \sin 3x = 0 \Rightarrow \sin 3x (2\cos 2x + 1) = 0$
$\Rightarrow \sin 3x = 0$ or $2\cos 2x + 1 = 0$

$\sin 3x = 0 \Rightarrow 3x = n\pi, x = \frac{n\pi}{3}$

$2\cos 2x + 1 = 0 \Rightarrow \cos 2x = -\frac{1}{2} \Rightarrow 2x = 2n\pi \pm \frac{2\pi}{3} \Rightarrow x = n\pi \pm \frac{\pi}{3}.$

NB. i) Make sure you do not forget the factor $\sin 3x = 0$. Many candidates cancel the $\sin 3x$ terms and consequently omit the solutions from $\sin 3x = 0$

ii) The pairings $\sin x + \sin 3x$ or $\sin 3x + \sin 5x$ would not have produced any common factors since
$\sin x + 3x = 2\sin 2x \cos x$ and $\sin 3x + \sin 5x = 2\sin 4x \cos x$

TRINOMIAL

◀ Factorisation ▶

TURNING POINT

◀ Maximum and minimum ▶

UNBIASED ESTIMATOR

◀ Estimator ▶

UNBIASED VARIANCE ESTIMATOR

◀ Variance ▶

UNIFORM (OR RECTANGULAR) DISTRIBUTION

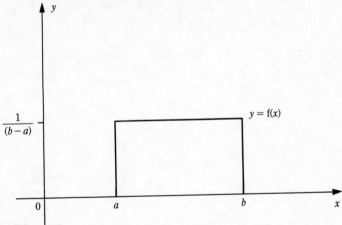

Fig. U.1

The continuous **random variable** X has the uniform (or rectangular) distribution on $[a, b]$ if its **probability density function** is given by

$$f(x) = \frac{1}{b - a} \qquad \text{if } a \leq x \leq b$$
$$= 0 \qquad \text{otherwise}$$

The graph of $f(x)$ is as shown in Fig. U.1. The mean and variance are given by

$$E(X) = \frac{a+b}{2} \text{ and } Var(X) = \frac{(b-a)^2}{12}$$

UNIT MATRIX

◀ Matrix/matrices ▶

UNIT VECTOR

A unit **vector** is a vector of unit length. In three-dimensional cases, it is customary to define perpendicular unit vectors **i**, **j**, **k**.

The vector
$$\mathbf{a} = a_x\mathbf{i} + a_y\mathbf{j} + a_z\mathbf{k}$$
is a unit vector if
$$a_x^2 + a_y^2 + a_z^2 = 1$$

In two-dimensional cases, the vector
$$\mathbf{a} = a_x\mathbf{i} + a_y\mathbf{j}$$
is a unit vector if
$$a_x^2 + a_y^2 = 1$$

VARIANCE

▶ VARIANCE OF A DISTRIBUTION

The (population) variance σ^2 of a continuous distribution with **probability density function** $f(x)$ is defined by

$$\sigma^2 = E[(X - \mu)^2]$$

$$= \int_{-\infty}^{\infty} (x - \mu)^2 f(x) dx$$

$$= \int_{-\infty}^{\infty} x^2 f(x) dx - \mu^2$$

where the population mean μ is defined by

$$\mu = \int_{-\infty}^{\infty} x f(x) dx$$

The population variance σ^2 of a discrete distribution with probability function p_x is defined by

$$\sigma^2 = E[x - \mu)^2]$$

$$= \sum_x (x - \mu)^2 p_x$$

$$= \sum_x x^2 p_x - \mu^2$$

where the population mean μ is defined by

$$\mu = \sum_x x p_x$$

and the summations are over all possible values of the **random variable**.

▶ SAMPLE VARIANCE

The sample variance S^2 of the random sample $X_1, X_2, \ldots X_n$ is defined by

$$S^2 = \sum_{i=1}^{n} \frac{(X_i - \bar{X})^2}{n}$$

$$= \sum_{i=1}^{n} \frac{X_i^2}{n} - \bar{X}^2$$

where the sample mean $\bar{X}$ is defined by

$$\bar{X} = \sum_{i=1}^{n} \frac{X_i}{n}$$

It should be noted that S^2 is not an unbiased estimator of σ^2, in fact

$$E(S^2) = \left(\frac{n-1}{n}\right)\sigma^2$$

It follows from this that if

$$\hat{\sigma}^2 = \frac{nS^2}{(n-1)} = \sum_{i=1}^{n} \frac{X_i^2}{(n-1)} - \frac{n\bar{X}^2}{(n-1)}$$

then $\hat{\sigma}^2$ is an unbiased estimator of σ^2, that is
$$E(\hat{\sigma}^2) = \sigma^2$$

Because of this, some texts call $\hat{\sigma}^2$ the *sample variance*; a more common term for $\hat{\sigma}^2$ is the *unbiased variance estimator*.

VECTOR

A vector is a quantity which has both magnitude and direction, such as displacement or force. The diagram in Fig. V.1 shows the displacement vector $\overrightarrow{AB}$. The modulus of $\overrightarrow{AB}$, written $|\overrightarrow{AB}|$ or AB, is defined as the length of the vector.

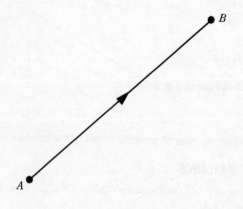

Fig. V.1

ADDITION OF VECTORS

Given the displacement vectors $\overrightarrow{AB}$, $\overrightarrow{BC}$ in the case shown in Fig. V.2, it is reasonable to define their sum as $\overrightarrow{AC}$.

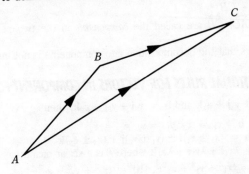

Fig. V.2

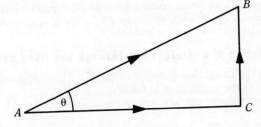

Fig. V.3

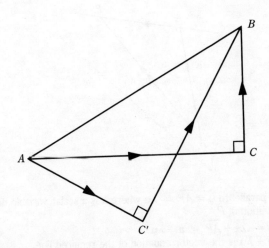

Fig. V.4

▶ COMPOSITION OF VECTORS

Given the vector $\overrightarrow{AB}$, it is possible to express it as the sum of two perpendicular vectors $\overrightarrow{AC}$, $\overrightarrow{CB}$ as shown in Fig. V.3. We write

$$\overrightarrow{AB} = \overrightarrow{AC} + \overrightarrow{CB}$$

The vectors $\overrightarrow{AC}$, $\overrightarrow{CB}$ are called the *components* in the two perpendicular directions.

Fig. V.4 shows that the decomposition into components is not unique.

▶ OPERATIONAL RULES FOR VECTORS IN COMPONENT FORM

Let $\mathbf{a} = x_1\mathbf{i} + y_1\mathbf{j} + z_1\mathbf{k}$ and $\mathbf{b} = x_2\mathbf{i} + y_2\mathbf{j} + z_2\mathbf{k}$, then

Rule 1 $\mathbf{a} = \mathbf{b} \Rightarrow x_1 = x_2, y_1 = y_2, z_1 = z_2$

Rule 2 $\mathbf{a} \pm \mathbf{b} = (x_1 \pm x_1)\mathbf{i} \pm (y_1 \pm y_2)\mathbf{j} \pm (z_1 \pm z_2)\mathbf{k}$

Rule 3 $\lambda\mathbf{a} = \lambda x_1\mathbf{i} + \lambda y_1\mathbf{j} + \lambda z_1\mathbf{k}$ where λ is a scalar quantity

Rule 4 $|\mathbf{a}| = (x_1^2 + y_1^2 + z_1^2)^{\frac{1}{2}}$, $|\mathbf{b}| = (x_2^2 + y_2^2 + z_2^2)^{\frac{1}{2}}$

Rule 5   If point A has position vector $\mathbf{a}$ and point B has position vector $\mathbf{b}$, then

$$AB = |\overrightarrow{AB}| = |\mathbf{b} - \mathbf{a}| = [(x_2 - x_1)^2 + (y_2 - y_1)^2 + (z_2 - z_1)^2]^{\frac{1}{2}}$$

Vector equation of a straight line through one fixed point

The equation of a straight line passing through a fixed point A, position vector $\mathbf{a}$ and parallel to the vector $\mathbf{u}$, is as follows.

Let P, position vector $\mathbf{r}$ be any point on the straight line shown in Fig. V.5.

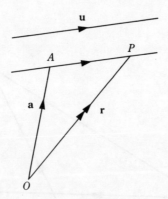

Fig. V.5

Then $\overrightarrow{AP}$ is parallel to $\mathbf{u} \Rightarrow \overrightarrow{AP} = \lambda\mathbf{u}$ where λ is a scalar variable dependent upon the position of P.

$$\overrightarrow{OP} = \mathbf{r} = \overrightarrow{OA} + \overrightarrow{AP} = \mathbf{a} + \lambda\mathbf{u}$$

$\Rightarrow \mathbf{r} = \mathbf{a} + \lambda\mathbf{u}$ is the vector equation of the required line.

If $P \equiv (x, y, z)$, $A \equiv (x_1, y_1, z_1)$ and $\mathbf{u} = l\mathbf{i} + m\mathbf{j} + n\mathbf{k}$ then
$\mathbf{r} = \mathbf{a} + \lambda\mathbf{u} \Rightarrow x\mathbf{i} + y\mathbf{j} + z\mathbf{k} = x_1\mathbf{i} + y_1\mathbf{j} + z_1\mathbf{k} + \lambda(l\mathbf{i} + m\mathbf{j} + n\mathbf{k})$
and comparing coefficients of $\mathbf{i}$, $\mathbf{j}$ and $\mathbf{k}$ $\Rightarrow$
$x = x_1 + \lambda l,\ y = y_1 + \lambda m,\ z = z_1 + \lambda n$

or $\dfrac{x - x_1}{l} = \dfrac{y - y_1}{m} = \dfrac{z - z_1}{n}\ (= \lambda)$

which are the cartesian equations of the line passing through the point (x_1, y_1, z_1) and parallel to the vector $\mathbf{u} = l\mathbf{i} + m\mathbf{j} + n\mathbf{k}$.
(l, m, n) are known as the direction ratios of the line.

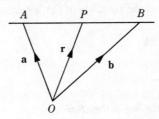

Fig. V.6

Vector equation of a straight line through two fixed points

The equation of a straight line passing through two fixed points A and B having position vectors $\mathbf{a}$ and $\mathbf{b}$ respectively, relative to an origin O, can be explained with reference to Fig. V.6.
$\overrightarrow{OA} + \overrightarrow{AB} = \overrightarrow{OB} \Rightarrow \overrightarrow{AB} = \overrightarrow{OB} - \overrightarrow{OA} = \mathbf{b} - \mathbf{a}$

Let P, position vector $\mathbf{r}$, be any point on the straight line.
$\overrightarrow{AP} = \lambda\overrightarrow{AB} = \lambda(\mathbf{b} - \mathbf{a})$ where λ is a scalar variable dependent upon the position of P relative to A and B.
$\overrightarrow{OP} = \mathbf{r} = \overrightarrow{OA} + \overrightarrow{AP} = \mathbf{a} + \lambda(\mathbf{b} - \mathbf{a})$
$\Rightarrow \mathbf{r} = \mathbf{a} + \lambda(\mathbf{b} - \mathbf{a})$ is the vector equation of the required line.
If $P = (x, y, z)$, $A = (x_1, y_1, z_1)$, $B = (x_2, y_2, z_2)$ then
$\mathbf{r} = \mathbf{a} + \lambda(\mathbf{b} - \mathbf{a}) \Rightarrow x\mathbf{i} + y\mathbf{j} + z\mathbf{k}$
$= x_1\mathbf{i} + y_1\mathbf{j} + z_1\mathbf{k} + \lambda(x_2\mathbf{i} + y_2\mathbf{j} + z_2\mathbf{k} - x_1\mathbf{i} - y_1\mathbf{j} - z_1\mathbf{k})$
and comparing coefficients of $\mathbf{i}$, $\mathbf{j}$, $\mathbf{k}$ $\Rightarrow$
$x = x_1 + \lambda(x_2 - x_1),\ y = y_1 + \lambda(y_2 - y_1),\ z = z_1 + \lambda(z_2 - z_1)$

or $\dfrac{x - x_1}{x_2 - x_1} = \dfrac{y - y_1}{y_2 - y_1} = \dfrac{z - z_1}{z_2 - z_1}\ (= \lambda),$

called *cartesian equations* of the line.

Worked example A

The position vectors of the points A and B in Fig. V.7 are given by
$\overrightarrow{OA} = 2\mathbf{i} + \mathbf{j} - 4\mathbf{k},\ \overrightarrow{OB} = -2\mathbf{i} + 4\mathbf{j} - 2\mathbf{k}$

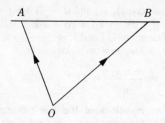

Fig. V.7

Find a vector equation of the line passing through A and B.

Find the position vector of the point where this line meets the plane $z = 0$

Here,
$$\mathbf{b} = -2\mathbf{i} + 4\mathbf{j} - 2\mathbf{k}$$
and
$$\mathbf{a} = 2\mathbf{i} + \mathbf{j} - 4\mathbf{k}$$
and
$$\mathbf{b} - \mathbf{a} = -4\mathbf{i} + 3\mathbf{j} + 2\mathbf{k}$$

The vector equation of the line is therefore
$$\mathbf{r} = \mathbf{a} + \lambda(\mathbf{b} - \mathbf{a})$$
$$= 2\mathbf{i} + \mathbf{j} - 4\mathbf{k} + \lambda(-4\mathbf{i} + 3\mathbf{j} + 2\mathbf{k})$$

The line meets the plane $z = 0$ where the **k** component, that is $-4 + 2\lambda$ equals zero. Thus $\lambda = 2$ and the position vector of the point of intersection is (putting $\lambda = 2$) $-6\mathbf{i} + 7\mathbf{j}$.

Equations of a plane

An equation of the plane through points A, B and C having position vectors $\mathbf{a}$, $\mathbf{b}$ and $\mathbf{c}$ respectively with respect to an origin O is as follows (see Fig. V.8).

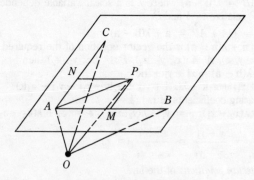

Fig. V.8

Let P, position vector $\mathbf{r}$, be any point in the plane. Then, constructing a parallelogram $AMPN$ such that AP is a diagonal and M and N are on AB and AC (or AC, AC produced if necessary) respectively

$$\Rightarrow \overrightarrow{AP} = \overrightarrow{AM} + \overrightarrow{MP} = \overrightarrow{AM} + \overrightarrow{AN}$$

But $\overrightarrow{AM} = s\overrightarrow{AB}$ and $\overrightarrow{AN} = t\overrightarrow{AC}$ where s and t are scalar variables depending upon the position of P in the plane with respect to A

$$\Rightarrow \overrightarrow{AP} = s\overrightarrow{AB} + t\overrightarrow{AC}$$
$$\Rightarrow \mathbf{r} - \mathbf{a} = s(\mathbf{b} - \mathbf{a}) + t(\mathbf{c} - \mathbf{a})$$

or $\mathbf{r} = (1 - s - t)\mathbf{a} + s\mathbf{b} + t\mathbf{c}$; a vector equation of plane ABC

An equation of a plane which passes through a fixed point A, position vector $\mathbf{a}$ with respect to an origin O and which is perpendicular to the direction given by a unit vector $\hat{\mathbf{n}}$ (or a vector $\mathbf{n}$) is as follows (see Fig. V.9).

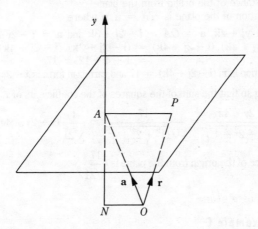

Fig. V.9

Let P position vector $\mathbf{r}$ be any point in the plane
$$\Rightarrow \overrightarrow{AP} = \mathbf{r} - \mathbf{a}$$
But AP is perpendicular to $\hat{\mathbf{n}} \Rightarrow \hat{\mathbf{n}} . (\mathbf{r} - \mathbf{a}) = 0$
$\Rightarrow \hat{\mathbf{n}} . \mathbf{r} = \hat{\mathbf{n}} . \mathbf{a} = OA\cos \angle NAO = AN$, where N is the foot of the perpendicular from the origin to the normal to the plane through A, that is, $AN = $ perpendicular distance p, of the origin from the plane.
$\Rightarrow$ vector equation of the plane is $\hat{\mathbf{n}} . \mathbf{r} = p$, where p is the perpendicular distance of the origin from the plane; or $\mathbf{n} . \mathbf{r} = \mathbf{n} . \mathbf{a}$ where $\mathbf{n}$ is any vector normal to the plane and $\mathbf{a}$ is the position vector of any point in the plane.

Cartesian form

If $P \equiv (x, y, z)$, $A \equiv (x_1, y_1, z_1)$ and $\hat{\mathbf{n}} = l\mathbf{i} + m\mathbf{j} + n\mathbf{k}$ then
$\hat{\mathbf{n}} . \mathbf{r} = \hat{\mathbf{n}} . \mathbf{a} \Rightarrow (l\mathbf{i} + m\mathbf{j} + n\mathbf{k}) . (x\mathbf{i} + y\mathbf{j} + z\mathbf{k})$
$\qquad = (l\mathbf{i} + m\mathbf{j} + n\mathbf{k}) . (x_1\mathbf{i} + y_1\mathbf{j} + z_1\mathbf{k})$
$\Rightarrow lx + my + nz = lx_1 + my_1 + nz_1$ (or p)
or $l(x - x_1) + m(y - y_1) + n(z - z_1) = 0$
The general equation of a plane is therefore $Ax + By + Cz = D$, where A,

B, C are the direction ratios of the normal to the plane and D is a constant. If the unit normal $\hat{n}$ is used rather than n so that $\sqrt{(A^2 + B^2 + C^2)} = 1$ then A, B, C are called the *direction cosines* of the normal to the plane and D will be the distance of the origin from the plane.

Worked example B

Find i) a vector equation, ii) a cartesian equation of the plane which passes through the point A $(1, -2, 3)$ and is normal to the vector n where $n = i - 2j + 4k$
Find the distance of the origin from the plane
Vector equation of the plane is $r.n = a.n$ where

$r = xi + yj + zk$, $a = \overrightarrow{OA} = i - 2j + 3k$ and $n = i - 2j + 4k$
$\Rightarrow (xi + yj + zk).(i - 2j + 4k) = (i - 2j + 3k).(i - 2j + 4k)$
$= 1 + 4 + 12 = 17$

Vector equation is $r.(i - 2j + 4k) = 17$ and cartesian form is $x - 2y + 4z = 17$

Rearranging so that the sum of the squares of the coefficients of x, y and z is 1

$$\Rightarrow \frac{x - 2y + 4z}{\sqrt{(1^2 + 2^2 + 4^2)}} = \frac{17}{\sqrt{(1^2 + 2^2 + 4^2)}} \Rightarrow \frac{1}{\sqrt{21}}(x - 2y + 4z) = \frac{17}{\sqrt{21}}$$

$\Rightarrow$ distance of the origin from the plane is $\dfrac{17}{\sqrt{21}}$

Worked example C

With respect to a fixed origin O, a point P has position vector $3i - j + 2k$ and a plane Π has equation $r.(2i - 4j - k) = 8$
Show that P lies in the plane Π
The point Q has position vector $7i - 9j$

a) Show that $\overrightarrow{QP}$ is perpendicular to the plane Π
b) Calculate, to the nearest one tenth of a degree, $\angle OQP$

If P lies in the plane Π then the coordinates of P satisfy the equation of $\Pi \Rightarrow r.(2i - 4j - k) = (3i - j + 2k).(2i - 4j - k) = 6 + 4 - 2 = 8$
$\Rightarrow P$ lies in the plane

$\overrightarrow{QP}$ is perpendicular to the plane Π provided $\overrightarrow{QP}$ is parallel to a vector which is normal to the plane, that is, provided $\overrightarrow{QP}$ is parallel to the vector $2i - 4j - k = n$, say
$\overrightarrow{QP} = \overrightarrow{OP} - \overrightarrow{OQ} = (3i - j + 2k) - (7i - 9j) = -4i + 8j + 2k$
$= -2(2i - 4j - k) = -2n$

$\Rightarrow \overrightarrow{QP}$ is perpendicular to the plane Π
$\overrightarrow{QO} = -7i + 9j$, $\overrightarrow{QP} = -4i + 8j + 2k$

$$\overrightarrow{QO}.\overrightarrow{QP} = |\overrightarrow{QO}|.|\overrightarrow{QP}| \cos \angle OQP \Rightarrow \cos \angle OQP$$

$$= \frac{(-7\mathbf{i} + 9\mathbf{j}).(-4\mathbf{i} + 8\mathbf{j} + 2\mathbf{k})}{|-7\mathbf{i} + 9\mathbf{j}|.|-4\mathbf{i} + 8\mathbf{j} + 2\mathbf{k}|}$$

$$\Rightarrow \cos \angle OQP = \frac{28 + 72}{\sqrt{(49 + 81)}.\sqrt{(16 + 64 + 4)}} = \frac{100}{\sqrt{130}.\sqrt{84}} = 0{\cdot}9569$$

$$\Rightarrow \angle OQP = 16{\cdot}9°$$

◀ Scalar (and vector), Vector product ▶

VECTOR GEOMETRY

▶ EQUATION OF A STRAIGHT LINE

Let the fixed point A in Fig. V.10 have position vector $\mathbf{a}$ with respect to an origin O. Consider the line l passing through A having direction vector $\mathbf{d}$.

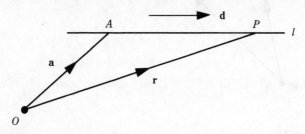

Fig. V.10

Let P be a general point on l having position vector $\mathbf{r}$. Then
$$\overrightarrow{OP} = \overrightarrow{OA} + \overrightarrow{AP}$$
that is,
$$\mathbf{r} = \mathbf{a} + \lambda\mathbf{d}$$
where λ is a scalar. This is the vector equation of l.

An alternative cartesian form can be obtained as follows. Let
$$\mathbf{r} = x\mathbf{i} + y\mathbf{j} + z\mathbf{k}$$
$$\mathbf{a} = a_x\mathbf{i} + a_y\mathbf{j} + a_z\mathbf{k}$$
and $\quad \mathbf{d} = d_x\mathbf{i} + d_y\mathbf{j} + d_z\mathbf{k}$

Then
$$x\mathbf{i} + y\mathbf{j} + z\mathbf{k} = a_x\mathbf{i} + a_y\mathbf{j} + a_z\mathbf{k} + \lambda(d_x\mathbf{i} + d_y\mathbf{j} + d_z\mathbf{k})$$
whence,
$$x = a_x + \lambda d_x$$
$$y = a_y + \lambda d_y$$
and $\quad z = a_z + \lambda d_z$

It follows that
$$\frac{x - a_x}{d_x} = \frac{y - a_y}{d_y} = \frac{z - a_z}{d_z} \ (= \lambda)$$

► *EQUATION OF A PLANE*

Consider the plane in Fig. V.11 containing the point A with position vector **a** and perpendicular to the vector **n**. Let P be a general point on the plane having position vector **r**.

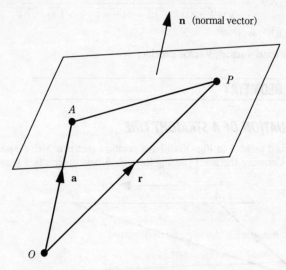

Fig. V.11

Then, since $\overrightarrow{AP}$ is perpendicular to **n**, it follows that

$$\overrightarrow{AP}.\,\mathbf{n} = 0$$

that is, $(\mathbf{r} - \mathbf{a}).\,\mathbf{n} = 0$

or $\mathbf{r}.\,\mathbf{n} = \mathbf{a}.\,\mathbf{n} = \mathbf{k}$ (constant)

The cartesian form of the equation can be derived by putting

$$\mathbf{r} = x\mathbf{i} + y\mathbf{j} + z\mathbf{k}$$

and $\mathbf{n} = n_x\mathbf{i} + n_y\mathbf{j} + n_z\mathbf{k}$

Thus

$$n_x x + n_y y + n_z z = k$$

An alternative form is

$$ax + by + cz = d$$

where (a, b, c) are the components of the normal vector.

VECTOR PRODUCT (OR CROSS PRODUCT)

The vector product of the two vectors **a**, **b**, written $\mathbf{a} \times \mathbf{b}$, is a vector of magnitude $ab \sin \theta$ perpendicular to both **a** and **b**, where θ denotes the angle between **a** and **b**. The sense of $\mathbf{a} \times \mathbf{b}$ is such that **a**, **b** and $\mathbf{a} \times \mathbf{b}$ form a right-handed set of vectors, that is a corkscrew whose handle moves from **a** towards **b** will move in the direction of $\mathbf{a} \times \mathbf{b}$.

It follows that $\mathbf{a} \times \mathbf{b} = 0$ if $\theta = 0°$, that is, if $\mathbf{a}$, $\mathbf{b}$ are parallel. If $\mathbf{a}$, $\mathbf{b}$ are expressed in component form, which is

$$\mathbf{a} = a_x\mathbf{i} + a_y\mathbf{j} + a_z\mathbf{k}$$
and $\quad \mathbf{b} = b_x\mathbf{i} + b_y\mathbf{j} + b_z\mathbf{k}$

where $\mathbf{i}$, $\mathbf{j}$, $\mathbf{k}$ is a right-handed set of unit vectors, then

$$\begin{aligned}
\mathbf{a} \times \mathbf{b} &= (a_x\mathbf{i} + a_y\mathbf{j} + a_z\mathbf{k}) \times (b_x\mathbf{i} + b_y\mathbf{j} + b_z\mathbf{k}) \\
&= a_xb_x\mathbf{i} \times \mathbf{i} + a_xb_y\mathbf{i} \times \mathbf{j} + a_xb_z\mathbf{i} \times \mathbf{k} \\
&\quad + a_yb_x\mathbf{j} \times \mathbf{i} + a_yb_y\mathbf{j} \times \mathbf{j} + a_yb_z\mathbf{j} \times \mathbf{k} \\
&\quad + a_zb_x\mathbf{k} \times \mathbf{i} + a_zb_y\mathbf{k} \times \mathbf{j} + a_zb_z\mathbf{k} \times \mathbf{k} \\
&= (a_yb_z - a_zb_y)\mathbf{i} + (a_zb_x - a_xb_z)\mathbf{j} + (a_xb_y - a_yb_x)\mathbf{k} \\
&= \begin{vmatrix} \mathbf{i} & \mathbf{j} & \mathbf{k} \\ a_x & a_y & a_z \\ b_x & b_y & b_z \end{vmatrix}
\end{aligned}$$

Since $\mathbf{i} \times \mathbf{i} = \mathbf{j} \times \mathbf{j} = \mathbf{k} \times \mathbf{k} = 0$; $\quad \mathbf{j} \times \mathbf{k} = -\mathbf{k} \times \mathbf{j} = \mathbf{i}$
$\mathbf{k} \times \mathbf{i} = -\mathbf{i} \times \mathbf{k} = \mathbf{j}$; $\quad \mathbf{i} \times \mathbf{j} = -\mathbf{j} \times \mathbf{i} = \mathbf{k}$

◀ Vector ▶

VELOCITY

Velocity is the rate of change of **displacement** with time, *or* the rate of change of distance with time in a stated direction. Velocity is a **vector**. The units will therefore be m/s in a stated direction.

$$\text{Velocity} = \frac{\text{change of displacement}}{\text{time taken}}$$

◀ Kinetics, Polar components ▶

VOLUME OF A REVOLUTION

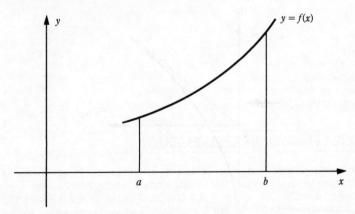

Fig. V.12

If the graph $y = f(x)$ between $x = a$ and $x = b$ (see Fig. V.12) is rotated through four right-angles about the x-axis, then the volume of the solid generated is

$$V = \pi \int_a^b y^2 \, dx$$

If the graph between $y = c$ and $y = d$ is rotated through four right-angles about the y-axis, then the volume of the solid generated is

$$V = \pi \int_c^d x^2 \, dy$$

Worked example A

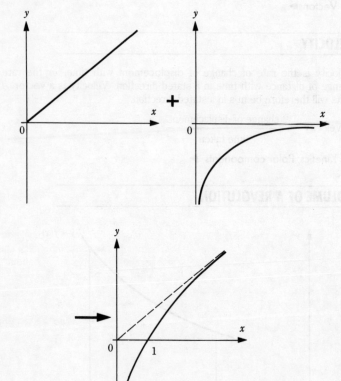

Fig. V.13

Sketch the curve with equation $y = x - \dfrac{1}{x}$, $x > 0$

The area bounded by the curve, the x-axis and the lines $x = 2$, $x = 3$ is rotated completely about the x-axis. Calculate the volume of the solid of revolution so formed.

The sketch can easily be obtained by adding the known curves $y = x$ and

$y = -\dfrac{1}{x}$ (see Fig. V.13).

⬤ SHELL METHOD

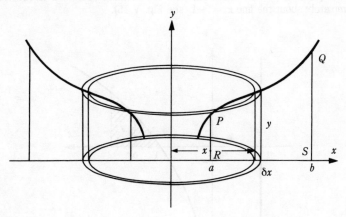

Fig. V.14

When the strip of area yx is revolved about the y-axis it produces a cylindrical shell of volume $2\pi xy\mathrm{d}x$ (see Fig. V.14). Summing all such elementary shells from $x = a$ to $x = b$ the volume, V, of revolution of area $PRSQ$ about the y-axis is given by:

$$V = 2\pi \int_a^b xy\mathrm{d}x$$

$$= \pi \int_2^3 y^2\mathrm{d}x$$

$$= \pi \int_2^3 \left(x - \frac{1}{x}\right)^2 \mathrm{d}x$$

$$= \pi \int_2^3 \left(x^2 - 2 + \frac{1}{x^2}\right) \mathrm{d}x$$

$$= \pi\left[\frac{x^3}{3} - 2x - \frac{1}{x}\right]_2^3$$

$$= \pi\left(9 - 6 - \frac{1}{3} - \frac{8}{3} + 4 + \frac{1}{2}\right)$$

$$= \frac{9\pi}{2}$$

Worked example B

Find the volume generated when the finite region enclosed between the curve with equation $y = \ln x$, the x-axis and the ordinate at $x = 2$ is revolved completely about the line $x = -1$ (see Fig. V.15).

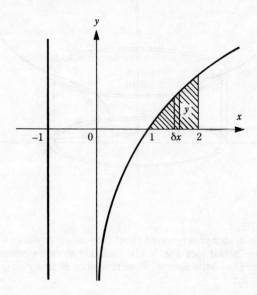

Fig. V.15

The graph of $y = \ln x$ crosses the x-axis at $x = 1$. The region revolved is the shaded region. The strip of area $y\delta x$ is parallel to and at a distance $(x + 1)$ from the line $x = -1$. Consequently, when this strip is revolved completely about the line $x = -1$, a cylindrical shell of volume $2\pi(x + 1)y\delta x$ is obtained. Hence, summing all such strips between $x = 1$ and $x = 2$ gives a volume of revolution

$$V = \int_1^2 2\pi(x + 1)y\,dx = \int_1^2 2\pi(x + 1)\ln x\,dx$$

Integrating by parts

$$V = \left[2\pi\left(\frac{1}{2}x^2 + x\right)\ln x\right]_1^2 - \int_1^2 2\pi\left(\frac{1}{2}x^2 + x\right)\frac{1}{x}\,dx$$

$$= 2\pi\left[(2+2)\ln 2 - \left(\frac{1}{2}+1\right)\ln 1\right] - \int_1^2 2\pi\left(\frac{1}{2}x + 1\right)dx$$

$$= 2\pi.4\ln 2 - 2\pi\left[\frac{1}{4}x^2 + x\right]_1^2 = 8\pi\ln 2 - 2\pi\left[(1+2) - \left(\frac{1}{4}+1\right)\right]$$

$$= 8\pi\ln 2 - 3\frac{1}{2}\pi = \pi\left(8\ln 2 - 3\frac{1}{2}\right)$$

VOLUME

Volume is the space occupied by a solid, three-dimensional shape. It is measured in cubes, that is cubic metres or m^3.

You ought to be familiar with the following formulae for finding volumes:

Cuboid = length × breadth × height

Prism = regular cross-section × length

$$\textit{Sphere} = \frac{4}{3}\pi r^3$$

$$\textit{Pyramid} = \frac{1}{3} \times \text{base area} \times \text{vertical height}$$

WEIGHT

The weight of a body is the downward **force** on the body due to gravity. A body of mass m kg has weight mg N, where g is the acceleration due to gravity.

WORK

The work done when a **force** F (Newtons) moves through a distance d (metres) in the direction of the force is equal to Fd (Joules).

More generally, if the **displacement d** is not in the direction of the force F, then

Work done $= \mathbf{F} \cdot \mathbf{d}$

$\qquad = |F|\ |d| \cos \theta$

where θ is the angle between the force and the displacement.

▶ WORK AND ENERGY

A particle of mass m is moving in a straight line under the action of a constant force of magnitude F. The particle covers a distance s in time t, the initial speed is u, the final speed v and the acceleration has magnitude a.

We have $F = ma$

and $v^2 = u^2 + 2as$, since the motion is uniformly accelerated.

By combining these two equations and eliminating a we obtain

$$Fs = \frac{1}{2}mv^2 - \frac{1}{2}mu^2 \tag{1}$$

The product force × distance, where the force is constant, is called the work done by the force over the space interval covered. The unit of work is the newton-metre (Nm) and the unit is called the joule, denoted by J. The expression $\frac{1}{2}mv^2$ is defined as the **kinetic energy** (K.E.) of a particle of mass m moving with speed v.

Equation (1) illustrates a particular case of a more general result which may be given as:

Work done by a force = change in K.E. produced by the force

For example, suppose that a particle of mass m is moving along the x-axis under the action of a force of magnitude P, where P depends only on x, the distance of the particle from the origin.

The equation of motion is

$$P = mv \frac{dv}{dx} \tag{2}$$

$$\left(\text{remember acceleration can be written as } v \frac{dv}{dx} \right)$$

Given that $v = v_1$, when $x = x_1$ and $v = v_2$ when $x = x_2$, equation (2) may be integrated with respect to x to give

$$\int_{x_1}^{x_2} P \, dx = \int_{x_1}^{x_2} mv \frac{dv}{dx} dx$$

$$= \int_{v_1}^{v_2} mv \, dv$$

$$= \left[\frac{1}{2} mv^2 \right]_{v_1}^{v_2}$$

$$= \frac{1}{2} mv_2{}^2 - \frac{1}{2} mv_1{}^2$$

We define $\displaystyle\int_{x_1}^{x_2} P \, dx$ to be the work done by the force P over the space interval

$x = x_1$ to $x = x_2$, and, we then have

Work done by a force = change in K.E. produced by the force

▶ WORK, DRIVING AND RESISTIVE FORCES

Worked example A

A lorry of mass 8 tonnes moves at constant speed $12 \, \mathrm{m\,s^{-1}}$ up a road inclined at θ to the horizontal, where $\sin \theta = 1/20$. The non gravitational resistances are of magnitude 2500 N. Taking the acceleration due to gravity to be $10 \, \mathrm{m\,s^{-2}}$, calculate the rate, in kW, at which the engine of the lorry is working (see Fig. W.1).

Let us suppose that the engine of the lorry is working at H kW. The tractive force at $12 \, \mathrm{m\,s^{-1}}$ is $(1,000H/12)$ N. The forces opposing the motion of the lorry are the resistances and the component of the weight of the lorry along the line

of motion. We have, therefore, $1,000H/12 = 2,500 + 8,000 \times 10 \times 1/20$
leading to $H = 78$
The engine of the lorry is working at 78kW

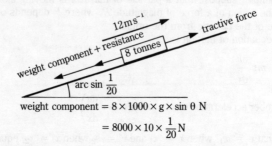

weight component $= 8 \times 1000 \times g \times \sin \theta$ N

$$= 8000 \times 10 \times \frac{1}{20} \text{N}$$

Fig. W.1

Worked example B

A car, of mass 800kg, moves down a road inclined at an angle θ to the horizontal at constant speed $30 \, \text{ms}^{-1}$. At this speed the resistive forces are of magnitude $1,200$N and the engine of the car is working at 30kW. Taking the acceleration due to gravity to be of magnitude $10 \, \text{ms}^{-2}$, calculate $\sin \theta$. On another occasion the car is moving along a horizontal straight road with the engine working at a constant rate HkW. At a particular instant the speed of the car is $15 \, \text{ms}^{-1}$ and the acceleration is of magnitude $0 \cdot 5 \, \text{ms}^{-2}$. Given that the resistive forces are of magnitude 300N at this speed, calculate the value of H

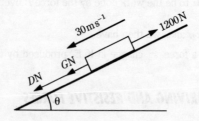

Fig. W.2

We consider the forces acting on the car in the line of motion as shown in Fig. W.2. These forces are the driving force of magnitude DN, the resistive forces of magnitude $1,200$N and the weight component of the car of magnitude GN.

Since Power = Force × Speed, $30D = 30 \times 1,000 \Rightarrow D = 1,000$. Also $G = 800g \sin \theta = 8,000 \sin \theta$.

Since the car is moving with constant speed, by Newton's first law
$D - 1,200 + G = 0$
because the net force acting on the car in the line of motion is zero.
We have therefore $1,000 - 1,200 + 8,000 \sin \theta = 0$
$\Rightarrow \sin \theta = 1/40$

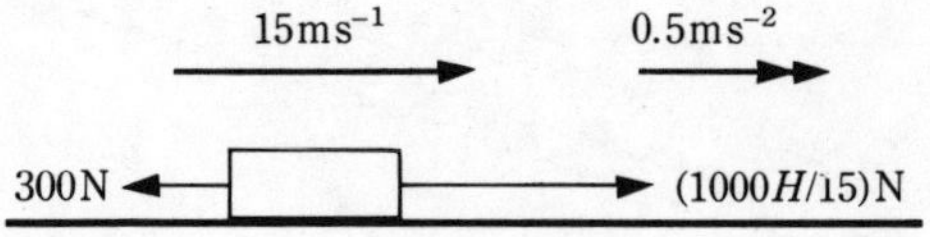

Fig. W.3

In Fig. W.3, we show the forces acting on the car in the line of motion when it is moving along a level road with *instantaneous* speed $15\,\text{ms}^{-1}$ and *instantaneous* acceleration of magnitude $0.5\,\text{ms}^{-2}$, with the engine of the car working at $H\,$kW. At this *instant*, the driving force is of magnitude $(1,000H/15)\text{N}$, the resistive forces are of magnitude $300\,\text{N}$ and the force producing acceleration is of magnitude $800 \times 0.5\,\text{N}$ (from Newton's second law). The *instantaneous difference* between the magnitudes of the driving force and the resistive forces is equal to the magnitude of the force making the car accelerate,
and so, $1,000H/15 - 300 = 400$
$$\Rightarrow H = 10.5$$